W9-BSQ-031

MULTIPLE-CHOICE
&
CONSTRUCTED-RESPONSE QUESTIONS
IN PREPARATION FOR THE
AP CHEMISTRY EXAMINATION

(SIXTH EDITION)

David W. Hostage
The Taft School
Watertown, CT

Patsy W. Mueller
Regina Dominican College Preparatory School for Young Women
Wilmette, IL

Dr. Arden Zipp
Distinguished Teaching Professor, Emeritus
SUNY College at Cortland
Cortland, NY

D&S MARKETING SYSTEMS, INC.
1205 38th Street Brooklyn, NY 11218

w w w . d s m a r k e t i n g . c o m

ISBN # 978-1-934780-29-9 / 1-934780-29-4

PREFACE

The three authors of this book recognize that their primary responsibility is to prepare students to be successful on the AP Chemistry exam. The practice questions at the end of the chapters and the Sample Exams at the end of the book have been constructed with the newly-written Learning objectives and Science Practices in mind, so that these questions will be similar to those to be anticipated on these exams. A number of topics are included here, even though some of these are excluded in the Redesign. For the most part, these topics, [including but not limited to Arrhenius acids and bases, numerous gas laws, a zero order kinetics equation, nuclear half-life (kinetics) calculations, etc.] are ones that the AP Chemistry Redesign Committee have labeled "Assumed Prior Knowledge," typically taught in first year chemistry classes, but whose mastery is a necessary foundation for successful work involving the revised expectations and rigor imbedded in the new curriculum. For the same reasons, examples using concentrations beyond molarity and the applications involving predictions or explanations requiring a **conceptual understanding** of the Van der Waal equation for non-ideal gases are provided. Based upon on our many years of teaching experience, we authors strongly believe that these topics should be included in an advanced chemistry course in order to better prepare students for college and university work as well as Regional and national exams or competitions. We have also included summaries and explanations which review the salient topics in each chapter, and these summaries precede the multiple-choice and constructed-response questions. Additionally, we have taken pains to include discussions of and questions dealing with the recently added topics in the Redesign. These topics include Photon Emission Spectroscopy (PES), Mass Spectroscopy and much more work involving Beer's Law as applied to colored solutions.

The authors of this book and its Student's Solution Manual have spent thousands of hours in planning, collaborating, writing, and reviewing since the changes to the AP Chemistry curriculum and examination were announced in late April 2013. We wish to thank a number of contributors to the project. Our students over the years have challenged us as much as we have challenged them. The freshness and originality of their thinking in our own classrooms has prompted us to look frequently at chemistry in a new light. All past students who have written the AP Chemistry exam have caused us, through each response to each question, to reflect upon our understanding of their understanding of the chemistry as we evaluated their work. Participants in our daylong and summer workshops have also helped us, especially through their innovative analyses of our laboratory procedures. Our colleagues and reviewers, Mark Case of Emmaus (PA) High School and Fred Vital of Darien (CT) High School, offered invaluable advice about both the content and intent of our prose, questions, and solutions. Finally, our families and friends supported us through many, many hours of writing, reviewing, and editing. Their patience has been boundless.

This work is dedicated to the memory of Peter E. Demmin, author of several previous editions of this series of AP Chemistry review books. Pete was an exemplary teacher at Amherst (NY) Central High School and a longtime workshop consultant who guided thousands and thousands of AP Chemistry students and teachers alike through the intricacies of the subject. He was a Reader and Table Leader at the grading of AP Chemistry examinations for decades. He wrote articles, standardized tests, and textbooks in profusion. And he was a great friend, always ready for a serious discussion or to share his wry sense of humor. We miss you, Pete!

We would also like to remember and pay tribute to our co-author, Arden Zipp, whose death precedes the publication of this work. He was an enthusiastic, knowledgeable contributor, and a terrific friend to all who became involved in chemistry education in general and AP Chemistry in particular. His quick smile, his patience, his consummate professionalism, and his understanding of how students learn chemistry touched thousands of AP Chemistry Readers and Table Leaders over four decades. All of us who worked with Arden became better question writers of both multiple choice and constructed response questions in our own classrooms. Arden Zipp was also a personal friend of many of us and is another individual who will truly be missed.

INTRODUCTION

The Redesigned Advanced Placement Chemistry Course and Its Relationship to this Book

In 2002 the National Academy of Sciences (NAS) published the report, "Learning and Understanding: Improving Advanced Study of Mathematics and Science in U.S. High Schools", in which they assessed the science and mathematics programs offered by the College Board and International Baccalaureate Organization. This report prompted an extensive revision of the Advanced Placement science courses offered by the College Board that has taken place over the last decade. This revision was undertaken with financial support from a number of granting agencies and the redesign of the chemistry program involved a broad spectrum of teachers, chemists and other educators. One of the members of the 2002 National Academy of Sciences (NAS) team that published the report, Patsy W. Mueller, is also one of the authors of this new work.

The redesigned AP Chemistry course is organized around six Big Ideas, which encompass virtually all of chemistry. These are:

Big Idea 1
The chemical elements are fundamental building materials of matter, and all matter can be understood in terms of arrangement of atoms. These atoms retain their identity in chemical reactions.

Big Idea 2
Chemical and physical properties of materials can be explained by the structure and the arrangement of atoms, ions, or molecules and the forces between them.

Big Idea 3

Changes in matter involve the rearrangement and/or reorganization of atoms and/or the transfer of electrons.

Big Idea 4

Rates of chemical reactions are determined by details of the molecular collisions.

Big Idea 5

The laws of thermodynamics describe the essential role of energy and explain and predict the direction of changes in matter.

Big Idea 6

Any bond or intermolecular attraction that can be formed can be broken. These two processes are in a dynamic competition, sensitive to initial conditions and external perturbations.

Each Big Idea is divided into a series of statements (referred to as Enduring Understandings), each of which addresses a particular aspect of it Big Idea. For example, the first Enduring Understanding under Big Idea 1 is: "All matter is made of atoms. There are a limited number of types of atoms; these are the elements."

Science Practices

In addition to the 6 Big Ideas, the AP Chemistry Redesign Committee has included the Seven Science Practices that are an integral part of all three AP Science Curricula that have been redesigned: AP Biology, AP Chemistry and AP Physics. These are also included by the authors in the Students' Solutions Manual. You will find that after each answer, both the specific Learning Objective(s) and Science Practices from which the question stems have been annotated. The format is the same as those associated with the Practice questions provided by the Redesign Committee. An example would be following the explanation and correct multiple choice answer to question 1 in Chapter one, the bracketed reference code, [LO 1.6, SP 5.1], is included, so that the student knows exactly which area of the new curriculum might need to be revisited in greater depth. More in depth examples of how the codes apply to each question are provided in the Students' Solutions Manual that goes along with this book, and a complete description of all the Learning Objectives, Science Practices, etc., can be found by visiting the website link: http://media.collegeboard.com/digitalServices/pdf/ap/11_3461_AP_CF_Chemistry_WEB_110930.pdf.

Enduring Understandings, in turn, are subdivided into statements of Essential Knowledge, which summarize the material required of students and include under them the details of this material. For example, Big Idea 1 comprises five Enduring Understandings, each of which includes two or three Essential Knowledge statements for a total of twelve such statements. The Enduring Understandings are also connected to seven Science Practices, each of which specifies a particular skill that students are expected to display on exams.

Each of the **Essential Knowledge** statements and the supporting material in them culminates in one or more Learning Objectives. An example of a Learning Objective that should be familiar to everyone who has taken a chemistry course is the following (LO 1.2): "The student is able to select and apply mathematical routines to mass data to identify or infer the composition of pure substances and/or mixtures." The Science Practice that accompanies this LO is SP 2.2 that states: The student can apply mathematical routines to quantities that describe natural phenomena."

In all, there are 117 **Learning Objectives**. Theoretically, a student could prepare for the AP exam by ensuring that he/she could respond successfully to each of these Learning Objectives because every question that is used on the exam must be linked to a specific Learning Objective and Science Practice.

A schematic diagram of the Redesign Project and the relationship among the various aspects described above is given below.

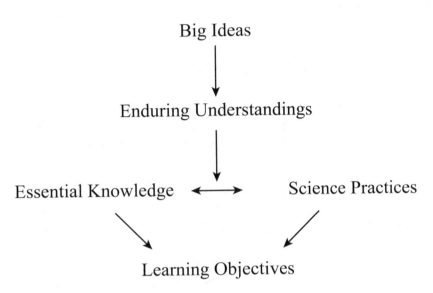

Another result of the redesign effort was the elimination of certain topics that had been a part of the previous AP Chemistry curriculum in an effort to decrease the breadth of the subject. (One of the criticisms of AP Chemistry in the NAS Report was that it had too much breadth and too little depth.) These explicit exclusions include:

1. memorization of exceptions to the Aufbau principle for atomic structure.

2. assignment of quantum numbers to electrons

3. phase diagrams

4. colligative properties

5. calculations of molality, percent by mass and percent by volume

6. knowledge of specific types of crystal structures

7. The use of formal charge to explain why certain molecules do not obey the octet rule

8. Learning how to defend Lewis models based on assumptions about their limitations

9. an understanding of the derivation and depiction of hybrid orbitals

10. recall of filling of molecular orbital diagrams

11. study of the specific varieties of crystal lattices for ionic compounds

12. Lewis acid-base concepts

13. language of reducing agent and oxidizing agent

14. labeling an electrode as positive or negative

15. Nernst equation

16. calculations involving the Arrhenius equation

17. collection of data pertaining to experimental detection of reaction intermediates

18. numerical computation of the concentration of each species present in the titration curve for polyprotic acids

19. computing the change in pH resulting from the addition of an acid or a base to a buffer

20. the production of the Henderson-Hasselbach equation by algebraic manipulation of the relevant equilibrium constant expression

21. memorization of solubility rules other than for Na^+, K^+, NH_4^+ and NO_3^-

22. computations of solubility as a function of pH

23. computations of solubility in solutions where one of the ions is an acid or a base

TABLE OF CONTENTS

TABLE OF CONTENTS

PERIODIC TABLE OF THE ELEMENTS

1 H 1.008																	2 He 4.00
3 Li 6.94	4 Be 9.01											5 B 10.81	6 C 12.01	7 N 14.01	8 O 16.00	9 F 19.00	10 Ne 20.18
11 Na 22.99	12 Mg 24.30											13 Al 26.98	14 Si 28.09	15 P 30.97	16 S 32.06	17 Cl 35.45	18 Ar 39.95
19 K 39.10	20 Ca 40.08	21 Sc 44.96	22 Ti 47.90	23 V 50.94	24 Cr 52.00	25 Mn 154.94	26 Fe 55.85	27 Co 58.93	28 Ni 58.69	29 Cu 63.55	30 Zn 65.39	31 Ga 69.72	32 Ge 72.59	33 As 74.92	34 Se 78.96	35 Br 79.90	36 Kr 83.80
37 Rb 85.47	38 Sr 87.62	39 Y 88.91	40 Zr 91.22	41 Nb 92.91	42 Mo 95.94	43 Tc (98)	44 Ru 101.1	45 Rh 102.91	46 Pd 106.42	47 Ag 107.87	48 Cd 112.41	49 In 114.82	50 Sn 118.71	51 Sb 121.75	52 Te 127.60	53 I 126.91	54 Xe 131.29
55 Cs 132.91	56 Ba 137.33	57 *La 138.91	72 Hf 178.49	73 Ta 180.95	74 W 183.85	75 Re 186.21	76 Os 190.2	77 Ir 192.2	78 Pt 195.08	79 Au 196.97	80 Hg 200.59	81 Tl 204.38	82 Pb 207.2	83 Bi 208.98	84 Po (209)	85 At (210)	86 Rn (222)
87 Fr (223)	88 Ra 226.02	89 †Ac 227.03	104 Rf (261)	105 Db (262)	106 Sg (266)	107 Bh (264)	108 Hs (277)	109 Mt (268)	110 Ds (271)	111 Rg (272)							

* Lanthanide Series

58 Ce 140.12	59 Pr 140.91	60 Nd 144.24	61 Pm (145)	62 Sm 150.4	63 Eu 151.97	64 Gd 157.25	65 Tb 158.93	66 Dy 162.50	67 Ho 164.93	68 Er 167.26	69 Tm 168.93	70 Yb 173.04	71 Lu 174.97

† Actinide Series

90 Th 232.04	91 Pa 231.04	92 U 238.03	93 Np (237)	94 Pu (244)	95 Am (243)	96 Cm (247)	97 Bk (247)	98 Cf (251)	99 Es (252)	100 Fm (257)	101 Md (258)	102 No (259)	103 Lr (262)

USEFUL EQUATIONS, SYMBOLS AND CONSTANTS

Symbols of General Use:

L, ML = liters(s), milliliters(s)
g = grams(s)
mm Hg = millimeters of mercury
nm = nanometer(s)
atm = atmosphere(s)
J, kJ = Joule(s), kiloJoule(s)
V = volt(s)
mol = mole(s)

Chapter 1: Atomic Structure

Equations:

$E = h\nu$
$c = \lambda\nu$

$$E = h\frac{c}{\lambda \times 10^{-9}}$$

Constants:

h = Planck's constant = 6.626×10^{-34} J s
c = speed of light = $2.998 \times 10^8 \, ms^{-1}$
Avogadro's Number = $6.022 \times 10^{23} \, mol^{-1}$
e = electron charge = -1.602×10^{-19} coulomb

Symbols:

E = energy
λ = wavelength
m = meter
ν = frequency
J = joule
s = second

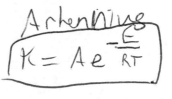

Arhennius

$$K = Ae^{-\frac{E}{RT}}$$

Chapter 3: Gases

Equations:

$PV = nRT$

$PA = P_T \times X_A$, where $X_A \times \dfrac{\text{moles of A}}{\text{total moles}}$ total moles

$P_{total} = P_A + P_B + P_C + \ldots$

$K = °C + 273$

$D = m/V$

$n = m/M$

KE per molecule $= \frac{1}{2} mv^2$

Constants:

R = Gas Constant $= 8.314$ J mol^{-1}K^{-1}

$\hspace{3.5cm} = 0.08206$ L atm mol^{-1}K^{-1}

$\hspace{3.5cm} = 62.36$ L torr mol^{-1}K^{-1}

1 atm $= 760$ mm Hg

$\hspace{1.8cm} = 760$ torr

STP $= 0.00°$C and 1.000 atm

Symbols:

P = pressure

D = density

KE = kinetic energy

V = volume

n = number of moles

T = temperature

X_A = mole fraction

v = velocity

m = mass

M (or MM) = molar mass

Chapter 5: Solutions

Equations:

M (Molarity) = moles of solute per liter of solution

$A = abC$

Symbols:

A = absorbance

a = molar absorptivity

b = path length

C = concentration

Chapter 7: Kinetics

Equations:

$$\ln[A]_t - \ln[A]_0 = -kt$$
$$1/[A]_t - 1/[A]_0 = kt$$
$$t_{1/2} = 0.093/k$$

Symbols:

k = rate constant
t = time
$t_{1/2}$ = half life

Chapter 8: Equilibrium

Equations:

$$K_c = \frac{[C]^c [D]^d}{[A]^a [B]^b}, \text{ where } a\,A + b\,B \leftrightarrow c\,C + d\,D$$

$$K_p = \frac{(P_C)^c (P_D)^d}{(P_A)^a (P_B)^b}$$

Symbols:

K_c (molar concentrations)
K_p (gas pressures)

Chapter 9: Thermodynamics

Equations:

$$q = mc\Delta T$$
$$\Delta S^\circ = \Sigma S^\circ \text{ products} - \Sigma S^\circ \text{ reactants}$$
$$\Delta H^\circ = \Sigma \Delta H^\circ_f \text{ products} - \Sigma \Delta H^\circ_f \text{ reactants}$$
$$\Delta G^\circ = \Sigma \Delta G^\circ_f \text{ products} - \Sigma \Delta G^\circ_f \text{ reactants}$$
$$\Delta G^\circ = \Delta H^\circ - T\Delta S^\circ$$
$$= -RT\ln K$$
$$= -nFE^\circ$$

Symbols:

q = heat
m = mass
c = specific heat capacity
T = temperature
S° = standard entropy
H° = standard enthalpy
G° = standard free energy
n = number of moles
E° = standard reduction potential

Constant:

F = Faraday's Constant = 96,500 coulombs per mole of electrons

Chapter 10: Acid-Base Equilibrium

Equations:

$$K_a = \frac{[H^+][A^-]}{[HA]}$$

$$K_b = \frac{[OH^-][HB^+]}{[B]}$$

$$K_w = [H^+][OH^-] = 1.0 \times 10^{14} \text{ at } 25°C$$

$$= K_a \times K_b$$

$$pH = -\log[H^+], \ pOH = -\log[OH^-]$$

$$14 = pH + pOH$$

$$pH = pK_a + \log\frac{[A^-]}{[HA]}$$

$$pK_a = -\log K_a, \ pK_b = -\log K_b$$

Equilibrium Constants:

K_a (weak acid)

K_b (weak base)

K_w (water)

Chapter 11: Electrochemistry

Equations:

$$I = q/t$$

$$\Delta G° = -nFE°$$

Constant:

F = Faraday's Constant = 96,500 coulombs per mole of electrons

Symbols:

$E°$ = standard reduction potential

n = moles

I = current (amperes)

q = charge (coulombs)

t = time (seconds)

1 volt = 1 joule/1 coulomb

CHAPTER 1

ATOMIC STRUCTURE

The chemical elements are fundamental building materials of matter, and all matter can be understood in terms of arrangements of atoms. These atoms retain their identity in chemical reactions.

The foundation of modern chemistry is John Dalton's Atomic Theory (1808) in which he stated that:

(1) An element is composed of tiny indivisible particles called atoms.
(2) Atoms move from one substance to another in chemical reactions but do not disappear or change into atoms of other elements.
(3) Compounds form when two or more atoms combine.

This work provided a theoretical basis for the experimental laws of conservation of mass, constant composition, and multiple proportions.

An understanding of atomic structure did not begin until the late 19th and early 20th centuries when tools became available to study these tiny particles. The names and accomplishments of several of the major contributors to this work are given below.

Scientist	Date	Accomplishment	Significance for Atomic Theory
Henri Becquerel	1896	observed radioactive decay of U	atoms are not unchangeable
J. J. Thomson	1897	discovered electrons	atoms are not indivisible
Max Planck	1900	studied blackbody radiation	proposed the quantization of energy
Albert Einstein	1905	examined light-metal interaction	photoelectric effect - light behaves as particles
Ernest Rutherford	1908	studied radioactive emissions	named α, β, γ radiation
Robert Millikan	1908	measured electron charge	determined electron mass
Ernest Rutherford	1911	used α radiation to bombard Au	discovered nucleus
Henry Moseley	1913	studied x-ray spectra of atoms	defined atomic number
Neils Bohr	1913	investigated atomic spectra	proposed quantized levels
Louis deBroglie	1924	theoretician	proposed matter exhibits wave-like behavior
Werner Heisenberg	1927	did theoretical work	developed Uncertainty Principle
Erwin Schrodinger	1926	did calculations on H atom	developed wave equation
James Chadwick	1932	studied nucleus	discovered neutron

These studies produced a model of the atom with a positively charged nucleus containing protons and, with the exception of the simplest and most abundant form of hydrogen, neutrons. In a neutral atom the nucleus is surrounded by a number of electrons equal to the charge on the nucleus resulting from the protons present. While the identity of an atom is established by the number of protons in its nucleus (the atomic number) the atomic mass equals the total of the number of protons and neutrons. (Electrons have little effect on an atom's mass because the mass of an electron is only about 1/2000 that of a proton or neutron, which are the same to three decimal places.)

Particle	Grams	Atomic Mass Units	Charge
electron	9.109383×10^{-28}	0.0005485799	-1
proton	1.672622×10^{-24}	1.007276	$+1$
neutron	1.674927×10^{-24}	1.008665	0

Atoms with a specified number of protons and a variable number of neutrons are known as isotopes. For example, hydrogen has three isotopes designated $_1^1H$, $_1^2H$ and $_1^3H$, where the subscript gives the atomic number and the superscripts are the mass numbers or the total of the number of protons and neutrons.

Isotopes can be separated and characterized by mass spectrometry, a technique in which gaseous atoms are bombarded with high-energy electrons. This process removes one or more electrons from an atom to form positive ions that can be separated according to their masses when subjected to a magnetic field. Mass spectrometry provides data to calculate the relative abundance of the isotopes in a sample of an element and can be used to determine the molar masses of compounds.

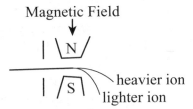

Magnetic Field

heavier ion
lighter ion

The current understanding of the arrangement of electrons within atoms began with studies of the interaction of electromagnetic radiation with atoms. The electromagnetic spectrum is shown below.

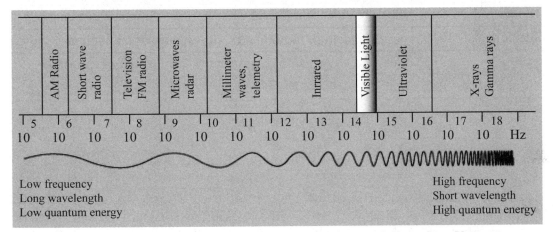

Reprinted with permission from HyperPhysics by Rod Nave, Georgia State University

Calculations involving light can be carried out with the equations: $c = \lambda \nu$ where c, the speed of light, equals the wavelength, λ, times the frequency, ν and $E = h\nu$ (energy of a photon equals Planck's constant, h, times the frequency using the constants: c = speed of light $(3.0 \times 10^8 \text{m s}^{-1})$, h = Planck's constant $(6.63 \times 10^{-34} \text{J s})$.

In his representation of the atom Neils Bohr used Coulomb's law: $F = \dfrac{q_1 q_2}{r^2}$

(F is the force between two particles with charges q_1 and q_2 and r is the distance separating them) to calculate the force between a proton and an electron in the hydrogen atom and account for the lines observed in the visible hydrogen spectrum.

The current view of the atom is based on the quantum mechanical model developed by Schrodinger and others. In this model electrons surround the nucleus in energy levels related to but more involved than the circular orbits suggested by Bohr. Each electron can be identified by a set of quantum numbers obtained from the solution of the Schrodinger equation. The possible values and limits on these quantum numbers are given in the table below.

Label	Name	Physical significance	Possible values
n	Principal quantum number	Distance from nucleus	1, 2, 3, …
l	Orbital quantum number	Sublevels (s, p, d, f)	0, 1, 2, … (n − 1)
m_l	Magnetic quantum number	Orbital orientation	0, ±1, ±2, … ±l
m_s	Spin quantum number	Clockwise/anti-clockwise	±1/2

Although quantum numbers other than "n" are not included in the revised AP Chemistry curriculum they are part of most first year university courses as well as regional and national chemistry competitions. For this reason, the authors recommend strongly that they be discussed but not necessarily reviewed before the AP exam in May.

Electron arrangements are typically designated with the principal quantum, a letter (s, p, d or f) for the sublevel and the number of electrons in that sublevel. The electron in the H atom is specified $1s^1$, while the two electrons in He would be $1s^2$ (with the two electrons spinning in opposite directions) and the three in Li–$1s^2$ $2s^1$. Additional electrons are placed in successive levels by means of the Aufbau (i.e. building-up) Principle. The order of filling can be determined by following the diagonal arrows in the diagram below.

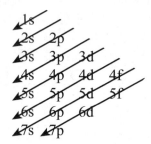

The electron configurations of the 118 elements that are currently known can be specified with these sublevels. Each s sublevel can hold two electrons with opposed spins, each p sublevel, consisting of three orbitals, can hold six electrons. A d sublevel with five orbitals can hold ten electrons and an f sublevel, with seven orbitals, can hold 14. For sublevels with multiple orbitals, one electron enters each orbital before any pair up. This diagram correctly predicts the filling of the 4s before the 3d and other "exceptions". The electrons in the outermost orbitals (i.e. those with the highest quantum number) are called valence electrons and those in inner orbitals are core electrons. For each of the main energy levels (1–7), the number of possible orbitals equals n^2, and with 2 electrons per orbital, the maximum number of electrons per energy level is $2n^2$. (This rule applies only to $n = 1 - 4$ because some sublevels have not been accessed for $n \geq 5$.)

Electrons repel one another, which decreases the attraction of the nucleus for a given electron and makes it appear that the electron is attracted by an effective nuclear charge (Z_{eff}) that is less than the actual charge. An electron in the same principal energy level cancels a fraction of a nuclear charge while an electron in an inner level (i.e. a core electron) cancels a full nuclear charge. Thus, the Z_{eff} increases from left to right across the Periodic Table (PT) but changes very little down the PT.

When the elements are listed in order of increasing atomic number, regular variations in chemical and physical properties occur that are related to electron configurations and chemical families in the PT.

Atomic radius – (distance between nuclei of adjacent atoms in an element)

- increases down the PT due to the increase in principal energy levels.
- decreases across the PT from left to right as electrons in the same principal energy level are attracted to nuclei with greater Z_{eff}.

Ionization energy (the energy required to remove an electron from a gaseous atom)

- decreases down the PT as electrons are removed from higher principal energy levels that are screened or shielded from the nucleus by core electrons. (This is often referred to as the shielding effect.)
- increases from left to right across the PT due to greater attractions to more highly-charged nuclei. Exceptions to this increase are observed for Group 13 (B, Al, Ga, In, Tl) due to the outermost electron occupying a p sublevel and Group 16 (O, S, Se, Te, Po) where the fourth electron in the p sublevel is paired.

For elements with two or more electrons the IE for each subsequent electron is greater than that for the previous one because subsequent ones are removed from species with greater positive charges containing fewer electrons to repel (i.e increased Z_{eff}). This effect is especially pronounced for an electron removed from an inner shell, which experiences a greater nuclear attraction due to both decreased shielding and a smaller distance to the nucleus. For example, the first three IEs for Mg (in kJ/mol) are; 738, 1451, 7732. The large difference between the second and third IEs offers an explanation for the observation that Mg ions are +2 in its compounds.

Electron affinity (energy released* [see note below] when a gaseous atom gains one or more electrons to form a negative ion)

- generally decreases down the PT as the attraction between the nucleus and the added electron becomes smaller with the distance from the nucleus. The elements Al, Si, P, S and Cl have higher EAs than those above them due to the greater electron repulsion in these smaller atoms (B, C, N, O, F, respectively).
- generally increase from left to right across the PT although Group 2 is less than expected due to the added electron having to occupy a higher energy sublevel and Group 15 is lower than predicted because the added electron must pair with another.

*Note: When more than one electron is added to an atom the extra repulsion may require the absorption rather than the release of energy.

Electronegativity (the relative ability of an atom in a bond to attract electrons)

- generally decreases down a given family in the PT with exceptions for the main group elements that follow the first transition series (Ga - Br).
- increases from left to right across the PT.

Metallic behavior (lose electrons, exhibit three-dimensional electrical and thermal conductivity)

- decreases from left to right across the PT as electrons are held more tightly in the smaller atoms and are more difficult to remove.

- increases down the PT as electrons in higher principal energy levels are released more readily due to the increased distance from the nucleus to the outermost occupied energy level.

Ion formation (certain atoms lose or gain electrons to form positive or negative ions)

• cations are formed when atoms with low IEs lose one or more electrons

+1	Group I and ammonium	Li, Na, K, Rb, Cs, NH$_4^+$
+2	Group II and transition metals	Mg, Ca, Sr, Ba, Ra, Mn, Fe, Co, Ni, Cu, Zn
+3	Group III	Al

• anions are formed when atoms with high EAs gain one or more electrons

−1	Group 17 atoms (halogens)	F, Cl, Br, I
−2	Group 16 atoms (chalcogens)	O, S, Se, Te
−3	Group 15 atoms (pnictogens)	N, P, As, Sb, Bi

Spectroscopy

• Most forms of spectroscopy begin with the absorption of a photon that has enough energy to promote a transition within an atom or molecule. Examples include:

1. infra-red (IR) spectroscopy – Photons can cause stretching and bending vibrations in molecules. A vibration that is accompanied by a change in the molecule's dipole moment will be infra-red active. H_2 and O_2 do not absorb IR because these non-polar molecules cannot undergo a dipole moment change. In contrast, the non-polar CO_2 is infrared-active because its dipole moment changes when it bends (and stretches asymmetrically).

Vibrational modes of carbon dioxide

←O = C = O→   →O = C = O→   O = C = O

symmetric stretch   asymmetric stretch   bend
IR inactive   IR active   IR active

2. ultraviolet (UV)-visible spectroscopy – Photons cause changes in the energy levels of electrons in atoms and molecules. Colored substances result when the absorbance occurs in the visible region of the spectrum and the complementary color is transmitted. Transition metal ions appear colored due to electron transitions between d orbitals.

absorption of a photon of visible light excites e⁻

3. photoelectron spectroscopy (PES) – When high energy UV or x-ray photons strike an atom, molecule or surface they cause the ejection of valence or bonding (UV) or core (x-ray) electrons. Because the energy of the photon equals the kinetic energy of the ejected electron plus the energy binding it in the atom ($h\nu = \text{KE} + \text{BE}$), by measuring the kinetic energy of the ejected electron it is possible to determine the energy with which it was held in the substance.

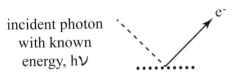

incident photon
with known
energy, hν

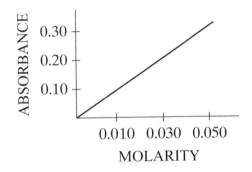

ejected electron with energy equal to the difference
between that of the photon and the energy
holding the electron in the substrate

Quantitative Spectra

The amount of light absorbed at a specific wavelength by a solution or collection of molecules is proportional to the concentration of the absorbing species, the thickness of the sample, and a constant (called the molar absorptivity) that is characteristic of the substance as summarized in the equation; $A = abc$. This equation is known as Beer's Law and provides a means of determining the concentration of a sample from a measurement of the absorbance (A) if the molar absorptivity (a) and the sample thickness (b) are known. Alternatively, the concentration of an unknown can be found by locating its absorbance on a graph of absorbance vs concentration for a series of samples of known concentration.

CHAPTER 1
MULTIPLE-CHOICE QUESTIONS

Questions 1–4 should be answered using the following responses.

    (A) Infrared
    (B) Ultraviolet
    (C) Visible
    (D) X-ray

1. Which type of electromagnetic radiation has the highest frequency?

    X-ray

2. Which type of electromagnetic radiation has the longest wavelength?

    Infrared

3. A photon of which type of electromagnetic radiation has the greatest energy?

    X-ray

4. Which type of radiation is shown mainly by fireworks displays?

    Visible

5. What is the energy of a photon (in units of h) that has a wavelength of 300 nm?
   ($c = 3.00 \times 10^8$ m/s)

    (A) $1 \times 10^{17} h$
    (B) $1 \times 10^{15} h$
    (C) $1 \times 10^6 h$
    (D) $1 \times 10^{-2} h$

    $c = \lambda \nu$ *$E = h\nu$*

    $3.00 \times 10^8 \, m/s = 300 \, \nu$

    $1.0 \times 10^6 = \nu$

6. An atom of which element forms an ion with a charge of –2 ?

    (A) Sodium
    (B) Magnesium
    (C) Sulfur
    (D) Chlorine

7. The elements listed all react with H_2O to produce H_2 gas and the respective cations. Which element reacts most vigorously?

(A) Sodium
(B) Magnesium
(C) Potassium
(D) Calcium

8. Which of the atoms below has the largest atomic radius?

(A) Nitrogen
(B) Oxygen
(C) Phosphorus
(D) Sulfur

Questions 9–10 should be answered with the following ionization energy data.

	I	II	III	IV	V
IE kJ/mol	496	4562	6912	9544	13353

9. How many valence electrons are present in this atom?

(A) One
(B) Two
(C) Three
(D) Four

10. The increase in ionization energies for these five electrons is best attributed to a(n)

(A) increase in the charge on the nucleus
(B) increase in the size of the nucleus
(C) decrease in the repulsion between electrons
(D) decrease in the charge on the ion formed

11. Which of the elements below has the highest first ionization energy?

(A) Li
(B) Be
(C) Na
(D) Mg

12. What is the electron configuration of an atom that has eight electrons?

(A) $1s^2\ 2s^2\ 2p^2\ 2p^2$
(B) $1s^2\ 2s^2\ 2p^2\ 3s^2$
(C) $1s^2\ 1p^2\ 2s^2\ 2p^2$
(D) $1s^2\ 2s^2\ 2p^2\ 2p^1\ 2p^1$

$1s^2\ 2s^2\ 2p^4$

13. According to Coulomb's Law ($F = q_1q_2/r^2$), how does the force between a hydrogen nucleus and an electron in the n = 2 level compare with that for one in the n = 1 level if the distance between the nucleus and the n = 2 level is twice as great as that between the nucleus and the n = 1 level?

(A) one-quarter as strong
(B) one-half as strong
(C) twice as strong
(D) four times as strong

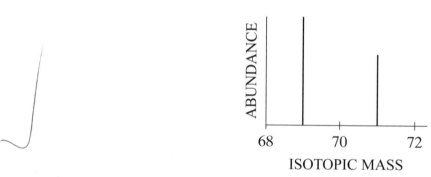

14. The mass spectrum of a sample of an element is shown below. What is the average atomic mass of this element?

ABUNDANCE

68   70   72
ISOTOPIC MASS

(A) 69.0
(B) between 69.0 and 70.0
(C) 70.0
(D) between 70.0 and 71.0

Questions 15–17 should be answered using the following responses.

  (A) infra-red spectroscopy
  (B) mass spectrometry
  (C) photoelectron spectroscopy
  (D) UV-visible spectroscopy

15. Which technique should be used to determine the energy of vibration of the atoms in a molecule?
    infra-red spectroscopy

16. Which technique should be used to determine the energy of excitation of the electrons in a molecule?
    UV-visible spectroscopy

17. Which technique should be used to determine the energies of core electrons?
    photo electron spectroscopy

Questions 18–19 should be answered by reference to the graph below.

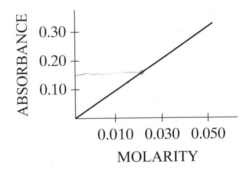

18. If 2.00 mL of a solution is diluted to 20.0 mL and the absorbance of the 20.0 mL solution is found to be 0.15, what is the molarity of the 2.00 mL solution?

  (A) 0.025 *M*
  (B) 0.050 *M*
  (C) 0.25 *M*
  (D) 0.50 *M*

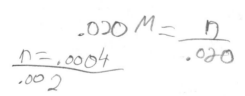

$$.020\,M = \frac{n}{.020}$$

$$n = .0004$$

$$\frac{n = .0004}{.002}$$

19. If the graph above was obtained using a 1 cm cell, what are the units of the slope of the graph?

  (A) mol/L
  (B) L/mol
  (C) mol•cm/L
  (D) L/mol•cm

LiF

20. The formulas of lithium fluoride and lithium nitride are LiF and Li_3N, respectively. If the formula of magnesium fluoride is MgF_2, what is the formula for magnesium nitride?

(A) MgN
(B) MgN_2
(C) Mg_3N
(D) Mg_3N_2

21. The spectrum of a hydrogen atom contains a total of 26 lines, and that of lithium possess approximately eight times as many. This provides evidence for the quantum mechanical model of the atom due to the

(A) larger mass of the lithium atom
(B) greater number of lithium isotopes
(C) greater attraction between the electrons and the lithium nucleus
(D) greater number of occupied sublevels in the lithium atom

Questions 22–24 should be answered using the responses, which refer to the ionization energies of four consecutive elements in the table below.

(A) I
(B) II
(C) III
(D) IV

	I	II	III	IV
Ionization Energy, kJ/mol	1314	1681	2080	496

22. Which element is a noble gas?

23. Which element is an alkali metal?

24. Which element is a halogen?

25. All of the following increase from left to right across the second period of the periodic table (Na - Ar) EXCEPT

(A) atomic number
(B) effective nuclear charge
(C) number of valence electrons
(D) number of core electrons

CONSTRUCTED-RESPONSE QUESTIONS

1. The model of the atom changed dramatically during the late nineteenth and early twentieth century.

   (a) Briefly outline the atomic model that existed during the late 1800s.
   (b) Describe one experiment that was conducted during this period that led to the change in the atomic model and state the specific change in the model that this experiment prompted.
   (c) List three characteristics of the current model of the atom that differ from the model that was popular during the late 1800s.

2. A student has a 0.100 M solution of $Cu(NO_3)_2$ and a solution with an unknown concentration of about 0.00500 M. She wants to determine the concentration of the unknown by measuring its absorbance and plotting it on a graph of absorbance against concentration.

(a) List the equipment needed to prepare the solutions required for the graph.
(b) State and explain the number of standard solutions that should be prepared.
(c) Briefly describe the procedure needed to prepare one of the solutions in (b).
(d) Outline how the concentration of the unknown can be found from its measured absorbance.

3. An x-ray photon with an energy of 2.382×10^{-16} J ejects an electron with a kinetic energy of 1.911×10^{-16} J from a $1s$ orbital in carbon.

   (a) Calculate the binding energy of the $1s$ orbital in C in joules.

   (b) Calculate the binding energy of this orbital in kJ/mol.

   (c) Calculate the velocity of the ejected electron in m/s.
      [KE = $1/2mv^2$, m = 9.11×10^{-31} kg, 1 J = 1 kg•m^2/s^2]

   (d) Determine the ratio of the energy of a C $1s$ electron to that of a C $2p$ orbital (IE = 1086 kJ/mol).

CHEMICAL BONDING

Big Idea 2 of the new AP Chemistry Curriculum Framework states that "chemical and physical properties of materials can be explained by the structure and the arrangement of atoms, ions, or molecules and the forces between them." Enduring Understanding 2.C continues with the idea that "the strong electrostatic forces of attraction holding atoms together in a unit are called chemical bonds."

Forces that hold atoms together are called chemical bonds. Bonds form in order to allow a minimal energy state for the participating atoms, so bond formation is an exothermic process (and bond breaking is an endothermic process). The type and strength of bond that forms between reacting particles dictates the physical and chemical characteristics of the molecule or polyatomic ion in question.

Covalent, Ionic, and Metallic Bonding

Ionic bonds occur between ions due to electrostatic attraction between cations and anions. They form between atoms with large differences in electronegativity (> 1.5 on the Pauling scale), typically between a metal and a non-metal. The relative strength of an ionic bond can be predicted using Coulomb's Law (the strength of the bond is directly proportional to the magnitude of the charges involved and indirectly proportional to the square of the distance between them). Because they are polar in nature, ionic solids are soluble in polar solvents, such as water. Ionic attraction is very strong so ionic solids tend to have high melting points.

Pure or non-polar covalent bonds form between non-metals of nearly identical electronegativities while polar covalent bonds form between non-metals with dissimilar electronegativity values. While covalent bonds within molecules are strong, the binding forces between molecules are relatively weak (see IMFs or intermolecular forces). Thus molecular solids with covalent bonds tend to have low melting points and can be soluble in non-polar solvents like carbon tetrachloride (tetrachloromethane).

Metallic bonding occurs between metal atoms. Metals tend to have a nucleus with a large positive charge and relatively few valence electrons. The positively charged nuclei are positioned regularly in a lattice by electrostatic repulsion while the valence electrons are equally attracted by adjacent nuclei. This leads to the "sea of electrons" model, wherein the nuclei bob like islands in a stream of free-flowing electrons. This model is useful for explaining physical characteristics such as electrical and thermal conductivity; for example, pushing an electron into one side of a metallic solid eventually pushes an extra electron out elsewhere, thus causing an electrical current. Since the attraction between nuclei and valence electrons varies widely, metals have a wide range of melting points.

Intermolecular Forces

Intermolecular forces (IMFs) are a group of weaker attractive forces between atoms or molecules that are not bonds. Known generically as "van de Waals forces", they include two general types. London forces are common to all atoms and molecules. These are caused by temporary dipoles that occur when electrons shift around the nuclei, thus forming ephemeral attractions and repulsions. Although these are very weak, they are found in all atoms and molecules. The strength of the temporary dipole formed depends on the number of electrons that are moving around the molecule, so molecules with larger molecular mass (and therefore more electrons) have greater London forces. The other general sort of IMF is the dipole force, an attraction between the opposite polarity ends of adjacent molecules which have permanent dipoles. An exaggerated form of the dipole force, the "hydrogen bond", occurs when an electropositive hydrogen atom bonds with a very electronegative partner, such as fluorine, oxygen, or nitrogen. The "H-FON" bond formed is thus very polar, and the strongly positive and negative ends of adjacent molecules have noticeably stronger interaction that a simple London force. IMFs will be discussed in depth in Chapter 4.

Lewis Structures

Lewis structures are drawn with a technique that encourages grouping valence electrons in octets around each nucleus. Covalent bonds are represented as shared pairs of electron dots between nuclei or as a dash. A short line or pair of dots can also represent an unshared electron pair. If the overall species is an ion, then square brackets enclose it and the charge is placed to the upper right of the brackets. The technique can be extended to grouping atoms to form molecules or polyatomic ions. The positioning of electron pairs around a central atom can be predicted using a technique known as Valence Shell Electron Pair Repulsion Theory (VSEPRT). The polarity of the predicted species can then be used to predict physical characteristics such as vapor pressures or melting and boiling points.

Vocabulary: Bonds and Bonding

Covalent bond   bond formed from shared electrons

Bond length   average distance between nuclei of two bonded atoms in a molecule

Bond energy   energy needed to break one particular chemical bond in a gaseous substance

Lewis Structures   representation of molecules and atoms using symbols for atoms with dots and lines for electrons

Bond energy   a measure of the stability of a chemical bond; the amount of energy needed to break the bond. This depends on the atoms that form the bond specified and on the effects of all the other atoms in the molecular structure. Bond energy is also determined by the number of electrons shared; bond strength increases with bond multiplicity. It also increases with increase in electronegativity difference, due to increased stability from coulombic attractions. Bond strength decreases with decreased orbital overlap between atoms. Because those valence electrons are more diffuse and electron density is more spread out, overlap on the axis and resulting attraction decreases.

Bond length   characteristic distance of separation between two atoms, influenced by principal quantum number, because a greater number of core electrons decreases the ability of two atoms to get very close to each other due to electron repulsion. Increased multiplicity of a bond decreases bond length because the placement of additional electrons between atoms increases coulombic attraction. Higher effective nuclear charge (Z_{eff}) decreases bond length because higher attraction results in smaller atomic size, allowing the atoms to get closer to each other. Increased electronegativity decreases bond length because the partial charges increase the coulombic attraction, allowing the atoms to get closer. The ability to form a *pi* bond is dependent on atomic size. For example C=C is possible due to the relatively small atomic size, but Si=Si is not because the Si atoms are much larger. Breaking a bond *always* requires energy; forming a bond always releases energy.

Molecular orbitals   When two atomic orbitals from different atoms interact, two new molecular orbitals are generated, on additive and one subtractive. The additive orbital (**bonding molecular orbital**) has high electron density between the nuclei. The subtractive orbital (**antibonding molecular orbital**) has low electron density between the nuclei. The bonding antibond σ_s orbitals are more stable than any molecular orbital from $2p$, because $2s$, which forms σ_s and σ_s^*, is more stable that $2p$. The two π bonding orbitals are of equal energies, as are the π^* orbitals. The $2p$ antibonding orbitals are the least stable molecular orbitals, with σ_p^* less stable than π^*

Bond order   net amount of bonding between two atoms, BO = $\frac{1}{2}$ the number
                         ($e^-_{bonding} - e^-_{antibonding}$)

Vocabulary: Sharing Electrons

Bonding orbitals	orbital with high electron density between the atoms
Sigma (σ) **bond**	bond formed by the end-on overlap of atomic orbitals giving high electron density along the axis, with one pair of electrons shared between two atoms.
Pi (π) **bond**	bond formed by side-by-side overlap of atomic orbitals accounting for electron density above and below the axis.
Double ($\sigma + \pi$) **bond**	chemical bond containing two pairs of electrons, involving two orbital orientations, with one pair end-on-end and a second pair side by side
Triple ($\sigma +$ **two** π) **bond**	chemical bond with three shared pairs of electrons, involving three orientations, one end-on and two side-by-side
Nonbonding electrons	valence electrons that do not participate in bonding
Lone pairs	a pair of valence electrons that is localized on one atom instead of being involved in a chemical bond
Formal charge (FC)	"bookkeeping" of valence electrons in Lewis structures; calculate the apparent charge on any atom in a Lewis structure as follows: • all unshared electrons assigned to atom where located • half the bonding electrons in a shared pair assigned to each of the bonded atoms The formal charge for each atom in the Lewis structure is equal to the number of valence electrons in that isolated atom minus the number of electrons assigned as above to that atom in the Lewis structure.
Resonance structures	two or more equivalent Lewis structures representing a molecule with delocalized electrons
Delocalized π **orbitals**	formed when more than two p orbitals from three or more atoms overlap in the appropriate geometry. Evidence for the orbitals is provided by bond lengths: in ozone, O_3, all bond lengths are equal and intermediate between that of O–O and O=O. Delocalized π orbitals affect absorption spectra/color, bond stability, and redox. For example, many organic molecules with these orbitals are colored (eg. chlorophyll).
Polar covalent bond	asymmetric electron distribution between two bonded nuclei
Electronegativity	measure of an atom's ability to attract shared electrons in a bond
Dipole moment	the net electrical character arising from asymmetrical charge distribution in a molecule or polyatomic ion

Vocabulary: Molecular and Electron Pair Geometry

VSEPR principle of minimizing electron-electron repulsion by placing electron pairs as far apart as possible

Hybridization formation of a set of hybrid orbitals with favorable directional characteristics by blending two or more valence orbitals of the same atom

Coordination structure the number of atoms to which an atom is bonded

Steric number the sum of the coordination number of an atom and its number of lone pairs of electrons

Molecular shapes

(a) tetrahedron electron or molecular geometry that features four identical faces that are equilateral triangles

    trigonal pyramid pyramid shape with an equilateral triangle base and isosceles triangle sides due to a lone pair distorting three shared pairs of electrons and the corresponding bond angles

    bent shape shape of a triatomic molecule with a bond angle $< 180°$, due to two lone pairs

(b) trigonal bipyramidal double pyramid with triangular base and two apices along a linear axis perpendicular to the plane of the base, dsp^3 hybrid.

    trigonal bipyramid five atoms arranged around central atom, with bond angles of $90°$ and $120°$

    seesaw shape four outer atoms and one central atom; one equatorial lone pair; bond angles of $< 120°$ and $90°$ due to lone pair

(c) octahedral shape double pyramid with square base; six vertices for atoms and/or lone pairs, d^2sp^3 hybridication

    octahedron six outer atoms, with bond angles $= 90°$

    square planar four outer atoms and two axial lone pairs, bond angles $= 90°$

    square pyramid fiver outer atoms and one axial lone pair, bond angles $< 90°$

(d) trigonal planar sp^2 hybrid with three atoms arranged to form a triangle bond angle $= 120°$

    linear geometry three atoms arranged in a line

Molecular Geometry

The best way to address the concept of molecular geometry is to consider first the distribution of electron pairs. Then consider the location of shared and unshared (lone pairs) of electrons. In general, pairs of electrons are distributed to minimize repulsion. Unshared pairs are located so as to be as from far from each other as possible. A systematic presentation of electron pair distribution is given below. Consult your textbook for detailed diagrams that include representation of three dimensions.

Covalent bonds; electron pair distribution and hybridization

- Two pairs; linear distribution; two *sp* hybrid orbitals

$$-A-$$

shared pairs	
two	linear – three atoms arranged in a straight line

- Three pairs: trigonal planar distribution; three *sp*^{2} hybrid orbitals

shared pairs	
two	bent – three atoms arranged in a bent line
three	trigonal planar – central atom plus three bonded atoms

- Four pairs: tetrahedral distribution; four *sp*^{3} hybrid orbitals

shared pairs	
two	bent – three atoms arranged in a bent line
three	trigonal pyramid – central atom plus three bonded atoms
four	tetrahedral – central atom plus four bonded atoms

- Five pairs: trigonal bipyramidal distribution; five *dsp*^{3} hybrid orbitals

shared pairs	
two	linear – three atoms arranged in a straight line
three	trigonal planar – central atom plus three bonded atoms
four	see-saw – central atom plus four bonded atoms
five	trigonal bipyramid – central atom plus five bonded atoms

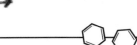

- Six pairs: octahedral distribution; six d^2sp^3 hybrid orbitals

<u>shared pairs</u>

two	linear – three atoms arranged in a straight line
three	T-shaped – central atom plus three bonded atoms
four	square planar – central atom plus four bonded atoms
five	square pyramid – central atom plus five bonded atoms
six	octahedron – central atom plus six bonded atoms

A summary of distribution of electron pairs and resulting molecular geometry is found in Figure 2.3.

Electron Pairs	Geometrical Arrangement	Electron-pairs (*sigma* bonds)		Set of Hybrid Orbitals	Molecular Shape	Examples
		Shared	Unshared			
2	linear	2	0	sp	linear	$BeCl_2$; CO_2
3	trigonal planar	3	0	sp^2	trigonal planar	BF_3; SO_3
		2	1		bent	SO_2
4	tetrahedral	4	0	sp^3	tetrahedral	CH_4
		3	1		trigonal pyramidal	NH_3; SO_3^{2-}
		2	2		bent	H_2O
		1	3		linear	HF
5	trigonal bipyramidal	5	0	dsp^3	trigonal bipyramidal	PCl_5
		4	1		see-saw	SF_4
		3	2		T-shaped	ClF_3
		2	3		linear	XeF_2
6	octahedral	6	0	d^2sp^3	octahedral	SF_6; $Fe(CN)_6^{3-}$
		5	1		square pyramidal	BrF_5
		4	2		square planar	XeF_4; $Cu(H_2O)_4^{2+}$

Figure 2.3 Distribution of electron pairs

CHAPTER 2
MULTIPLE-CHOICE QUESTIONS

Questions 1–5: The set of lettered choices below is a list of classes of solids and refers to the numbered phrases immediately following it. Select the one lettered choice that best fits each phrase. A choice may be used once, more than once, or not at all.

(A) an ionic solid
(B) a metallic solid
(C) a network solid with covalent bonds
(D) a molecular solid with nonpolar molecules

1. Al, aluminum wire

2. CO_2, dry ice

3. $C_{12}H_{22}O_{11}$, sucrose or table sugar

4. NH_4NO_3, ammonium nitrate crystals

5. C(gr), powdered graphite

6. All of these molecular shapes can be explained by d^2sp^3 hybridization of electrons on the central atom EXCEPT

(A) linear
(B) T-shaped
(C) square planar
(D) trigonal bipyramid

7. Which of the following molecules is predicted to have the smallest molecular dipole moment?

(A) HBr
(B) HCl
(C) HI
(D) H_2

8. Each species below has a Lewis diagram that illustrates the octet rule EXCEPT

   (A) nitrate, NO_3^-
   (B) ammonia, NH_3
   (C) ammonium, NH_4^+
   (D) nitrogen monoxide, NO

9. Which species exhibits a bent molecular geometry?

   (A) HCl
   (B) PH_3
   (C) CH_4
   (D) SO_2

Questions 10–12: Consider the chemical bonds found in solid sodium hydrogencarbonate. For each bond specified, choose the best description from the list of bond types below.

   (A) ionic bond
   (B) single covalent bond
   (C) double covalent bond
   (D) resonance covalent bond

10. carbon/oxygen bond

11. sodium/hydrogencarbonate bond

12. oxygen/hydrogen bond

_____

Questions 13–15: Use the following descriptions of electron distribution around a central atom to answer the following questions.

   (A) 4 shared pairs
   (B) 3 shared pairs, 1 unshared pair
   (C) 2 shared pairs, 2 unshared pairs
   (D) 1 shared pair, 3 unshared pairs

13. In the water molecule, the H-O-H bond angle is 105°. Which distribution of electrons around the central carbon atom provides the best explanation for this bond angle?

14. The H-N-H bond angle in ammonia, NH_3, is 107°. Which distribution of electron pairs around the central nitrogen atom provides the best explanation for this bond angle?

15. In the tetrachloromethane (carbon tetrachloride) molecule, the Cl-C-Cl bond angle is 109.5°. Which distribution of electron pairs around the central carbon atom provides the best explanation for this bond angle?

Questions 16–18: use the set of lettered choices below to answer the following questions.

(A) see-saw
(B) T-shaped
(C) tetrahedral
(D) trigonal planar

16. The shape of the BF_3 molecule is best described as

17. The shape of the IF_3 molecule is best described as

18. The shape of the SF_4 molecule is best described as

---

19. Which of the following identifies the species that occupies the lattice points in crystals of xenon and xenon difluoride?

(A) Some lattice points in each substance contain anions.
(B) The lattice points in xenon are occupied by ions while the lattice points in xenon difluoride are occupied by molecules.
(C) The lattice points in xenon are occupied by atoms while the lattice points in xenon difluoride are occupied by molecules.
(D) The lattice points in xenon are occupied by cations while the lattice points in xenon difluoride are occupied by atoms.

Questions 20–24: use the set of lettered choices below to answer the following questions.

(A) Linear
(B) Bent
(C) T-shaped
(D) Trigonal planar

20. beryllium fluoride, BeF_2

21. boron trihydride, BH_3

22. bromine triiodide, BrI_3

23. water, H_2O

24. sulfur trioxide, SO_3

---

25. The $Fe(CN)_6^{3-}$ complex ion is known to have octahedral geometry. Explanation of its bonding includes all of the following EXCEPT

(A) bond angles of 90°
(B) resonance structures
(C) expanded octet
(D) d^2sp^3 hybridization

CONSTRUCTED-RESPONSE QUESTIONS

1. Using principles of chemical bonding and/or intermolecular forces, explain each of the following.

   (a) The normal melting point of iodine, I_2, is $113.5°C$, greater than the normal melting point of chlorine, Cl_2, at $-100.98°C$.

   (b) Both solid Ag and molten Ag are excellent conductors of electricity. However, solid silver nitrate, $AgNO_3$, is a good conductor only when melted or dissolved in water. As a solid, it is a poor conductor of electricity.

   (c) The normal boiling point of H_2O is higher than the normal boiling point of H_2S even though the molar mass of H_2O is lower.

   (d) Arsenic, As, reacts with the metal sodium, Na, to form Na_3As but it reacts with the nonmetal chlorine, Cl_2, to form $AsCl_3$.

2. The shape of the carbonate ion, CO_3^{2-}, is known to be trigonal planar (triangular coplanar), with three equivalent C-O bonds.

(a) Draw a Lewis electron dot diagram for any one of the three equivalent contributing resonance structures of the carbonate ion, CO_3^{2-}.

(b) Discuss the hybridization of the atomic orbitals on the central carbon atom that is most likely to account for the bonding, geometry and distribution of electrons within this polyatomic ion. Include the role of *sigma* (σ) and *pi* (π) bonds in determining geometry and electron distribution.

(c) Draw a reasonable 3-dimensional representation of this ion. Clearly label *sigma* and *pi* bonds.

(d) Using a chemical symbol or formula, identify the atom, ion or molecule found at each lattice point in the solid crystalline form of calcium carbonate.

3. Although the number of atoms and overall charge of the azide (N_3^-) and triiodide (I_3^-) ions are similar, the bonding in the two polyatomic ions is quite different.

    (a) Draw a Lewis structure for each of the ions. Indicate the electron pair geometry, molecular geometry, and hybridization that applies to the central atom for each ion.

    (b) Which, if any, of the ions is polar? Explain.

    (c) Which, if any, of the ions has delocalized π bonds? Explain.

THE GAS PHASE

The Kinetic Molecular Theory

The Kinetic Molecular Theory (KMT) describes what we believe to be true about gases-beliefs from collected observations and indirect evidence spanning hundreds of years. For example, when one sees a white vapor trail in the sky that is growing longer and longer, one can reasonably conclude a jet airplane must be passing overhead, even if the altitude or the angle of the Sun obscures the actual airplane and makes it invisible to the naked eye.

The beliefs result in a mental picture of a rigid vessel containing individual particles, be they isolated atoms such as neon or helium, or molecules such as N_2 or CO_2. These particles may collide with the container walls and with each other, but rebound without a loss of energy, Our indirect evidence for believing the last statement is that, when temperature remains constant, there is a constant pressure inside the container, which would not be the case if molecules were to lose energy and then slow down.

The ideas we believe to be true about gases are often referred to as Postulates and the **Postulates of the Kinetic Molecular Theory** includes:

1. Ideal gases consist of small, invisible particles that are far apart in comparison to their own size and considered to be dimensionless points which occupy zero volume.
2. Ideal gas molecules move in rapid, random straight line motion.
3. The collisions of ideal gas molecules with the walls of a container or with other molecules are perfectly elastic: there is no loss of energy.
4. There are no attractive forces between ideal gas molecules or between gaseous molecules and the walls of the container.

5. At any particular instant, the molecules in a container do not all possess the same amount of kinetic energy. The average kinetic energy of the sample is directly proportional to the absolute Kelvin temperature.

An Ideal Gas is one in which the molecules conform to the above behaviors. Ideal gas behavior is promoted by conditions in which the gas molecules remain very far apart relative to their size: high temperatures and low pressures. The KMT allows us to make only accurate qualitative predictions about what happens to the gas sample when we change the conditions of temperature, pressure, volume or the number of molecules

When the distances between molecules decreases, attractions between molecules may become appreciable and deviations from ideal behavior may be observed. Such gases are then referred to as non-ideal or "real gases." In general, gases are most likely to deviate from ideal behavior when they reach conditions approaching the liquid phase. These typically include high pressure and/or or low temperature (near their boiling points).

THE GAS LAWS include

1. **Avogadro's Hypothesis** Equal volumes of gases at the same temperature and pressure (are equal because they) contain the same number of molecules.
An extension of this is the "balloon principle" – that the volume of a flexible container at constant temperature is directly proportional to the number of gas molecules in the container (balloon).

2. **Boyle's Law** The volume of a trapped sample of gas (at constant temperature) is inversely proportional to the applied pressure.

3. **Charles' Law** The volume of a gas is directly proportional to absolute (K) temperature (pressure held constant).

4. **Dalton's Law of Partial** For a mixture of gases, the total pressure exerted by the mixture is equal to the sum of the partial pressures of the individual gases.

5. **Graham's Law** The speed of the gas molecules is inversely proportional to the square root of their mass (temperature held constant). The lighter the molecules, the faster they move.

6. **Gay-Lussac's Law** When gases chemically combine, the ratios of their reacting volumes are small whole numbers.

Helpful Graphical Representations

Examinations frequently use graphical representations as frameworks for both the multiple choice and free-response questions.

Directly Proportional (e.g.Charles' Law)
Temperature and volume or
molecules and volume

Inversely Proportional (e.g.Boyle's Law)
pressure and volume

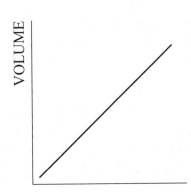

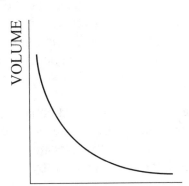

THE MATHEMATICS OF GAS LAWS

1. **The Ideal Gas Law** – The KMT accounts for the directly proportional relationships between the number of molecules and volume as well as temperature (K) and volume.[V = kT and V = k'n] It also accounts for the inverse relationship between pressure and volume. [PV = k]

These relationships can be combined into one equation: PV = k nT, where k is a proportionality constant which converts the proportional relationships to a mathematical equality. This k is more commonly known as R, the universal gas constant and the general gas law becomes

$$PV = nRT,$$

with the value of R = 0.0821 L atm $mol^{-1}K^{-1}$. P is pressure (in atm); V is volume (in Liters); n is the number of gas moles, and T is the Kelvin temperature. The equation and R values are found in the List of Equations provided by AP Chemistry for use during the exam, and the ability to successfully apply the equation is an absolute necessity in demonstrating mastery of gas principles. Given any three of the four values, one must be able to determine the fourth. A common mistake is neglecting to convert a °C temperature to a kelvins temperature in problems where only the °C temperature is provided.

Often two of the variables are held constant, so the problem requires one to determine the fourth quantity when a third variable is given or changed.

The van der Waals equation of state for a real gas is as follows:

van der Waals Equation $\left(P + \dfrac{n^2a}{V^2}\right)(V - nb) = nRT$

Calculations involving the van der Waals equation are no longer part of the A.P. Chemistry curriculum, but knowledge of the equation is helpful in explaining why the volume occupied by "real" gases is larger than the volume of ideal gases and why the pressures exerted by "real" gases are lower than the ideal pressures: hence the need for the "correction factors" inserted into the Ideal Gas Law. Energy is expended in overcoming attractions occurring during collisions between gas particles, lowering the velocity and the frequency of collisions against the container walls. Real gas particles are not points, but occupy a finite volume, so the total volume of the sample is larger than the ideal volume.

2. **Molar Volume** – KMT tells us that equal volumes of gases are equal because they contain the same number of molecules at the same temperature and pressure. Therefore, if standard temperature (0°C) and standard pressure (1atm) are inserted into the Ideal Gas Law, $PV = nRT$, the **molar volume** (volume occupied by 1 mole of any gas) at S.T.P. = 22.4 L mol^{-1}.

3. **Density** – Density is always expressed in terms of mass per unit volume, so the units of density become g L^{-1}. An application of this occurs where one may be asked to determine the density of oxygen gas at S.T.P. The density becomes 32.0 g mole $^{-1}$/22.4 L mol^{-1} = 1.43 g L^{-1}.

4. **Mixtures of Gases** – Frequently, two or more gases are present in a gas sample. All the molecules occupy the same volume and exist at the same temperature, but they do not necessarily have the same number of particles or exert the same (partial pressure). Daltons Law states that, $P_{total} = P_1 + P_2 + P_3 + \ldots$ where P_{total} = the total pressure exerted by the gas mixture and $P_1 + P_2 + P_3$ are the individual partial pressures exerted by the separate gases.

    Two common applications of the above principle suggest themselves here.

    (a) 2.0 mol of He and 4.0 mol of Ne are combined and result in a total pressure of 0.36 atm. Determine the partial pressure of each gas (P_{He} = 2/6 of 0.36 atm = 0.12 atm. P_{Ne} = 0.36 – .12 atm etc.)

    (b) If H_2 gas is produced when Mg is reacted with $HCl_{(aq)}$ and collected over water, determine the pressure of the "dry hydrogen" if the vapor pressure of water at this temperature is 18.2 mm Hg, and the total pressure in the collecting tube is 755 mm Hg.
    $$(P_{H_2} = 755 - 18.2 = 736.8 \text{ mm})$$

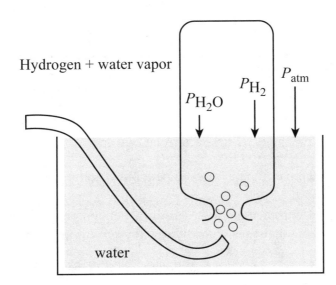

Hydrogen + water vapor

P_{H_2O} P_{H_2} P_{atm}

water

5. Molar mass and molecular velocity – The common illustration of appyling Graham's Law comes when we are asked to compare the relative velocities of equal volumes of gases at the same temperature, which means they have the same average kinetic energies.
½ mv^2 of the first gas = ½ mv^2 of the second gas, where m and v represent (molar) mass and velocity, respectively. $mv^2_a = mv^2_b$. Another variation might deal with the rates of diffusion. Two such examples might be

(a) Compare the relative velocity of He molecules to CH_4 molecules if both exist at 25°C.
$mv^2_{He} = mv^2_{CH4}$, $4v^2_{He} = 16\ v^2_{CH4}$ **$v_{He} = 2\ v_{CH4}$**

(b) If He diffuses through a tube in 15 seconds, how long will it take an equimolar amount of CH_4 to diffuse through the same tube. Assume constant temperature at 25°C.

Referring to the relative velocity calculation in (a), the v_{CH4} is 1/2 as fast as the velocity of He, so it will require twice the time – **30 seconds**.

EQUATIONS AND CONSTANTS

$PV = nRT$ — the fundamental relationship for successful mastery of gas gas law problems

$P_{total} = P_A + P_B + P_C + \ldots$ — Law of Partial pressures – for mixtures of gases, especially those collected over water

$n = m/molar\ mass$ — fundamental first year relationship

$K = \degree C + 273$ — converting Celsius temperature to kelvins

$\dfrac{P_1 V_1}{T_1} = \dfrac{P_2 V_2}{T_2}$ — Combined gas law – useful when temperature and pressure are simultaneously changing with a resulting change in volume

$D = m/V$ — classic mathematical definition of density

$K.E. = \frac{1}{2} mv^2$ — calculation of kinetic energy per molecule

$\dfrac{r_1}{r_2} = \sqrt{\dfrac{M_1}{M_2}}$ — re-arrangement of Graham's law useful with diffusion **rates**

$R = 0.0821\ L\ atm\ mol^{-1}\ K^{-1}$ — for use in $PV = nRT$

RECOMMENDED EXPERIMENTS

1. Determination of molar mass by vapor density (a.k.a. Dumas method)

2. Determination of molar volume of a gas- "Assumed Prior Knowledge"

3. % H_2O_2 – Production of Oxygen via $KMnO_4$ titration with H_2O_2

MULTIPLE-CHOICE QUESTIONS

1. Which of the following gases contains the fewest number of molecules?

   (A) 6.0 g of H_2
   (B) 14 g of N_2
   (C) 17 g of NH_3
   (D) 34 g of H_2S

2. Which of the following gases is NOT diatomic?

   (A) HCl
   (B) Hydrogen
   (C) Carbon monoxide
   (D) Neon

Questions 3–5: Select from the gases below at 25.°C and 1 atm.

   (A) CO_2 (molar mass 44)
   (B) NH_3 (molar mass 17)
   (C) H_2O (molar mass 18)
   (D) C_4H_{10} (molar mass 58)

3. Which molecule would move the fastest in the gas state at 25.0°C and 1 atm?

4. Which gas would dissolve in distilled water to form a basic solution?

5. Which gas is an odorless gas frequently used in fire extinguishers?

6. What is the ratio of the average speed of gaseous Ne atoms to gaseous SO_3 molecules, if equal volumes of both gases are measured at the same temperature and pressure?

(A) 8 to 1
(B) 4 to 1
(C) 2 to 1
(D) 1 to 1

7. The temperature of 36.0 mL of CH_4 gas is raised from 27.0°C to 327°C at constant pressure. What is the final volume of the CH_4 gas after heating ?

(A) 18.0 mL
(B) 36.0 mL
(C) 72.0 mL
(D) 327 mL

8. A real gas closely approaches the behavior of an ideal gas under conditions of

(A) low pressure and high temperature
(B) low pressure and low temperature
(C) high pressure and low temperature
(D) high pressure and high temperature

9. A mixture of 0.40 mole of He gas and 0.50 mole of N_2 gas exerts a total pressure of 0.90 atm. at 25°C. What is the partial pressure of the He gas?

(A) 0.36 atm
(B) 0.40 atm
(C) 0.45 atm
(D) 0.81 atm

10. What is the final gas pressure exerted by a sample of gas if the absolute (Kelvin) temperature of a gas is doubled and the volume is tripled?

(A) 1/6 the original pressure
(B) 2/3 the original pressure
(C) 3/2 the original pressure
(D) 6 times the original pressure

11. An inverse relationship is to Boyle's Law as a direct relationship is to

    (A) Ideal Gas Law
    (B) Grahams Law of Gas Diffusion
    (C) Hess's Law
    (D) Charles' Law

12. When water is heated to boiling in an open soda can and then inverted into a bucket containing cold water,

    (A) the can expands due to rapid expansion of the water vapor inside
    (B) the can implodes due to the rapid change in room air pressure
    (C) the can implodes due to rapid condensation of the inside water vapor
    (D) the can implodes due to the rapid change in room air pressure and rapid condensation of the inside water vapor

13. When a sample of an ideal gas is heated from 30°C to 60°C, the average kinetic energy of the gas changes. Which factor describes this change?

    (A) 1/2
    (B) 333/303
    (C) 333/273
    (D) 2/1

14. The dissolving of CO_2 gas in room temperature distilled water will typically

    (A) increase if the temperature of the water is increased
    (B) decrease if the temperature of the water is decreased
    (C) result in a change of pH from that of the pure water
    (D) result in the formation of a precipitate as the CO_2 dissolves

15. A rigid metal contains nitrogen gas. Which of the following statements applies to the N_2 gas in the tank if 10% of the gas is allowed to escape? (Assume the temperature remains constant.)

    (A) The volume of the gas decreases.
    (B) The pressure of the gas decreases.
    (C) The average kinetic energy of the N_2 gas decreases.
    (D) The mass of the gas remains the same.

Questions 16–17: Hydrogen gas is produced and then collected over water at 24°C in a long gas-collecting tube, which is inverted in a battery jar. The water levels in the battery jar and the tube are made equal, and the volume of the gas is 37.20 mL The gas, mixed with evaporated water vapor, exerts a total pressure of 751.0 mm.

16. If the water vapor pressure at this temperature is 23.1 mm, what is the pressure of the "dry" hydrogen at 24°C?

    (A) 774.1 mm Hg
    (B) 751.0 mm Hg
    (C) 727.9 mm Hg
    (D) 23.1 mm Hg

17. The purpose of leveling the gas measuring tube in the above experiment is to

    (A) determine the volume of the gas at room temperature
    (B) ensure that the gas pressure inside the tube is equal to room pressure
    (C) prevent further water molecules from evaporating in the tube
    (D) prevent the gas molecules from escaping from the tube

Questions 18–19: Use the balanced equation $2C_2H_6(g) + 7\ O_2(g) \rightarrow 6H_2O(g) + 4\ CO_2(g)$ to answer the following questions.

18. What minimum volume of oxygen will be required to completely react with 6.0 liters of C_2H_6? (Assume room pressure and temperature remain constant.)

    (A) 21.0 L
    (B) 14.0 L
    (C) 6.0 L
    (D) 3.5 L

19. How many molecules of $H_2O(g)$ will result if 1×10^{23} molecules of C_2H_6 completely react with excess oxygen?

    (A) 1×10^{23} molecules
    (B) 3×10^{23} molecules
    (C) 4×10^{23} molecules
    (D) 6×10^{23} molecules

20. When a balloon filled with helium gas is released, it rises and floats away. Which statement below is the best <u>explanation</u> for this observed behavior?

    (A) The helium density inside the balloon is less than that of the surrounding air.
    (B) The temperature of the surrounding air is less than the temperature of the helium.
    (C) Air pressure is greater than the pressure exerted by the helium.
    (D) The rate of diffusion of cooler air is less than that of warmer air.

Questions 21–22: The density of a mystery gas is 2.0 g/Liter at 0°C and 1 atm (STP) conditions.

21. What is the molar mass of this gas?

    (A) 2.0×22.4
    (B) $22.4/2.0$
    (C) $2.0/22.4$
    (D) 2.0×24.5

22. What is the most likely formula of this mystery gas?

    (A) Ne
    (B) CH_4
    (C) CO
    (D) C_3H_8

23. $2NH_3(g) \rightarrow 3H_2(g) + N_2(g)$. Consider the decomposition of NH_3 gas in the equation above at constant room temperature and pressure. Compared to the initial pressure, the final pressure exerted by the products will be

    (A) 2 times greater
    (B) 3 times greater
    (C) the same as the initial pressure
    (D) one-half the initial pressure

24. Which statement is typically true about gaseous molecules?

    (A) The heavier the molecules, the faster they travel.
    (B) The heavier the molecules, the greater their average kinetic energy.
    (C) The hotter the molecules, the faster they travel.
    (D) The larger the volume of the container, the greater the pressure exerted by the gaseous molecules.

25. A sample of N_2 gas is heated from 200 K to 400 K in a rigid container. Which of the following does **NOT** double?

(A) he average $\sqrt{\text{speed}}$ of the N_2 molecules
(B) he pressure of the N_2 gas
(C) he density of the N_2 gas
(D) he average kinetic energy of the N_2 gas

FREE-RESPONSE QUESTIONS

1. Consider 1.0 L volume of nitrogen and sulfur trioxide in the diagram below. Both containers exist at 25°C and a pressure of 1 atm.

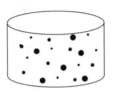 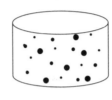

      1.0 L of N_2 1.0 L of SO_3

Decide whether each statement below is true or false and explain your reasoning for your decision.

(a) The number of moles of SO_3 is larger than the number of moles of N_2.
(b) The average speed of the SO_3 molecules is lower than the average speed of of the N_2 molecules.
(c) The average kinetic energy of the SO_3 molecules is greater than the average kinetic energy of the N_2 molecules.
(d) The mass of the SO_3 present in the 2nd container will be the same as the mass of N_2 present in the first container.

2. A mystery gas weighing 1.55 g occupies a volume of 0.560 L at 800 mm Hg and 0.00°C.

    (a) How many moles of the mystery gas are contained in the sample?

    (b) What is the molar mass of the gas?

3. A 4.00 g sample of $NH_4NO_3(s)$ is exploded, and the products are $H_2O(g)$, N_2, and O_2.

    (a) Write the balanced equation for the reaction.
    (b) If all the products are in the gas phase, what is the total number of moles of gaseous products?
    (c) What is the total number of molecules produced?
    (d) If the temperature is 527 K and the pressure is 745 mm Hg, what is the volume of the final mixture?

4. A 8.25 gram sample of PCl$_5$ is placed in an evacuated 2.00 liter flask and is completely vaporized at 400 K.

    (a) Calculate the pressure in the flask if no chemical reaction were to occur.

    (b) However, at 400 K, the PCl$_5$ is partially dissociated according to the following equation:

$$PCl_5(g) \rightleftharpoons PCl_3(g) + Cl_2(g)$$

The observed pressure is found to be 0.900 atm. Calculate the partial pressures of PCl$_5$ and PCl$_3$ in the flask.

INTER-MOLECULAR FORCES AND CONDENSED PHASES OF MATTER

SOLIDS, LIQUIDS AND PHASE CHANGES

I. From the Molecular Viewpoint

One way to think about liquids and solids is to visualize the gas particles so close to each other that they touch. When their temperature decreases, so does the distance between particles, and when the attractive forces between the particles are sufficiently strong, the particles no longer rebound from one another. This process is condensation, the opposite of evaporation: overcoming attractive forces and entering the (ideal) gas phase, and the temperature at which this happens is the boiling point

When phase changes occur, both the entropy and the enthalpy change. Values for these changes can be determined experimentally by using the liquid state as the starting point. These values are often referred to as the heat of fusion (liquid to solid at the normal freezing point) or the heat of vaporization (liquid to gas at the normal boiling point).

II. Summary chart – Phase changes

Phase change	ΔH Enthalpy change	ΔS Entropy change	ΔG Free Energy change
Vaporization	positive	positive	Temperature dependent – negative at high temps
Solidification	negative	negative	Temperature dependent – negative at low temps

III. Graphical Representations

Cooling or warming curves are one form of illustrating temperature changes and accompanying phase changes that occur when a pure substance is heated at a constant rate. Careful experiments result in plateau regions despite the fact that the substance is continuing to absorb heat, and these plateaus represent changes in **potential energy**- the distance between molecules changes as the incoming energy is used to *overcome attractions between the particles* in solid or liquid phases. The other regions, those with a rise in temperature, represent an increase in **kinetic energy** (as measured by temperature increases) for the substance. Note that the plateau for vaporization (boiling) is longer than the plateau for melting. This tells us that the heat of vaporization is typically much larger than the heat of fusion (heat of solidification).

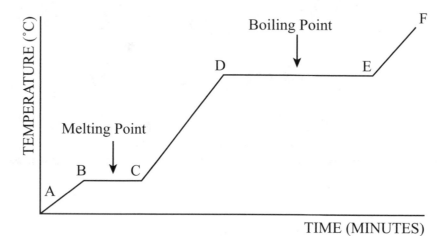

Regions depicted in the graph above:

Kinetic energy changes	Potential energy changes
A-B Solid warming	B-C Solid to liquid
C-D Liquid heating	D-E Liquid to gas
E-F Gas heating	

Phase diagrams such as the one below are used to show pressure-temperature relationships. A "normal boiling point" is defined as the temperature at which the vapor pressure equals (cancels out) the atmospheric pressure at 1 atm. Normal boiling points can be determined by finding the temperature of the liquid that intersects the graph at 1 atm. Such graphs tell us that the lower the temperature of the liquid at 1 atm, the higher the vapor pressure of the liquid at room temperature, and the weaker the inter-moleular attractions between molecules. Such graphs are **no longer included in the current A.P. Chemistry curriculum** but are often included on other chemistry subject exams such as Chemistry Olympiad Tests.

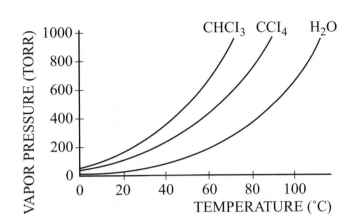

IV. Classification of Solid Crystals

True solids exhibit crystal structures which result in the formation of flat faces and sharp, reproducible angles. Materials in the solid phase which lack these characteristics are often referred to as amorphous solids or super-cooled liquids (glass) and, if made up or organic molecules, they are called "plastics." The chart below presents the common properties associated with these substances.

Summary Chart: Classification of Solid (Crystal) Structures

Type	Bonding Units	Bonding Strength	Factors	Examples
1. Atomic or Molecular Crystals	Neutral atoms or molecules (non-metallic elemnts)	**Very Weak** (Van der Waals) moderate to strong London Dispersion Forces	– surface area – Number of valence electrons – Symmetry – Polarity – "Hydrogen-bonding" (highest type of polarity	Ar, Kr, I_2 $C_6H_{12}O_6$ (sugar) H_2O
2. Metallic Crystals	Metal Atoms	**moderate to strong** "Delocalized Sea" of valence electrons surrounding + ions (kernels) – Conduction Bands aka Conduction Bands	– Ss size increases, down the Per. Chart, density of sea of e- decreases – Number of valence electrons	Zn, U Pb, Fe Au, Na, Al,
3. Ionic Crystals	positive and negative ions Metals + Non-metals	**Strong** ionic bonds - arise from electrostatic attractions (opposite charges attract)	$F = k \cdot \dfrac{q_1 \times q_2}{d^2}$ → charges → distance between ions (nuclei)	NaCl. KBr, BaO.NiS etc.
4. Covalent Crystals	Atoms of C, Si, or Ge	**Very strong** Covalent bonds between atoms	1. Network covalent or 2. planar covalent. structures 3. radius of atoms (as bond length increases, bond strength decreases)	Carbon (graphite) Carbon (diamond) Quartz, mica. (Si) Sand (SiO_2)

    A. If one focuses on **Molecular crystals** (consisting of non-metallic atoms) first, one observes trends in their melting and subsequent boiling points related to their molecular size, molecular shape and polarity, as well as to the number of outer (valence) electrons on the molecule's surface (Please refer to their inclusion in the above chart.) In general, the attractions between neutral molecules increases as the size (surface area) increases. The amount of the molecular surface in "touch" with an adjacent molecule increases attractions to the surface electrons on the **adjacent** molecules. In addition, the more symmetrical the molecules, the closer together they can pack in to one another, and again, attractions between **adjacent** molecules' surfaces increases. The more outer (valence) electrons on the surface, the stronger the attractions tend to be. Polar molecules, by their very label, have positive and negative "poles" of charge on the molecule; the electron distribution is NOT symmetrical. Strong attractions result between these positive and negative regions of these molecules (dipole-dipole attractions). The stronger these attractions, the more energy that is required to separate these molecules into liquid phase and the higher the melting points. The same reasoning can be applied to the liquid molecules becoming independent gas molecules and their subsequent boiling points.

In polar molecules containing the highly electronegative atoms of fluorine, oxygen or nitrogen (and occasionally chlorine, in terminal positions on the molecule) the electronegtivity differences may result in "hydrogen bonding." This is the additional attraction of H atoms of one molecule to the F,O, or N (and occasionally Cl, in terminal positions) atoms on an adjacent molecule. "Hydrogen bonding" accounts for the fact that even though H_2S has the same shape and is a larger molecule than H_2O, the attractions between H_2O molecules are **MUCH** stronger, so much so that, at room temperature, water is a liquid with stronger inter-molecular attractions and a significantly higher boiling point, and that H_2S is a gas, indicating weaker inter-molecular attractions. "Hydrogen bonding" also accounts for water expanding as is freezes, instead of shrinking, (as metals most frequently do), as the water molecules align into crystals and occupy a larger volume, taking into account this additional "bond " between molecules in all three dimensions. Hence we can usually successfully predict (a favorite "science practice") that molecules that include "hydrogen bonds" will typically have higher melting points and boiling points than similar molecules without these additional H-bonds.

B. If we investigate **Metallic crystals** next, we find correlations of properties here as well. The attractions between metallic atoms arise from the low ionization energies we typically observe in metals, which can give way to "delocalized" valence electrons - electrons no longer attracted to one specific nucleus but sufficiently delocalized into bands (conduction bands) surrounding the atoms that have become positive metal ions. Because Conduction Band Theory is not a part of the AP Chemistry curriculum, these electrons are often referred to as a delocalized "sea of electrons." The more electrons a metal atom contributes to the band the stronger the force "wrapped around" the positive ions, the higher the energy needed to separate the atoms, and the higher the melting point of the metal. Within this band of loosely held electrons, the easy mobility of these electrons also leads to the properties of electrical and thermal conductivity that we find in metals as well. As the size of the metal atoms increases, moving down a column of the Periodic Table, we find the same number of valence electrons but the "sea of electrons" or band is spread out over atoms with more filled inner layers of electrons leading to atoms with larger volumes. This "blanket" of electrons is stretched over larger atoms, with more shielding of the nuclear charge, resulting in **weaker attractions** of the electrons in the outer band to the positive "kernels." This accounts for the fact that we find that, with metal atoms, the melting points **decrease** as we move down the Periodic table. This is the opposite trend that we find with the halogen molecules, which are molecular solids. Very simply, these differences arise from the **differences in the nature or type of inter-molecular forces (IMF's)**.

C. Next, we move to **Ionic Crystals**, which are made up of *positive and negative ions* organized into an array of crystal structures. The attraction arises from the fact that opposite charges attract, resulting in forces known as "electrostatic attractions." The **greater the charges on the opposite ions, the stronger the attraction between the ions**, and the greater the energy required to separate the ions, leading to **higher melting points**. Conversely, **the larger the radius of the ions the greater the distance between the nuclei of the adjacent ions and the weaker the attraction** between oppositely charged ions. This results in lower melting points for ionic crystals with larger ions which typically result as we move down the Periodic Table. These can be summarized with an in "inverse square law" relationship, Coulomb's Law shown in the chart above:

$$F = k \cdot \frac{q_1 \times q_2}{d^2} \quad \begin{array}{l} \rightarrow \text{charges} \\ \rightarrow \text{distance between ions (nuclei)} \end{array}$$

where F is the force of attraction between ions, q= the amount of charge on the ions, and d = the distance between the nuclei (ions). For purposes here, k can be described as the proportionality constant that changes the proportional relationships into an equality. Again, we can often make useful predictions: we can predict, for example, that NaCl will have a higher melting point than CsBr, because although the charges are the same on the ions involved, the sizes are different, and the farther apart the ions are, the weaker the attraction between them.

D. Finally, we come to **Covalent crystals**, with the atoms most frequently involved found in the Upper IVA's of the Periodic Table: carbon, silicon and germanium. The two structures most frequently discussed are the planar covalent and network covalent crystals. In planar covalent crystals, the atoms have strong bonds within the plane, but much weaker bonds between planes of atoms, leading to the property of "cleavage," which we find in pencils. The incorrectly named pencil "leads," really consist of graphite, a planar covalent substance where the carbon readily rubs (cleaves) off onto the paper. This phenomenon occurs with mica (Si) as well, and, with the aid of a sharp fingernail or razor blade, one can peel off the layers of silicon atoms like the layers of an onion. With network covalent crystals, the atoms are strongly bonded in all three dimensions, leading to a network structure resulting in extraordinarily hard crystals that we find in diamond (carbon atoms) or quartz (silicon atoms). These strong bonds also explain the exceptionally high melting points we typically find in covalent solids, but who in their right mind would **melt** a diamond! We can apply this property to cutting tools. One thing that *can* cut a diamond is another diamond (used in the jewelry industry), and diamond cutting tools are frequently utilized in drilling processes or, in another era, were prized in phonograph record player needles.

MULTIPLE-CHOICE QUESTIONS

Questions 1–6 refer to the diagram below.

The graph below shows the temperature change as a sample of pure substance is cooled at a constant rate from a gas to a liquid to a solid. Separate regions are labeled I though V.

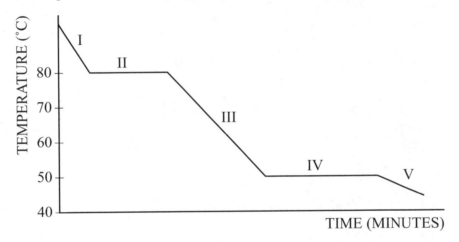

1. What is the approximate boiling point of the substance above?

   (A) 90°C
   (B) 80°C
   (C) 50°C
   (D) 40°C

2. What is the approximate freezing point of the substance above?

   (A) 90°C
   (B) 80°C
   (C) 50°C
   (D) 40°C

3. Which region represents the greatest change in potential energy?

(A) IV
(B) III
(C) II
(D) I

4. Which region represents the cooling of the liquid phase?

(A) IV
(B) III
(C) II
(D) I

5. Which region represents the region of highest kinetic energy?

(A) IV
(B) III
(C) II
(D) I

6. Which pairing lists the liquid with the higher vapor pressure first? Assume both liquids are observed at room temperature and 1 atm.

(A) motor oil, water
(B) rubbing alcohol, motor oil
(C) mineral oil, water
(D) milk, perfume

7. The term that describes the amount of heat required to convert one mole of a solid at its melting point to a liquid at this temperature is

(A) Heat of fusion
(B) Heat of sublimation
(C) Heat of combustion
(D) Heat of vaporization

8. The best explanation below for why C_3H_8 has a higher normal boiling point than CH_4 is the

   (A) greater molar mass
   (B) greater London Dispersion forces
   (C) greater polarity
   (D) presence of hydrogen bonding

Questions 9–13. Choose your answers from the choices below.

   (A) Germanium, Ge, is a solid where the atoms are bonded to each other much like those of carbon in a diamond.
   (B) Glycerol, $C_3H_5(OH)_3$, is an alcohol.
   (C) Lithium chloride, LiCl, is a white crystalline solid.
   (D) Propane, C_3H_8 is a gas which can be liquefied only at low temperatures or high pressures.

Considering only the above substances, identify the substance with:

 9. the highest melting point

10. the greatest hardness in the solid phase

11. the lowest heat of vaporization

12. conductivity in the fused or melted state, but not in the solid state

13. "hydrogen bonding"

_____

14. Ice cubes and snowmen shrink in size even when the temperature stays well below freezing, due to

   (A) vaporization
   (B) sublimation
   (C) excitation
   (D) evaporation

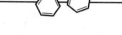

15. Which liquid below would be expected to have the highest equilibrium vapor pressure at room temperature, 25°C?

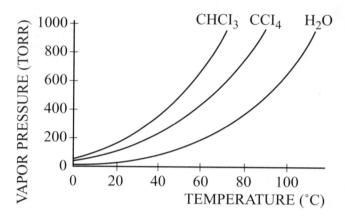

   (A) $CHCl_3$
   (B) H_2O
   (C) CCl_4
   (D) All three would have the same equilibrium vapor pressure at 25°C.

16. Which pairing has the substance with the higher melting point listed first?

   (A) Rb or K
   (B) LiCl or C_4H_{10}
   (C) CO_2 or CS_2
   (D) Cs or Fe

17. The explanation for why CH_4 is relatively insoluble in water is related to

   (A) the dipole-dipole attractions between H_2O molecules are stronger than the attractions between H_2O and CH_4 molecules
   (B) the size of CH_4 molecules is larger than the size of H_2O molecules
   (C) the dipole-dipole attractions between CH_4 molecules are greater than attractions between CH_4 and H_2O molecules
   (D) the attractions between CH_4 molecules are stronger than the attractions between CH_4 and H_2O molecules due to "hydrogen bonding" between CH_4 molecules

18. Which characteristic is most closely associated with covalent network solids?

   (A) High thermal conductivity, high degree of hardness
   (B) High electrical conductivity, high thermal conductivity
   (C) High melting points, high degree of hardness
   (D) High ductility, low electrical conductivity

Questions 19–23. Select your answers to questions 19–23 from the choices below.

(A) An ionic solid
(B) A metallic solid
(C) A planar covalent solid
(D) A molecular compound with non-polar molecules

19. Cu, copper wire

20. CO_2, dry ice

21. C_6H_6, benzene

22. $LiNO_3$ lithium nitrate crystals

23. $C_{(gr)}$ powdered graphite

---

24. Inexpensive sealed hand-boilers work on the principle that

(A) Liquids have just one characteristic boiling point
(B) Liquids boil when their vapor pressure = "atmospheric" (ambient) pressure.
(C) Liquids will not boil under low atmospheric pressure conditions.
(D) Heat from one's hand is insufficient to boil a liquid.

25. Which intermolecular forces are NOT found in liquified NH_3?

(A) Ionic bonds
(B) Dipole-dipole attractions
(C) London Dispersion forces
(D) "Hydrogen bonds"

CHAPTER 4

CONSTRUCTED-RESPONSE QUESTIONS

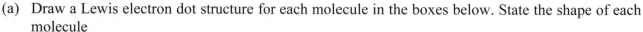

1. Consider 2 molecules : CH_4 and SF_4 .

   (a) Draw a Lewis electron dot structure for each molecule in the boxes below. State the shape of each molecule

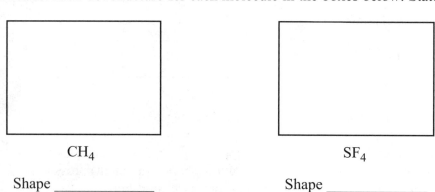

CH_4	SF_4
Shape _____	Shape _____

   (b) i. State and explain 2 factors that account for the fact that SF_4 has a higher boiling point than CH_4. Include **both** molecules with your reasoning and explanations of each factor

       ii. Which compound is more soluble in pure water at 25°C? Explain.

   (c) Which compound is predicted to be more soluble in carbon tetrachloride, CCl_4? Explain.

2. Using appropriate principles of chemical bonding and/or inter-molecular forces, explain each of the following.

   (a) The normal vapor pressure of water is lower than the normal vapor pressure of methanol, CH_3OH, when both are measured at 25°C.

   (b) The normal melting point of iodine, I_2 (113.5°C) is higher than the normal melting point of Cl_2 (−100.98°C).

   (c) Both solid silver (Ag) and molten Ag are excellent conductors of electricity. However, solid silver nitrate, $AgNO_3$ is a good conductor only when melted or dissolved in pure water; as a solid, it is a poor conductor.

   (d) The normal boiling point of water is higher than the normal boiling point of H_2S, even though the molar mass of H_2O is lower, and they both have the same shape.

3. Using appropriate principles of chemical bonding and/or inter-molecular forces, explain each of the following.

   (a) C(diamond) is used as a cutting tool but C(graphite) is not.
   (b) An aqueous solution of sucrose, $C_{12}H_{22}O_{11}$ does not conduct an electrical current, but an aqueous solution of potassium nitrate does.

Liquids maintained at 50 mm Hg pressure

Temp °C	H₂0	Ethyl alcohol	CCl₄	Methyl Salicylate	Benzene
0	4.6	12.2	33	.012	27
10	9.2	23.6	56	.012	45
25	23.8	59.0	114	.012	94
50	92.5	222.2	317	.012	271
80	355.1	812.6	843	4.41	753
100	760	1693	1463	12.8	1360

Vapor Pressure Information Chart in (mm Hg) for various liquids is given above

4. The questions below refer to the following experiment: Five flasks, each containing one of the five liquids listed in the table, are hooked to a vacuum pump. The pressure in each flask is **reduced to 50 mm Hg**, and the temperature of each flask is **maintained at 10°C**.

(a) Under these conditions, which liquids would you observe boiling? Explain.
(b) If the temperature is raised to 25°C and the pressure in each flask is maintained at 50 mm, will the same liquids be boiling or different liquids? Explain.

SOLUTIONS

Big Idea 3: Changes in matter involve the rearrangement and/or reorganization of atoms and/or the transfer of electrons.

A solution is defined as a homogeneous mixture of two or more substances in which the amounts of the two substances can be varied. These substances are known as the solvent (the substance that does the dissolving and is usually the more abundant one) and the solute (the substance that is dissolved, usually the less abundant). Although solutions can be formed by any state of matter (solid, liquid or gas) the most common solutions (and the most important for AP Chemistry) are those in which a liquid (often water) serves as the solvent and a solid, gas or another liquid is the solute. Solutions in which the solvent is water are called aqueous solutions and species dissolved in them are indicated with the notation (*aq*).

CONCENTRATION SCALES

A number of measures are commonly used to specify the concentration of solute in a solution; molarity, molality, mole fraction, percent by mass, and parts per million. Of these, molarity is the only concentration scale required for AP Chemistry but the authors believe students should know the definitions and be able to carry out calculations for each of the other scales as well.

Molarity, abbreviated *M*, is defined as the number of moles of solute per liter of solution. It has the advantage that solution volumes can be measured relatively easily but the disadvantage that molarities may vary with temperature changes as the solution expands or contracts.

Molality, *m*, is the number of moles of solute per kilogram of solvent. The molality of a solution does not vary with temperature because the amounts of solute and solvent are both specified by mass. Molality is used to determine molar masses by freezing point depression and boiling point elevation, using the equations: $\Delta T_f = -k_f m$ and $\Delta T_b = k_b m$ where the constants, k_f and k_b, vary with the solvent.

Mole fraction, χ, is the number of moles of one substance divided by the total number of moles. χ can be used to calculate the pressure of a gas from the total pressure with the expression; $P_A = \chi_A P_T$ where P_A is the pressure of gas A in the mixture with a total pressure of P_T.

Percent by mass, mass %, is the mass of one component divided by the total mass, multiplied by 100 to convert the decimal quantity to a percentage.

Parts per million, ppm, is defined as the mass of solute per million parts of solution. It is especially useful for specifying very low concentrations. e.g. 1.0 mg of solute in 1.0 liter (1,000 g) of H_2O would have a concentration of 1 ppm.

DISSOLVING MECHANISM

Solvents dissolve solutes in different ways. Non-polar solvents such as toluene (C_7H_8) or dichloromethane (CH_2Cl_2) interact with similar substances, e.g. I_2, by means of London dispersion (induced dipole-induced dipole) forces. In contrast, polar solvents, especially H_2O, do not interact with non-polar solutes well but are good solvents for polar and ionic solutes. The polar nature of the water molecule

enables it to interact with other polar molecules by dipole-dipole forces (including hydrogen bonding) and with ionic compounds through ion-dipole forces. Water can bond to cations via its negative end and with anions via the positive end.

Water does not dissolve monatomic and homo-nuclear diatomic gases to an appreciable extent because they are non-polar. In contrast, polar gases (e.g. HCl and NH_3) are quite soluble as they interact with H_2O either by hydrogen bonding as depicted below or by forming ions (shown above) as they dissolve.

ELECTROLYTES, NONELECTROLYTES AND WEAK ELECTROLYTES

The question of whether a solute remains in molecular form or breaks into ions when it dissolves in H_2O can be answered by measuring the electrical conductivity of the solution. Solutes that do not ionize are referred to as nonelectrolytes while those that ionize are electrolytes. As expected, most ionic compounds are electrolytes in H_2O. While many covalent substances dissolve in molecular form others, such as HCl, HBr and HI, ionize completely and some (e.g. NH_3, HF and CH_3COOH) interact with H_2O so that a fraction of the dissolved molecules form ions. The last group of substances exhibit electrical conductivities intermediate between electrolytes and nonelectrolytes and are known as weak electrolytes.

SOLUTION ENERGETICS

The solubility of a substance depends on differences in the energy and disorder of the system as the solute dissolves. Solubility is promoted by a release of energy and an increase in disorder. Energy changes are expressed in terms of the enthalpy (defined as heat absorbed or released at constant pressure) and the entropy.

Enthalpy effects

Enthalpy changes, ΔH, accompanying dissolution result from the relative strengths of the forces among solute molecules, among solvent molecules and between the solute and solvent. Energy is required to divide the molecules of a molecular solute or the ions of an ionic solute and to separate the molecules of the solvent sufficiently to allow the solute particles to fit into the holes produced. On the other hand, solute particles and solvent molecules interact to release energy, called hydration energy when the solvent is water. The dissolution of a solute is endothermic if the total enthalpy change for the first two processes is greater than the third and exothermic if the enthalpy change of the third process is greater.

Solute and solvent   Solution   ↑ ENERGY   Solute and solvent   Solution

Solvent-solvent / solute-solute
interactions STRONGER than
solute-solvent interactions
Dissolution is endothermic.

Solvent-solvent / solute-solute
interactions WEAKER than
solute-solvent interactions
Dissolution is exothermic

When a salt dissociates the energy associated with the separation of the ions (the lattice energy) is often so large that the dissolution process is endothermic. Because lattice energy increases with ionic charge as predicted by Coulomb's Law, $F = q_1q_2/r^2$, salts with highly charged ions are often insoluble unless they are paired with a counter ion with a low charge. Thus, alkali metal salts and nitrates are soluble, regardless of the charge on the opposing ions. The endothermic nature of the dissolving process of *most* ionic compounds causes their solubility to increase with increasing temperature. Because volumes usually change little with the introduction of solid or liquid solutes to water, modest changes in pressure have little effect on the solubility of these solutes.

When gases dissolve the process is usually exothermic. This is because energy is not needed to separate gas molecules from one another initially but energy is released when they dissolve, as water molecules interact with the molecules or the ions formed by the gas. As a consequence, gas solubility decreases as the temperature is increased. The aqueous solubility of gases increases with an increase in their pressure above a solution because the solution occupies a smaller volume than the gas and solvent do separately.

Entropy effects

A change in the disorder of the system, ΔS, often occurs when a solute dissolves. If the system becomes more disordered as the solute dissolves the entropy increases while the entropy decreases if there is an increase in order. Gases dissolve with a decrease in entropy as expected for the change of a substance from the freedom of the gas phase to a condensed phase. For example, when chlorine gas dissolves in water the entropy decreases by $102 \text{ J} \cdot \text{mol}^{-1} \cdot \text{K}^{-1}$.

Many ionic salts dissolve with an increase in entropy as expected for the release of ions from the rigidity of the solid to the freedom of solution. However, ions that bind H_2O molecules tightly to them (e.g. small, highly-charged ions) decrease the entropy of the system upon dissolution because they cause the H_2O molecules in the solution to pack tightly around them, increasing the order. For a salt containing such ions to be soluble this entropy decrease must be counterbalanced by a large decrease in enthalpy in order that the free energy, ΔG, for the process be negative.

REACTIONS IN AQUEOUS SOLUTION

Liquid solutions are important media for reactions because reactants can move relatively easily to contact one another. Water is an especially popular solvent because it is inexpensive and a good solvent for a variety of substances. While many different reactions occur in aqueous solution three types will be emphasized here: acid-base, precipitation, and oxidation-reduction.

Acids, bases, and neutralization reactions

Water ionizes to form $H^+(aq)$ and $OH^-(aq)$ to a small extent. (At 25°C approximately one molecule in 10^7 undergoes this process.) Aqueous solutions that have equal concentrations of $H^+(aq)$ and $OH^-(aq)$ are considered neutral while those with a concentration of $H^+(aq)$ higher than 1×10^{-7} M are referred to as acidic and those in which the $H^+(aq)$ is less than 1×10^{-7} M (and the $OH^-(aq)$ is greater than 10^{-7} M) are called basic or alkaline. The acidity of a solution can also be expressed in terms of its pH $(-\log[H^+])$, which ranges from 0 for $[H^+] = 1$ M to 14 for $[H^+] = 1 \times 10^{-14}$. On this scale, acidic solutions have pH values lower than 7, neutral ones have a pH = 7, and alkaline ones have pH values above 7. Similarly, pOH values are equal to $-\log[OH^-]$. In a given aqueous solution the values pH + pOH = 14.

Some molecules containing hydrogen atoms ionize completely to form H^+ ions and the corresponding anion when added to water so the $[H^+]$ concentration equals that calculated initially for the molecule. Such species are called strong acids and include HCl, HBr, HI, HNO_3, $HClO_4$, and H_2SO_4. Other hydrogen-containing molecules, called weak acids, ionize to smaller but varying degrees. The means of calculating the $[H^+]$ in such solutions and the structural factors that influence their degree of ionization will be discussed in chapter 10.

Substances that ionize completely to form cations and OH^- ions are referred to as strong bases. They include the hydroxides of Group I (the alkali metals Li, Na, K, Rb, Cs) which contain one OH^- for each cation and the hydroxides of the larger members of Group II (alkaline earths Sr, Ba, Ra) for which the $[OH^-]$ would be twice as large as the concentration of the cation. The solubility of these substances can be understood in terms of Coulomb's Law which would predict a small attraction between –1 anions and +1 cations (or large +2 cations). The complete ionization of strong acids and bases is promoted by the strong exothermic interactions of the very small H^+ and OH^- ions with H_2O molecules.

When acidic and basic solutions are mixed the excess $H^+(aq)$ and $OH^-(aq)$ in the respective solutions react rapidly with one another to form $H_2O(l)$ in a process called neutralization.

Salt solubility and precipitation reactions

Although many salts dissolve readily in water as described above, some dissolve to only a tiny extent and are considered to be insoluble. The following rules can be used to predict the solubility of a wide range of salts. (NOTE:The first rule {in bold} is the only one required for the AP exam but the others may be helpful in predicting precipitation reactions.)

SOLUBILITY GUIDELINES

1. **Alkali metal salts (those with Li^+, Na^+, K^+, Rb^+, and Cs^+ ions), and those containing NH_4^+ and NO_3^- ions are soluble.**

2. Sulfates (SO_4^{2-}) are soluble with the exception of those with Ca^{2+}, Sr^{2+}, Ba^{2+}, Pb^{2+}.

3. Most chlorides (Cl⁻), bromides (Br⁻), and iodides (I⁻) are soluble except for those of Ag^+, Pb^{2+}, and Hg_2^{2+}.

4. Carbonates (CO_3^{2-}), sulfides (S^{2-}), phosphates (PO_4^{3-}) other than those in Guideline 1 are insoluble.

5. Most metal hydroxides and oxides are insoliuble except for those with the ions in Guideline 1.

These solubility guidelines can be understood in terms of Coulomb's Law where the soluble substances are those with low charges and many of the insoluble species contain ions with higher charges. (According to this law the attractive forces between a +2 and a –2 ion is four times as strong as that between a +1 and a –1 ion of the same size.)

When solutions of two soluble salts containing ions that form an insoluble salt are mixed a precipitation reaction occurs. This behavior can be illustrated by mixing clear solutions of sodium hydroxide and magnesium sulfate to produce solid white magnesium hydroxide. (A suspension of this solid is sold as milk of magnesia to combat excess stomach acidity.)

Oxidation-reduction reactions

When certain reactants are combined they participate in a process in which one or more electrons are transferred from one reactant to the other. The reactant that donates the electron undergoes oxidation while the recipient becomes reduced. A simple example of this behavior occurs when a strip of zinc is placed in a solution of copper(II) chloride. The zinc quickly develops a dark deposit of copper metal and the blue color of the solution fades as electrons are transferred from the zinc metal to copper ions.

It is relatively easy to recognize oxidation-reduction reactions which involve the formation of a substance in its elemental form into or from one of its ions or compounds. Reactions in which a cation is converted to one with a different charge are equally easy to recognize as redox reactions. However, there are other reactions that are less easily recognized as redox reactions and require additional information to either place them in or exclude them from this category. As examples we might ask whether the process by which SO_2 and H_2O form H_2SO_3 is a redox reaction, or whether the formation of Cl^- from OCl^- (found in bleach) is one. These questions can be answered by using the concept of the oxidation number (ON), also called the oxidation state. The oxidation number can be assigned to any element in a compound with the rules below.

OXIDATION NUMBER (ON) RULES

1. H has an ON of +1 (except in compounds with active metals).

2. O has an ON of –2 (except in peroxides where it is –1 or in compounds with F).

3. Monatomic ions have ONs equal to their charges. (e.g. Na^+ has an ON of +1, F^- is –1.)

4. The ON of an element other than those listed above in a compound or polyatomic ion is obtained by adding the ONs of the other atoms and determining the difference between their sum and zero (for a neutral molecule) or the charge on the ion.

Thus, the ON for sulfur in SO_2 can be found from: The charge on the molecule, 0 = the ON of S + **2** (–2, ON of O).

$$0 = \text{ON of S} - 4. \quad \text{ON of S} = +4.$$

The ON for the S in H_2SO_3 is;

$$0 = \text{ON of S} + 2 \, (+1, \text{ON of H}) + 3 \, (-2 \text{ ON of O}) \qquad \text{ON of S} = +4.$$

Since the two ONs are the same, this is not a redox reaction.

The ON of Cl in Cl^- equals its charge of -1 (rule 3) while the ON of Cl in OCl^- is obtained from -1 (charge on ion) = ON of Cl $- 2$ (ON of O) from which the ON of Cl $= +1$. Therefore the conversion of OCl^- to Cl^- is a reduction reaction since the ON decreases.

The information about a reaction can be presented in a shorthand form as a chemical equation. When answering a question about chemical reactions, the first task is to assign the reaction to its proper category. This is because equations for many reactions, including some redox reactions, can be balanced by inspection, but equations for some redox reactions require special rules. The discussion here about writing and balancing equations will address those equations that can be balanced by inspection and the special rules for other redox equations will be deferred to the chapter on electrochemistry.

WRITING CHEMICAL EQUATIONS

Chemical equations to describe reactions in aqueous solution can be written in molecular form, ionic form, or net ionic form. A chemical equation is similar to a mathematical equation in that the two sides of the expression must equal one another. In the case of a chemical equation (other than nuclear equations) the number of atoms of each element must be equal.

Molecular equations

For the reaction of sulfuric acid with aluminum metal to form hydrogen gas and aqueous aluminum sulfate, one begins by writing the formulas of the reactants and products.

$$Al + H_2SO_4 \rightarrow H_2 + Al_2(SO_4)_3$$

State symbols can be added to give:

$$Al(s) + H_2SO_4(aq) \rightarrow H_2(g) + Al_2(SO_4)_3(aq)$$

Although this summarizes the information about the reactants and products satisfactorily (and even has the same number of hydrogens on both sides of the arrow), it is not balanced because the Al, S and O are not equal. If the Al and SO_4 are balanced as in

$$2\,Al(s) + 3\,H_2SO_4(aq) \rightarrow H_2(g) + Al_2(SO_4)_3(aq)$$

the hydrogen atoms are not equal on the two sides of the arrow. Fortunately this is achieved easily to give the final molecular equation:

$$2\,Al(s) + 3\,H_2SO_4(aq) \rightarrow 3\,H_2(g) + Al_2(SO_4)_3(aq)$$

Ionic equations

This equation can be written in ionic form, where the various species are shown as they exist in aqueous solution, where both $H_2SO_4(aq)$ and $Al_2(SO_4)_3(aq)$ are broken into ions.

$$2\,Al(s) + 6\,H^+(aq) + 3\,SO_4^{2-}(aq) \rightarrow 3\,H_2(g) + 2\,Al^{3+}(aq) + 3\,SO_4^{2-}(aq)$$

Net ionic equations

It is often desirable to limit the equation to those species that change form during the reaction. In this case the $SO_4^{2-}(aq)$ ions would be dropped from both sides of the equation.

$$2\,Al(s) + 6\,H^+(aq) \rightarrow 3\,H_2(g) + 2\,Al^{3+}(aq)$$

The combination of aqueous solutions of sodium carbonate and silver nitrate, both of which are soluble (Solubility Rule 1), forms sodium nitrate (soluble) and silver carbonate (insoluble, Rule 4).

Molecular

Reactants and products: $Na_2CO_3 + AgNO_3 \rightarrow NaNO_3 + Ag_2CO_3$

Add state symbols: $Na_2CO_3(aq) + AgNO_3(aq) \rightarrow NaNO_3(aq) + Ag_2CO_3(s)$

Balance: $Na_2CO_3(aq) + 2\,AgNO_3(aq) \rightarrow 2\,NaNO_3(aq) + Ag_2CO_3(s)$

Ionic

Break soluble substances into ions:

$$2\,Na^+(aq) + CO_3^{2-}(aq) + 2\,Ag^+(aq) + 2\,NO_3^-(aq) \rightarrow 2\,Na^+(aq) + 2\,NO_3^-(aq) + Ag_2CO_3(s)$$

Net ionic

Remove species that are the same on both sides of the arrow, referred to as "spectator ions":

$$CO_3^{2-}(aq) + 2\,Ag^+(aq) \rightarrow Ag_2CO_3(s)$$

In ionic and net ionic equations, the following should not be subdivided further: molecular substances, insoluble salts, and polyatomic ions.

SEPARATION METHODS

There are a variety of ways of separating solute and solvent or separating one solute from another in a solution. Distillation will be discussed first.

Distillation

The two types of distillation to be considered are a simple distillation, in which the solute and solvent differ substantially in volatility and a fractional distillation, where two or more volatile substance are to be separated from one another.

Simple distillation

For a solution of NaCl in H_2O, the liquid H_2O can be converted to vapor by heating to 100°C while the NaCl would require a much higher temperature to accomplish that transition. In order to recover the NaCl from an aqueous solution (or to obtain fresh water from sea water) one could heat the solution to form H_2O vapor leaving a more concentrated solution of NaCl behind. If the goal is to reclaim the H_2O the heated vessel could be connected to a condenser to convert the vapor back into liquid by circulating a cooling liquid through the outside of the condenser as shown in the diagram below.

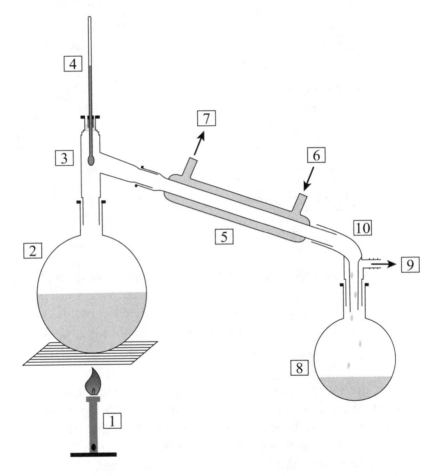

This process works because the forces among the H_2O molecules (hydrogen bonding) are weaker than those between the ions of NaCl or between the H_2O molecules and the cations and anions formed when NaCl dissolves.

Fractional distillation

In the separation of two or more volatile compounds, especially ones with boiling points that are close to one another (as in the petroleum industry) substances with weaker intermolecular forces evaporate more easily as in a simple distillation. However, the fractional distillation apparatus requires a device called a fractionating column, which causes less volatile components to re-condense. For the separation of a two-component mixture, the lower boiling component would distill first (with the second component condensing back into the still pot). If desired, after removing the first component the temperature could be increased to distill the second component into a different distillation receiver.

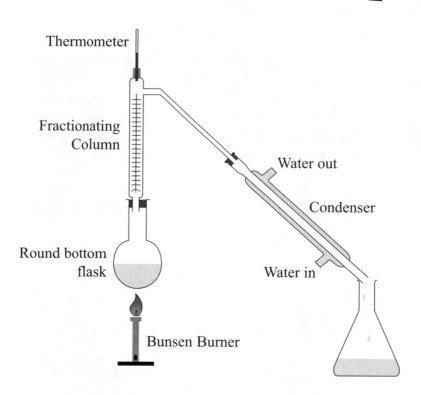

Filtration

Solids can be separated from solutions by pouring a mixture of them through a material such as filter paper that permits solvent molecules to pass through its pores but retains the solid particles. This technique is used in water purification plants and in gravimetric analysis (described below). It can also be used to separate insoluble salts, which will be caught in the filter paper, from soluble ones, which will move with the solvent.

Chromatography

This technique relies on the interactions of a solute with the solvent and the substrate (paper or the solid used to fill a chromatography column) to separate substances. Both types involve the same factors, the solubility of the solute in the solvent and its adsorption to the surface of the solid support to varying degrees. The distance that a specific solute travels along the substrate increases with the strength of attraction that a solute has for the solvent and decreases with its attraction for the substrate. The chromatographic behavior of a solute depends on both the adsorbent properties and the solvent characteristics (especially its polarity). For a given adsorbent, polar solutes will move better in a polar solvent (like H_2O or methanol) while non-polar solutes will move better in a non-polar solvent such as acetone or diethyl ether.

Paper Chromatography

Used primarily for identification of solutes in solution, this technique consists of placing one or more drops of a solution containing the substance(s) to be identified near one end of a piece of paper. The end of the paper is placed in an appropriate solvent that can move across the paper, carrying the solutes in the drop with it to different extents as can be seen for the unknown in the diagram below.

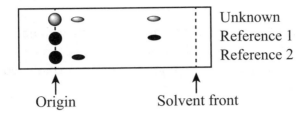

The unknown appears to contain two substances as suggested by the appearance of two spots, although the presence of more than two substances cannot be ruled out since additional ones could be unmoved by the solvent and remain at the origin (or travel with one of the other substances). One way to identify a substance is to run a reference material under the same conditions. If a spot in an unknown appears at the same distance from the origin as a reference spot it is reasonable to identify that unknown spot with that reference material. Alternatively, one can use a quantity called the Rf (the distance the spot moves from the origin divided by the distance the solvent moves). For example, if the distance from the origin to the spot for reference 1 in the above chromatogram is 5.7 cm and that to the solvent front is 6.5 cm, the Rf = 0.88.

Column Chromatography

This technique is often used when certain fractions are to be isolated from a complex mixture. A column fitted with a stopcock or valve at the bottom is filled with an adsorbent such as alumina or silica gel. The solution containing the substances to be separated is poured into the top and the mixture of solutes becomes adsorbed at the top. Solvent is added to the top of the column continuously and the solutes move down the column at different rates and exit the bottom of the column at different times so they can be collected separately as shown below (from Wikipedia).

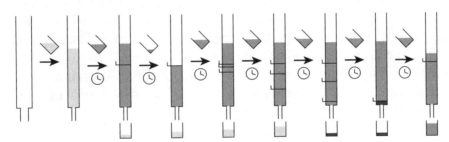

ANALYTICAL METHODS

Depending on their identity and the reactions they undergo, solutes can be measured quantitatively by one or more of the following methods.

Titrimetric

Titrations are one of the most common quantitative techniques in chemistry. A titration can be used for any reaction that: a) occurs rapidly, b) has a known stoichiometry, c) goes to completion, and d) has a detectable endpoint. The method consists of using a known amount of one reactant to determine the quantity or concentration of a second one and can be used for acid-base, precipitation, and oxidation-reduction reactions. Quantities can be measured by mass or volume but the latter is more common with concentrations expressed in molarity.

Gravimetric

The amount of an ion in solution can be determined by this technique if the ion forms an insoluble compound. A counter ion is added that reacts with the ion of interest, the resulting precipitate is filtered, dried and weighed. From the ratio of the desired ion's mass to that of the precipitated compound's mass the number of moles of the ion can be calculated.

Spectrophotometric

The basic principles of using this technique to determine concentrations were presented in chapter 1 but will be extended here. Spectra of colored substances in solution typically appear as broad bands rather than as sharp lines as depicted below where the visible spectrum of a substance is shown for two different concentrations.

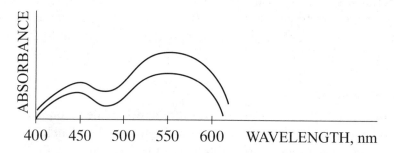

Before using Beer's Law or a standard curve (chapter 1) to determine a solute's concentration it is important to select the wavelength where the absorbance shows the greatest dependence on concentration. In the diagram above this wavelength is 550 nm. As long as all absorbance measurements for this substance are made using cells of constant thickness, b, at this wavelength the molar absorptivity, a, will not change and the absorbance, A, will be directly proportional to the concentration, c, in accordance with Beer's Law; $A = abc$. NOTE: Absorbance measurements are the most accurate over the range 0.10 to 0.70. If a solution absorbs so strongly that its absorbance is above the upper limit, it should be diluted quantitatively to give a value in the desired range. If the solution has an absorbance less than 0.10, a cell with a longer path length should be used to obtain a higher absorbance.

MULTIPLE-CHOICE QUESTIONS

Questions 1–3 should be answered using the responses below.

    (A) molarity
    (B) molality
    (C) mass percent
    (D) mole fraction

1. Which concentration unit can be calculated from masses of solute and solvent alone?

2. Which concentration unit varies with a change in temperature?

3. Which concentration unit is typically used to determine molar masses by freezing point depression?

---

4. What is the molarity of the Li^+ ion in a solution prepared by dissolving 2.20 g of Li_2SO_4 ($MM = 110.0$ g/mol) in enough H_2O to make 50.0 mL of solution?

    (A) $2.00 \times 10^{-2}\ M$
    (B) $4.00 \times 10^{-2}\ M$
    (C) $0.400\ M$
    (D) $0.800\ M$

5. How many moles of HNO_3 must be added to 200.0 mL of H_2O to give a solution with a pH $= 1.00$?

    (A) 0.020
    (B) 0.20
    (C) 0.50
    (D) 2.0

Questions 6–8 should be answered on the basis of the equations below.

(A) $NaCl(s) + H_2O(l) \rightarrow NaCl(aq)$
(B) $HCl(aq) + AgNO_3(aq) \rightarrow AgCl(s) + HNO_3(aq)$
(C) $2\ HCl(aq) + Mg(OH)_2(aq) \rightarrow MgCl_2(aq) + 2\ H_2O(l)$
(D) $2\ HCl(aq) + NaOCl(aq) \rightarrow NaCl(aq) + Cl_2(g) + H_2O(l)$

6. Which equation represents an oxidation-reduction reaction?

7. Which equation represents a precipitation reaction?

8. Which equation represents an acid-base reaction?

Questions 9–10 should be answered on the basis of the information below.

A student is asked to determine the molarity of Ca^{2+} ions in 50.0 mL of solution by adding a 10% excess of Na_2CO_3 to precipitate $CaCO_3$ (*MM* 100.0). The precipitate was filtered, washed, dried, and weighed to give 1.20 g of $CaCO_3(s)$.

9. Based on this information what molarity should the student report?

(A) 0.00060 *M*
(B) 0.012 *M*
(D) 0.24 *M*
(D) 4.2 *M*

10. If the actual value of the molarity is 10% higher than that reported by the student, which procedural error could be responsible?

(A) The student used a 20% excess of Na_2CO_3 rather than the suggested 10%.
(B) The student did not subtract the weight of the filter paper from that of the filter paper plus the precipitate.
(C) The precipitate was not washed sufficiently to remove excess Na_2CO_3.
(D) All of the precipitate was not transferred from the beaker to the filter.

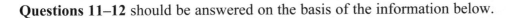

Questions 11–12 should be answered on the basis of the information below.

A student is asked to determine the molarity of a strong base solution by titrating it with a 0.250 M solution of H_2SO_4. The student is instructed to pipet a 20.0 mL portion of the strong base solution into a conical flask, to add two drops of an indicator that changes at pH = 7 and to dispense the standard H_2SO_4 solution from a buret until the solution undergoes a permanent color change. The initial buret reading is 5.00 mL and the final reading is 30.00 mL at the equivalence point.

11. What is the [OH⁻] in the strong base solution?

(A) 0.313 M
(B) 0.625 M
(C) 0.375 M
(D) 0.750 M

12. Which procedural error will result in a strong base molarity that is too high?

(A) Using 4 drops of indicator rather than the recommended 2 drops
(B) Using an indicator that changes at pH = 5 rather than at pH = 7
(C) Using a conical flask that contains several drops of H_2O
(D) Using a buret with a tip filled with air rather than the H_2SO_4 solution

13. Of the following the most acidic solution is the one with

(A) $[H^+] = 1 \times 10^{-2} \, M$
(B) $[OH^-] = 1 \times 10^{-3} \, M$
(C) pH = 3
(D) pOH = 9

14. Which equation best describes the net changes based upon the observation that solid silver nitrate and solid potassium chloride are soluble in water and these solutions react to form insoluble silver chloride and soluble potassium nitrate when mixed.

(A) $AgNO_3(s) + KCl(s) \rightarrow AgCl(s) + KNO_3(s)$
(B) $AgNO_3(s) + KCl(s) \rightarrow AgCl(s) + KNO_3(aq)$
(C) $AgNO_3(aq) + KCl(aq) \rightarrow AgCl(s) + KNO_3(aq)$
(D) $Ag^+(aq) + Cl^-(aq) \rightarrow AgCl(s)$

15. According to Coulomb's Law, which of the following compounds is least soluble?

(A) KOH
(B) K_2SO_4
(C) $Ca(OH)_2$
(D) $CaSO_4$

16. If the salt M^+X^- dissolves in H_2O with the absorption of energy, which of the interactions below is the strongest?

(A) M^+---X^-
(B) M^+--OH_2
(C) X^----HOH
(D) HOH---OH_2

17. What is the value of $\Delta H°$ for the process $MgF_2(s) \rightarrow Mg^{2+}(aq) + 2\,F^-(aq)$ based on the following information?

$$\Delta H°_{lat} = 2922\ kJ/mol \quad \Delta H°_{hyd}\,Mg^{2+} = -179\ kJ/mol \quad \Delta H°_{hyd}\,F^- = -74\ kJ/mol$$

(A) 2669 kJ/mol
(B) 2595 kJ/mol
(C) –2595 kJ/mol
(D) –2669 kJ/mol

18. The, $\Delta S°_{hyd}$, values (in J/mol K) in the table below represent the changes in $S°$ values relative to the $S°_{gas}$. Which of the following explanations accounts best for the trend in these values?

ion	Li^+	Na^+	K^+	Cs^+
$\Delta S°_{hyd}$, J/mol·K	–119	–88	–53	–37

(A) Hydration releases less heat as the ions become larger.
(B) Hydration releases more heat as the ions become larger.
(C) The H_2O molecules are held more tightly as the ions become larger.
(D) The H_2O molecules are held less tightly as the ions become larger.

19. What change occurs during the reaction $MnO_4^- \rightarrow Mn^{2+}$?

(A) Five electrons are gained.
(B) Five electrons are lost.
(C) Three electrons are gained.
(D) Three electrons are lost.

20. How many hydrogen bonds are shown in the diagram below?

$$H - \underset{\underset{H}{|}}{\overset{\overset{H}{|}}{N}} \!:\! \cdots H - \underset{\cdot\cdot}{\overset{\overset{H}{|}}{O}}\!:$$

(A) one
(B) two
(C) five
(D) six

Questions 21–22 should be answered using the following responses.

(A) column chromatography
(B) filtration
(C) fractional distillation
(D) simple distillation

21. Which technique should be used for the separation of two liquids with very similar boiling points?

22. Which technique should be used for the separation of a solid from a solution?

23. Which statement is correct about the separation of substances A, B and C in the paper chromatogram below?

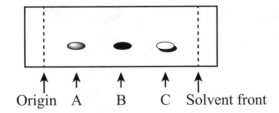

Origin   A   B   C   Solvent front

(A) A is more soluble in the solvent than B.
(B) B is more soluble in the solvent than C.
(C) B is adsorbed more strongly by the paper than C.
(D) B is adsorbed more strongly by the paper than A.

24. How many L of 0.0200 M KMnO$_4$ solution are required to react with 0.0400 mol of Cl$^-$ ions according to the equation below?

$$2\,MnO_4^-(aq) + 10\,Cl^-(aq) + 16\,H^+(aq) \rightarrow 2\,Mn^{2+}(aq) + 5\,Cl_2(g) + 8\,H_2O(l)$$

(A) 0.00800
(B) 0.0160
(C) 0.200
(D) 0.400

25. A 30.0 mL portion of 0.100 M Ba(OH)$_2$ is mixed with 20.0 mL of 0.200 M HNO$_3$. What is the molarity of the excess reactant, H$^+$ or OH$^-$, in the final solution?

(A) 0.0010 M H$^+$
(B) 0.020 M H$^+$
(C) 0.0020 M OH$^-$
(D) 0.040 M OH$^-$

26. What is the molality of a solution prepared by dissolving 3.00 g of urea, CO(NH$_2$)$_2$, ($MM = 60.0$) in 200. g of H$_2$O?

(A) 0.0100
(B) 0.0500
(C) 0.250
(D) 10.0

27. What is the molality of an aqueous solution that freezes at $-0.372°$C? ($k_f = -1.86°/m$)

(A) 0.0200
(B) 0.200
(C) 0.500
(D) 5.00

28. A solution prepared by dissolving 1.80 g of an unknown alcohol in 10.0 g of H$_2$O freezes at $-5.58°$C. What is the molar mass of the alcohol? ($k_f = -1.86°/m$)

(A) 54
(B) 60
(C) 180
(D) 300

29. A mixture of 56 g of N_2 and 32 g of O_2 exerts a total pressure of 1.5 atm. What is the partial pressure of O_2?

(A) 0.33 atm
(B) 0.50 atm
(C) 0.55 atm
(D) 1.0 atm

CHAPTER 5
CONSTRUCTED-RESPONSE QUESTIONS

1. Urea, $H_2NC(O)NH_2$, ($MM = 60.0$) is very soluble in water (up to 27 g in 25 mL of solution) but methoxyethane, $CH_3CH_2OCH_3$, ($MM = 60.1$) is only sparingly soluble.

   (a) Calculate the molarity of urea in a 25.0 mL solution that contains 27.0 g of urea.
   (b) Account for the differences in solubility of urea and methoxyethane in terms of the forces between the solute and solvent molecules.
   (c) Write a Lewis dot structure for urea.
   (d) Use the structure in (c) to sketch two different types of interactions between a urea molecule and water molecules.

2. A student is asked to determine the molarity of H_2SO_4 by titrating it with a NaOH solution of known molarity.

   (a) List the pieces of equipment needed to determine the H_2SO_4 molarity and describe briefly the purpose of each item.
   (b) List the measurements that must be made to determine the molarity.
   (c) Describe briefly how the student can tell when the reaction is complete.
   (d) Four successive titrations of the same volume of H_2SO_4 require 23.55, 22.66, 23.46 and 23.48 mL. State the average volume that should be reported. Outline your reasoning.

3. Consider the following unbalanced equations that occur in aqueous solution.

$$Na_3PO_4 + Ca(NO_3)_2 \rightarrow Ca_3(PO_4)_2 + NaNO_3$$

$$H_2SO_4 + Ba(OH)_2 \rightarrow BaSO_4 + H_2O$$

$$K_2Cr_2O_7 + SnCl_2 + HCl \rightarrow CrCl_3 + SnCl_4 + H_2O + KCl$$

(a) Identify each as an acid-base, oxidation-reduction, and/or precipitation reaction.
(b) Balance each equation.
(c) For each
   (i) acid-base reaction, give the formula of the base.
   (ii) oxidation-reduction reaction, identify the oxidizer and state the number of electrons gained by one unit of the oxidizer.
   (iii) precipitation reaction, give the formula of the insoluble substance.

CHAPTER 6
STOICHOIMETRY

Big Idea 3 states that "changes in matter involve the rearrangement and/or reorganization of atoms and/or the transfer of electrons." Observation, measurement, and calculation of these changes is the reason for stoichiometry. "Stoichoimetry" is a term meaning calculations regarding quantities of reactants or products involved in a chemical reaction. The term comes from the Greek work *stoicheio*, meaning a component, or *stoikheion*, meaning element. Thus the term can imply any mathematical comparison of participants in a chemical reaction or even fractions of a chemical compound. In practice, this means that stoichiometry problems themselves present in two ways: reaction and composition.

Atomic mass and weighted average atomic mass

The atomic mass unit (amu) is used for the very small masses of sub-atomic particles, atoms, and molecules. An amu is defined as one-twelfth the mass of a carbon-12 atom. Since a C-12 nucleus contains six protons and six neutrons, the amu is essentially the average of the mass of a proton and a neutron (electrons are much smaller in mass and are disregarded). Thus a carbon-12 atom has an atomic mass of 12 amu. A helium-4 atom has a mass of 4 amu. The weighted average atomic mass is the mass number that appears on the Periodic Table. It is calculated by taking into account the different isotopes of an element and their relative abundances.

Example: The vast majority of chlorine atoms fall into two isotopes; 75.53% of the atoms are Cl-35 and 24.47% are Cl-37. What is the weighted atomic average?
Solution: $(0.7553)(35) + (0.2447)(37) = 35.49$

Definition of mole

There are certain words or terms that imply a certain quantity.

Couple	2
Trio	3
Quartet	4
Basketball team	5
Volleyball team	6
Decade	10
Soccer team	11
Dozen	12
Century	100
Gross	144
Ream	500
Millenium	1000

The word *mole* is one of these words that refers to a quantity, just a very, very large one.

Mole	6.022×10^{23}

In practice, the mole can be viewed as an accelerator, one that brings us from consideration of masses of single atoms to that of masses that can be handled. It is a way to compare masses of single particles (in amu) to quantities of matter that can be weighed (in grams). Thus one H-1 hydrogen atom has a mass of 1 amu. One mole of hydrogen atoms has a mass of 1 gram. A single carbon-12 atom has a mass of 12 amu but one mole of C-12 atoms has a mass of 12 grams.

Problems using mole ratios from a balanced equation might appear in a variety of guises: mole:mole, mole:mass, mole:#particles, or even mole:volume (from Avogadro's Law of Combining Volumes). Note well that the mole is the central concept. You must always convert from a measured quantity in mass, number of particles, or volumes to moles before making a stoichiometric comparison via mole ratios from the balanced equation.

Chemical formulas: empirical and molecular

Chemical formulas may appear in two guises. The empirical formula for a compound contains the simplest whole number ratio of atoms of the elements in the compound. The molecular formula gives the ratio of the number of atoms of each element to the number of molecules of the compound. In other words, the molecular formula is an integral multiple of the empirical formula. The integral multiple can be determined by comparing the molar mass of the compound to its empirical mass (calculated by adding up the atomic masses within the empirical formula).

Chemical equations and balancing

A balanced chemical equation gives the quantitative basis for a reaction. It not only tells you what the reactants and products are. It also reveals how many grams of the reactants are required to give the same number of grams of products (plus any mass of excess reactant), an illustration of the Law of Conservation of Mass. It tells the ratio in which the reactants disappear and the products form (the Law of Definite Proportions). It indicates the relative number of atoms and molecules involved in the reaction. If the reaction involves gases, the ratios of volumes will be the same as the ratios of moles of reactants and products (Avogadro's Law of Combining Volumes).

Equation balancing tips

Both mass and charge must be conserved in a balanced reaction. There must be the same number of each type of atom on the reactant side of the equation as on the products side of the equation. Similarly, each side must have the same total charge as the other side (this is not necessarily zero).

1. Serendipity

Some reactions will already appear in balanced form once you write the skeleton equation.

Example: Magnesium ribbon is exposed to chlorine gas to form magnesium chloride.
Solution: $Mg(s) + Cl_2(g) \rightarrow MgCl_2(s)$

2. Fixed ratios and Leave the elemental forms until last

Example: Methane gas is combusted (reacts with oxygen) to produce carbon dioxide and water vapors.
Solution: $CH_4(g) + 2O_2(g) \rightarrow CO_2(g) + 2H_2O(g)$

Note that the only source of carbon and hydrogen atoms on the reactant side is the methane, which shows a 1:4 carbon:hydrogen ratio. Therefore the carbon dioxide and water coefficients must be 1 and 2 to maintain the appropriate number of carbon and hydrogen atoms. The elemental oxygen form is left until last since it is the only source of the oxygen atoms that show up in two species on the products side.

3. Odd/even rule

You cannot balance an odd number of atoms on one side of the equation with an even number on the other side. You must make both of them even by multiplying by an appropriate coefficient.

Example: Ethane gas is combusted to form carbon dioxide and water vapors.
Solution: $2C_2H_6(g) + 7O_2(g) \rightarrow 4CO_2(g) + 6H_2O(g)$

4. Keep polyatomic ions together

If at all possible, do not make separate consideration of each individual atom unless the polyatomic ion has been broken apart into other forms.

Example: Solutions of ammonium sulfate and barium nitrate are mixed and barium sulfate precipitates.
Solution: $Ba^{2+}(aq) + SO_4^{2-}(aq) \rightarrow BaSO_4(s)$

Reactions in solution

Since stoichiometric relationships from balanced equations are based on mole ratios, you must convert solution quantities to moles as soon as possible. Remember that the volume of a solution (in liters) multiplied by its molarity (in moles per liter) will yield the number of moles of a substance.

Limiting and excess reactants; % yield

When exact quantities of two (or more) reactants are given, that is a signal that you must decide which one of the reactants is limiting. That is, the limiting reactant is the one that runs out first. Some or most of the excess reactant(s) will react but there will always be some mass left behind. One way to consider this process is to select, just for sake of argument, one of the reactants as limiting, then to calculate the mass of the other reactant required to react all of the first reactant. Then compare your answer to the actual amount given in the problem. If there is more than enough of the second reactant, then that one must be in excess. If there is not enough of the second reactant, then you have guessed incorrectly and the second reactant must be limiting. Once you have established the limiting reactant, then that one must be used as the basis of all ensuing calculations.

In the laboratory, one does not always produce the amount of product predicted by a balanced equation. In this case, you might calculate the per cent yield by comparing the experimental value by the predicted value and converting to per cent:

$$\%\text{yield} = \frac{\text{experimental or lab value}}{\text{theoretical or predicted value}} \times 100\%$$

MULTIPLE-CHOICE QUESTIONS

1. Which of these alkali metal sulfides has the greatest mass percent of sulfur?

   (A) cesium sulfide
   (B) lithium sulfide
   (C) potassium sulfide
   (D) magnesium sulfide

2. Which expression gives the mass percent of carbon in methanoic (formic) acid, HCOOH?

   (A) $\frac{2}{46} \times 100$

   (B) $\frac{12}{46} \times 100$

   (C) $\frac{16}{46} \times 100$

   (D) $\frac{12}{29} \times 100$

3. Which oxide(s) of manganese have a mass percent of the metal that is greater than 50%?

$$MnO \quad MnO_2 \quad Mn_2O_3$$

   (A) 0
   (B) 1
   (C) 2
   (D) All of the above

4. Which describes the resulting system when 0.40 moles of $K_2CO_3(s)$ are added to 2.00 liters of 0.60 M $Ni(NO_3)_2$ solution?

   (A) A light-green precipitate forms; excess carbonate anion is found in solution.
   (B) A light-green precipitate forms; excess nickel(II) cation is found in solution.
   (C) A light-green precipitate forms; no excess reactants are found in solution.
   (D) A white precipitate forms and no excess ions are found in solution.

5. Which pair of samples contains the same number of oxygen atoms in each compound?

   (A) 0.10 mol Fe_2O_3 and 0.50 mol BaO
   (B) 0.20 mol Br_2O and 0.20 mol $HBrO$
   (C) 0.10 mol Na_2O and 0.10 mol Na_2SO_4
   (D) 0.20 mol $Ba(OH)_2$ and 0.10 mol H_2SO_4

6. Consider the reaction

$$2\,K_3PO_4(aq) + 3\,Mn(NO_3)_2(aq) \rightarrow Mn_3(PO_4)_2(s) + 6\,KNO_3(aq)$$

   A precipitate is formed when 1.0 L of 0.20 M potassium phosphate solution is mixed with 0.5 L of 1.6 M zinc(II) nitrate solution. After the reaction occurs, which list ranks the ions remaining in solution in order of decreasing concentration?

   (A) $NO_3^- > K^+ > Mn^{2+} > PO_4^{3-}$
   (B) $Mn^{2+} > PO_4^{3-} > K^+ > NO_3^-$
   (C) $PO_4^{3-} > Mn^{4+} > K^+ > NO_3^-$
   (D) $NO_3^- > K^+ > PO_4^{3-} > Mn^{2+}$

7. Limestone ($CaCO_3$) can be used to produce calcium carbide (CaC_2):

$$CaCO_3(s) \rightarrow CaO(s) + CO_2(g)$$
$$CaO(s) + 3C(s) \rightarrow CaC_2(s) + CO(g)$$

   If the process is started with 50. g calcium carbonate and the yield is 75%, what mass of calcium carbide can be produced?

   (A) 50 grams
   (B) 32 grams
   (C) 24 grams
   (D) 20 grams

8. Consider the reaction $2\,Al(s) + 3\,O_2(g) \rightarrow 2\,Al_2O_3(s)$

   Which expression approximates the volume of O_2 consumed, measured at STP, when 55 g Al reacts completely with excess O_2?

   (A) $2 \times 1.5 \times 22.4$
   (B) $0.5 \times 1.5 \times 22.4$
   (C) $2 \times 0.67 \times 22.4$
   (D) $0.5 \times 0.67 \times 22.4$

9. Assuming an equal mass of nitrogen in each compound, which oxide of nitrogen contains the greatest number of moles of oxygen atoms?

(A) NO
(B) N_2O_3
(C) NO_2
(D) N_2O_5

10. $2\,C_2H_6(g) + 7\,O_2(g) \rightarrow 4\,CO_2(g) + 6\,H_2O(g)$

A mixture of 2 L ethane gas and 10 L oxygen gas is ignited in a rigid container. After combustion is complete, the system is allowed to cool to its initial temperature. Which describes the change in pressure in the container after the reaction has finished?

(A) Total pressure is unchanged
(B) Pressure decreases by 12/13
(C) Pressure increases by 13/12
(D) Pressure increases by 12/10

11. When the equation for the following reaction is balanced using smallest whole numbers, which gives a correct description of the information in the equation?

$$..?..Fe(NO_3)_3 + ..?..Ba(OH)_2 \rightarrow ..?..Fe(OH)_3 + ..?..Ba(NO_3)_2$$

(A) The sum of all coefficients is 10.
(B) The total of all ions in solution is 34.
(C) The number of atoms represented is 40.
(D) The total charge of the cations remaining in solution is +12.

12. Which oxide of vanadium contains the greatest mass percent of the metal?

(A) VO
(B) V_2O_3
(C) VO_2
(D) V_2O_5

13. How many mL of 0.250 M $Ba(NO_3)_2$ solution are required to precipitate all the sulfate anions from 50.0 mL of 0.200 M H_2SO_4 solution?

(A) 2.50 mL
(B) 40.0 mL
(C) 50.0 mL
(D) 62.5 mL

14. How many moles of oxygen gas are required to burn completely 11.2 L propane (measured at STP)?

$$..?..C_3H_8 + ..?..O_2 \rightarrow ..?..CO_2 + ..?..H_2O$$

(A) 0.5 moles
(B) 1.0 moles
(C) 2.5 moles
(D) 5.0 moles

15. What volume of 0.0250 M HCl solution is required to titrate 25.0 mL of a 0.0100 M Ba(OH)$_2$ solution?

(A) 10.0 mL
(B) 20.0 mL
(C) 25.0 mL
(D) 40.0 mL

16. Consider the complete combustion of methane as shown in this equation:

$$..?..CH_4 + ..?..O_2 \rightarrow ..?..CO_2 + ..?..H_2O$$

How many moles of which reactant remains after the reaction of a mixture that containing 32 g each of CH$_4$ and O$_2$?

(A) Neither reactant remains since they are present in a stoichiometric ratio.
(B) 0.5 mol CH$_4$ remains
(C) 1.0 mol O$_2$ remains
(D) 2.0 mol CH$_4$ remains

Questions 17-19. A precipitation reaction is caused by mixing 100. mL of 0.25 M K$_2$Cr$_2$O$_7$ with 100. mL of 0.25 M Pb(NO$_3$)$_2$ solution. When the precipitate forms, it is filtered from the mixture.

17. What is the concentration of nitrate anion in the reaction mixture after filtration?

(A) 0.0 M
(B) 0.10 M
(C) 0.25 M
(D) 0.50 M

18. How many moles of solid product are formed?

(A) 0.010 mol
(B) 0.025 mol
(C) 0.050 mol
(D) 0.25 mol

19. Which describes the changes in concentration of the spectator ions K^+ and NO_3^- in the reaction mixture as the reaction occurs?

(A) Neither is affected.
(B) K^+ halved, NO_3^- halved
(C) K^+ doubled, NO_3^- halved
(D) Both are doubled.

20. Consider the reaction $2\,Mg(s) + O_2(g) \rightarrow 2\,MgO(s)$
What mass of MgO is produced when 0.15 mole of magnesium reacts with excess oxygen?

(A) 3.0 g
(B) 3.6 g
(C) 6.0 g
(D) 12.0 g

21. A source of zinc metal can be a zinc ore containing zinc(II) sulfide. The ore is roasted in pure oxygen to produce the oxide and then reduced with carbon to form elemental zinc and carbon monoxide:

$$2\,Zn(s) + 3\,O_2(g) \rightarrow 2\,ZnO(s) + 2\,SO_2(g)$$
$$ZnO(s) + C(s) \rightarrow Zn(s) + CO(g)$$

A crucible containing a sample of 0.50 mol ZnS was roasted in pure oxygen, then reduced with 1.00 mol carbon. What mass remained in the crucible after cooling?

(A) About 32 g
(B) About 40 g
(C) About 64 g
(D) About 80 g

22. The oxide of a certain metal is 64% oxygen by mass. The metal could be

    (A) beryllium
    (B) lithium
    (C) magnesium
    (D) sodium

23. Which volume of $O_2(g)$ (measured at STP) could be produced when 1.0 mol $NaClO_4(s)$ is heated?

    $$NaClO_4(s) \rightarrow NaCl(s) + 2\,O_2(g)$$

    (A) 11.2 L
    (B) 22.4 L
    (C) 33.6 L
    (D) 44.8 L

24. How many moles of $CaCl_2(s)$ should be added to 1.00 liters of 0.20 M $BaCl_2$ solution to increase the chloride concentration to 1.00 M? (Assume no change in volume as the solid is added to the solution.)

    (A) 0.20
    (B) 0.30
    (C) 0.40
    (D) 0.60

25. Copper(II) sulfate pentahydrate, $CuSO_4 \cdot 5\,H_2O$, (molar mass: 250 g) can be dehydrated by repeated heating in a crucible. Which value is closest to the percentage mass of water lost from the total mass of salt in the crucible when the crucible undergoes repetitive heatings until a constant mass is reached?

    (A) 13%
    (B) 25%
    (C) 26%
    (D) 36%

CONSTRUCTED-RESPONSE QUESTIONS

1. Dimethylhydrazine, used as a fuel in space excursion vehicles, contains atoms of carbon, hydrogen, and nitrogen.

   (a) When a 4.775 g sample of the fuel reacts with excess oxygen gas, 6.997 g carbon dioxide and 5.424 g water are produced. Determine the empirical formula of dimethylhydrazine.
   (b) At STP, a 26.83 g sample of dimethylhydrazine occupies 10.0 L. Determine the molar mass of the compound.
   (c) Determine the molecular formula of dimethylhydrazine.

2. Phosphine gas (phosphorus trihydride) is combusted with excess oxygen gas to form water vapor and solid tetraphosphorus decaoxide.

   (a) Write a balanced equation, including state symbols, to describe this reaction.
   (b) What mass of solid tetraphosphorus decaoxide can be produced from 1.25 mol phosphine?
   (c) What volume of water vapor can be produced from the reaction of 10.0 L phosphine with excess oxygen? Both gases are measured under identical conditions.
   (d) If 12.5 g each of phosphine and oxygen gases are placed in a 10.0 L rigid tank and allowed to react, what will be the total pressure in the tank if the temperature is allowed to return to 125°C after the reaction is complete?

3. When solutions of oxalic acid and potassium permanganate are allowed to react, solid manganese(IV) oxide and gaseous carbon dioxide are formed.

(a) Write a balanced net ionic equation to describe this reaction. Include state symbols.
(b) What is the oxidation number of manganese before and after the reaction?
(c) In a titration procedure, 30.0 mL of 0.200 M potassium permanganate are required to react with 26.5 mL oxalic acid solution. Calculate the molarity of the oxalic acid solution.
(d) During the titration described in the previous step, what mass of manganese(IV) oxide is formed?

CHEMICAL KINETICS

Kinetics, the study of reaction rates, pathways and reaction mechanisms is one of the core topics of the A.P. program and lends itself to both the "mathematical problems" sections (question 2 or 3) and the essay portion of the Free Response as well as appearing in the multiple choice part of the AP exam.

IONS AND MOLECULES IN COLLISIONS

The major conceptual models for kinetics are the "collision theory" theory and the absolute reaction rate theory (ARRT). The collision model describes chemical reactions as the sum of numerous collisions between reactant particles. Many of the collisions are ineffective, in which the reactants rebound upon collision and do not result in the formation of products. Those that are effective result in a rearrangement of the atoms to produce different substances.

Collisions

In order to be involved in an effective collision, the reactants must physically collide and meet two requirements; one factor is appropriate collision geometry (the steric factor) and the second is that the particles must be traveling with sufficient kinetic energy to break existing chemical bonds. Students are expected to be able to explain why an increase in temperature leads to an increase in reaction rates. The dominant factor is not that they are moving faster, although they are indeed, moving faster, but that there are more collisions with sufficient (activation) energy. **Catalysts** alter the rate of a reaction by providing a different pathway for the reaction. Those that slow down a reaction rate are referred to as "inhibitors." "Unleaded" gasoline contains inhibitors and replaces tetraethyl lead, often by adding small amounts of platinum (Shell Oil platformate) Fe or Mn which prevent premature combustion of the gasoline-air mixture. The AP Chemistry course focuses on "positive catalysts, " those which increase the reaction rate by providing a pathway with a **lower** energy requirement.

The Arrhenius Equation incorporates both of these ideas: $\ln k = \dfrac{Ea}{R} \times \left(\dfrac{1}{T}\right) + A$ (the steric factor).

$R = 8.314\ \text{Jmol}^{-1}\text{K}^{-1}$. If one carries out a given reaction at two different temperatures, two different rate constants, k, result and the A factor drops out. The more usable form becomes

$$\ln \frac{k_2}{k_1} = -\frac{Ea}{R}\left(\frac{1}{T_2} - \frac{1}{T_2}\right) \quad \text{Its alternate form,}$$

$$\ln \frac{k_2}{k_1} = +\frac{Ea}{R}\left(\frac{1}{T_1} - \frac{1}{T_2}\right) \quad \text{is frequently presented, and is the algebraic equivalent.}$$

Although AP no longer requires calculations involving this fundamental equation, knowledge of it can enhance the quality of one's understanding and explanations in the Free Response section of the test. One of its useful features is recognizing that one can use it to graphically determine the Ea (activation energy) value for a reaction.

Using the above equation,

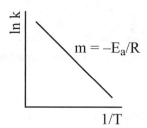

The equation is in the form of $y = mx + b$, and the slope would be $= -E_a/R$. Multiplying the slope by $-R$ would result in a value for E_a. (E_a would then need to be divided by 1000 to be reported in kJ mol^{-1}.

Reaction rates

Rate definitions require a Δ amount / Δ time, and any quantity which denotes an amount or concentration may be used. (e.g. Δ pressure/sec or Δ pH/minute) Reaction rate is often measured in mols, mL, mm Hg with per second or per minute as the most frequent time intervals that are readily measureable in a first year college lab. Reaction rates increase when concentration or temperature increases Aor when a catalyst is present. Using principles of Kinetic Molecular Theory, a student needs to be able to explain why such increases in reaction rate occur. These factors affecting reaction rate are summarized in Figures 7.1 below.

Temperature	At higher temperatures, particles collide with a greater transfer of energy
Concentration – including gas pressure & surface area	The more particles available for collisions, the faster the products are formed
Phase/ homogeneity of the system	The more similar the phase, the greater the probability that a collision will occur.
Presence of a catalyst	Catalyst results in a more favorable activated complex, requiring a lower activation energy
Complexity of reactants	As the number of bonds that need to be broken or formed increases, the likelihood of a longer reaction time increases.

Figure 7.1. Factors affecting rate of a reaction

These factors describe what we observe.

	Zero order	First order	Second order
Rate Law	$Rate = k[A]^0$	$Rate = k[A]^1$	$Rate = k[A]^2$
Integrated rate law (algebraic form)	$[A_2]-[A_1]=-k(t_2-t_2)$ $[A]-[A_0]=-kt^*$	$\ln[A_2]-\ln[A_1]=-k(t_2-t_1)$ $\ln[A]-\ln[A_0]=-kt^*$	$\dfrac{1}{[A]}-\dfrac{1}{[A_0]}=+kt^*$
Graphical form (for a straight line)	[A] vs TIME, straight line decreasing	ln[A] vs TIME, straight line decreasing	1/[A] vs TIME, straight line increasing
Relationship of slope (m) to rate constant	$m = -k$	$m = -k$	$m = +k$
Half-life expression	$t_{1/2} = \dfrac{1/2[A_0]}{k}$	$t_{1/2} = \dfrac{0.693}{k}$	$t_{1/2} = \dfrac{1}{k[A_0]}$

Figure 7.2 Reaction Mechanisms and Reaction Order Summary chart (for a reactant, A)

k is the rate constant, the proportionality constant that changes the proportional relationship between concentration and rate to an equality.

* Note: "t" is used as t_2, when $t_1 = 0$.

The Maxwell-Boltzmann energy distribution graph in Figure 7.3 shows the distribution of kinetic energies for the same sample of gas molecules at 2 different temperatures. Note that the curve at the higher temperature has a greater fraction of molecules that possess the minimum energy required to effectively start the reaction, E_a.

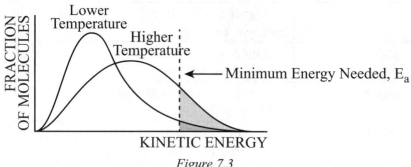

Figure 7.3

The graph of concentration of reactants in figure 7.4 (starting high and diminishing over time) and formation of products (increasing over time) shows us that a chemical equilibrium may be reached when both curves reach a horizontal line.

For the reaction below:

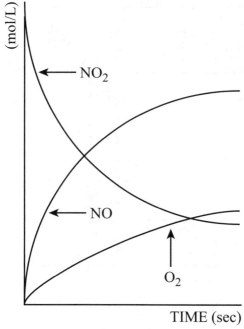

Figure 7.4 $NO + \frac{1}{2}O_2 \rightarrow NO_2$

VOCABULARY: REACTION KINETICS

Kinetics	the study of reaction rates and reaction mechanisms
Reaction Rate	the number of particle events occurring per unit of time (Δconc/Δtime)

Typical rate of consumption of reactant $A = \dfrac{\Delta[A]}{\Delta t}$

Half-life	time required for the concentration of a reactant to decrease by one-half its original value.
Catalyst	A substance that alters the rate of a reaction by providing a mechanism with a different activation energy for the reaction (usually a lower activation energy).
Reaction mechanism	the series of steps by which a reaction proceeds
Elementary reaction	(or process) a single step constitutes the reaction mechanism.
Unimolecular	one molecule breaks into two pieces or undergoes a rearrangement to form a new isomer
Bimolecular	two molecules collide and combine or transfer atoms
Termolecular	three molecules collide and combine to transfer atoms
Rate determining step	the slowest of the elementary steps in a reaction mechanism
Activated complex	the unstable intermediate species formed when the reactant collide
Activation energy (E_a)	the minimum energy needed for the reactants to collide and convert into products; the potential energy acquired by the reactants in forming the activated complex (transition state). This energy is provided by the kinetic energy of the colliding reactants, as shown in Figure 7.5

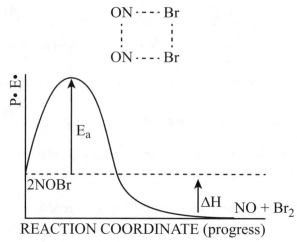

Figure 7.5: Potential Energy Diagram (e.g. an exothermic reaction) (activated complex - transition state)

For the reaction of $2\,NOBr \rightarrow NO + Br_2$

Rate Law

the mathematical expression that relates the rate of a reaction to the concentrations of the substances that dictate the rate of the reaction. rate = $k\,[A]^m\,[B]^n$ where k is the rate constant; A and B are reactants; and m and n are their respective reactant orders

Rate constant

the proportionality constant, k, that converts the proportional relationships into an equation (rate law). "k" is reaction specific and changes with temperature.

Reactant order

the effect a Δ concentration for a particular reactant has on the overall reaction rate; it becomes the exponent in the rate law. All reactant orders are experimentally determined and are NOT related to the coefficients in the balanced equation.

(A) zero order – when the concentration of a reactant changes, there is no (zero) change in the reaction rate.

(B) 1st order – when the concentration doubles or triples and the reaction rate also doubles or triples

(C) 2nd order – when the concentration doubles or triples, the reaction rate increases by a factor of 4 (2^2) or 9, (3^2) (squared) respectively.

(D) Note – another order that sometimes appears in AP essay questions is the one-half (1/2) order, in which if the concentration changes, the rate is the square root of that value.

Overall reaction order

the sum of the individual reactant orders. Given the rate law: rate = $k\,[A]^m\,[B]^n$, the overall reaction order = m + n.

Isolation experiment

kinetics experiments which isolate the effect of one reactant on the reaction rate, determining new rates as a result of concentration change. The experiment is often repeated varying a different reactant in the same manner. Please see table below. The assumption stated with such data is that temperature remains constant.

THE MATHEMATICS OF SIMPLE REACTION KINETICS

Analysis of Rate Law Data

Objective: to analyze rate data and determine the rate law. Typically, one reactant is held constant, in the beginning, but does not necessarily remain fixed in additional trials

Consider the hypothetical reaction of A + B → C, and the rate data table below

Trial	Initial [A]	Initial [B]	Initial rate
1	x	0.25 M	3.6 $M^{-1}min^{-1}$
2	2x	0.25 M	7.2 $M^{-1}min^{-1}$
3	x	0.50 M	3.6 $M^{-1}min^{-1}$
4	3x	0.50 M	?

Solution: When the [B] is held fixed in trials 1 and 2, and [X] doubles the rate also doubles, indicating 1st order as the reactant order of A. In trials 1 and 3, [A] is held constant and the [B] doubles, but the rate remains the same as in trial 1. Therefore changing the [B] has no effect on the rate: B is a zero order reactant. The rate law can now be written as rate = $k[A]^m[B]^n$ → rate = $k[A]^1[B]^0$ → rate = $k[A]^1$. One can now analyze the data in trial 4. If [A] triples, the rate in trial 4 will triple to 10.8 $M^{-1} min^{-1}$. Because B is a zero order reactant, simultaneously doubling [B] will have no effect on the rate in trial 4.

From the (Revised) Curriculum Redesign visit "advancesinap,collegeboard.com"

BIG IDEA #4   Rates of chemical reactions are determined by details of the molecular collisions.

SCIENCE PRECTICE # 5.0 The student can perform data analysis and evaluation of evidence

5.1 The student can analyze data to identify patterns or relationships.

5.2 The student can refine observations and measurements based on data analysis.

5.3 The student can evaluate the evidence provided by data sets in relation to a particular scientific question.

Learning objectives- Kinetics objectives -centered on Learning Objectives 4.1 through 4.9, 5.2, 5.3

Types of Constucted Response Questions:

- Lab I: Engaging in experimental design

- Lab II: Selection and analysis of authentic data/observations to identify patterns or explain phenomena

- Quantitative: Following a logical/analytical pathway to solve a problem

From the list of Equations and Constants

$[A] - [A_0] = -kt$ zero order kinetics

$\ln[A] - \ln[A_0] = -kt$ first order kinetics

$\dfrac{1}{[A]} - \dfrac{1}{[A_0]} = +kt$ second order kinetics

MULTIPLE-CHOICE QUESTIONS

Questions 1-4: Use the diagram below.

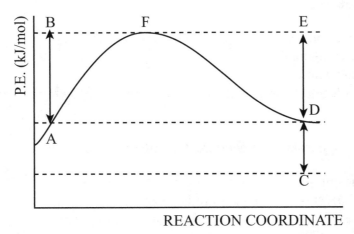

Choose from the answers below for Questions 1-4.

(A) AB
(B) CD
(C) DE
(D) F

1. Represents the ΔH of the forward reaction

2. Represents the activation energy of the forward reaction

3. If a catalyst were introduced, which value would remain unchanged?

4. Represents the activation energy for the reverse reaction

_____

5. The study of <u>altering reaction rates</u> by changing mechanisms and energy pathways is called

(A) thermodynamics
(B) catalysis
(C) materials studies
(D) kinetics

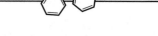

6. For the reaction: H_2 and $F_2 \rightarrow 2\,HF$, the step in the reaction mechanism involving $H \cdot + \cdot F \rightarrow H - F$ is described as

   (A) chain initiation
   (B) chain propagation
   (C) chain termination
   (D) over-all reaction mechanism

7. Which statement which best explains <u>why</u> a 10°C increase in temperature can result in a **substantial** increase in reaction rate is:

   (A) The collision geometry is more favorable at higher temperatures.
   (B) The molecules are moving faster.
   (C) There are more frequent collisions.
   (D) The number of molecules that have the necessary activation energy increases.

8. As a reaction proceeds at constant temperature, the rate of the reaction

   (A) remains the same unless a catalyst is added
   (B) remains the same because the temperature is constant
   (C) decreases because the concentration of reactant molecules decreases
   (D) decreases because the effectiveness of collisions between reactant molecules decreases

9. All of the following apply to the reaction $2C(g) \rightarrow A(g) + 2B(g)$ as it is carried out in a sealed rigid container at constant temperature EXCEPT

   (A) The total pressure increases.
   (B) The number of molecules of A decreases.
   (C) The entropy of the system increases.
   (D) The rate of the reaction decreases.

Questions 10–13: Consider the reaction and its rate law given below.

$$2A(g) + B(g) \rightarrow 2C(g)$$

Rate $= k[A][B]$

At the beginning of one trial of this reaction, $[A] = 3.0\ M$ and $[B] = 1.0\ M$. the observed rate for the formation of C is 0.36 mol L^{-1} sec^{-1}.

10. Determine the [A] when [B] drops to 0.50 M.

    (A) 2.0 M
    (B) 1.5 M
    (C) 1.0 M
    (D) 0.5 M

11. The numerical value of k, the rate constant is closest to

    (A) 0.040
    (B) 0.12
    (C) 108
    (D) 6.0

12. What are the units for k, the rate constant?

    (A) mol^{-1} L^{-1} sec
    (B) L mol^{-1} sec^{-1}
    (C) mol L^{-1} sec^{-1}
    (D) mol^{-1} L sec^{-1}

13. Which statement below describes how the rate for this trial, at constant temperature, changes as [B] approaches 0.5 M?

    (A) The rate remains the same because the rate constant remains the same,
    (B) The rate remains the same because the temperature remains the same.
    (C) The rate at which [C] forms is equal to the rate at which [A] decreases.
    (D) The rate decreases because the activation energy decreases.

14. Given the hypothetical reaction $A + B \Longrightarrow AB, \quad \Delta H = -50$ kJ

If an activation energy for the forward reaction is 75 kJ, the activation energy for the reverse reaction is

(A) 90 kJ
(B) −75 kJ
(C) 25 kJ
(D) 125 kJ

15. For the reaction, $2A + B_2 \rightarrow C + D_2$, the rate law is rate $= k[A]^2[B]^0$.

Which is a likely rate determining step?

(A) $A + B_2 \rightarrow X$
(B) $A + B \rightarrow X$
(C) $A + A \rightarrow X$
(D) $2A + B \rightarrow X$

Questions 16–17: FLOW RATES of water through two systems of funnels.

(Assume no overflow of any funnel occurs during flow rate studies)

funnel A = 2.0 mL/s   funnel B = 4.0 mL/s   funnel C = 8.0 mL/s

System I   System II

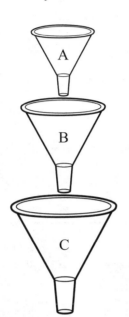 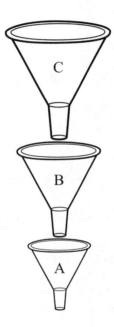

16. What will be the overall output (flow rate) in System I?

(A) 2.0 mL/s
(B) 4.0 mL/s
(C) 8.0 mL/s
(D) 14.0 ml/s

17. What will be the overall output (flow rate) in System II?

(A) 2.0 mL/s
(B) 4.0 mL/s
(C) 8.0 mL/s
(D) 14.0 mL/s

Questions 18–19: For the reaction of $N_2(g) + 3H_2(g) \rightarrow 2\,NH_3(g)$, the rate expression for the appearance of NH_3 in the forward reaction is: rate $= k[N_2]^1 [H_2]^2$

18. If the volume of the container is halved, doubling the concentration of all ingredients, at constant temperature, the reaction rate will increase by a factor of

   (A) 2
   (B) 4
   (C) 8
   (D) 9

19. The rate law for the disappearance of H_2 is

   (A) rate $= 3k[N_2]^1 [H_2]^2$
   (B) rate $= 3/2k[N_2]^1 [H_2]^2$
   (C) rate $= 2k[N_2]^1 [H_2]^2$
   (D) rate $= 2/3k[N_2]^1 [H_2]^2$

_____

Questions 20–22: Use the graphs below for questions 20-22, which refer to a first order reaction

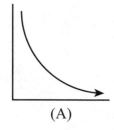   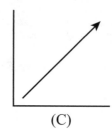   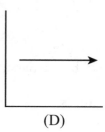

   (A)   (B)   (C)   (D)

20. Which of the above shows the relationship between reaction time and reaction rate?

21. Which of the above shows the relationship between activation energy and temperature?

22. Which of the above shows reaction rate as a function of concentration?

_____

Questions 23–24: Consider the graph possibilities shown below for a gaseous reactant.

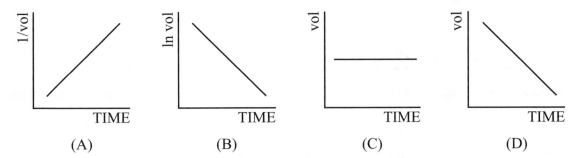

(A)   (B)   (C)   (D)

23. Which of the above graphs indicates a zero-order reactant?

24. Which of the above graphs indicates a second order reactant?

25. The following chart contains rate data for the reaction $X_2 + 2Y \rightarrow Z$.

Initial $[X_2]$	Initial $[Y]$	+d[Z]/dt (rate) M/minute
0.20 M	0.20 M	0.06
0.20 M	0.40 M	0.48
0.40 M	0.20 M	0.12

Which statement concerning the data table above is true?

(A) Reactant Y is zero order.
(B) Reactant X_2 is first order.
(C) The overall reaction order is 2.
(D) If the [Y] triples, the reaction rate is 9 times faster.

CHAPTER 7
CONSTRUCTED-RESPONSE QUESTIONS

1. Below are some of the steps in the reaction mechanism of $H_2 + Cl_2 \rightarrow 2\,HCl$.

     I $Cl - Cl + energy \rightarrow 2Cl\cdot$
    II $\cdot Cl + H_2 \rightarrow HCl + H\cdot$
  III $\cdot Cl + \cdot H \rightarrow HCl$
  IV $\cdot Cl + \cdot Cl \rightarrow Cl_2$
    V $H\cdot + \cdot H \rightarrow H_2$
  VI $\cdot H + Cl_2 \rightarrow HCl + Cl\cdot$

(a) Which step(s) is/are chain propagating steps? Explain.
(b) Which step(s) is/are chain-terminating steps? Explain.

2. Given the following data for a hypothetical reaction: L → M + N

Potential energy of the reactants	50 kJ/mol
Activation energy for the forward reaction	90 kJ/mol
ΔH for the forward reaction	+30 kJ/mol

(a) Draw a potential energy diagram, starting with the reactants, proceeding to the activated complex and ending with the products for the reaction above. Include numerical values on the vertical axis.

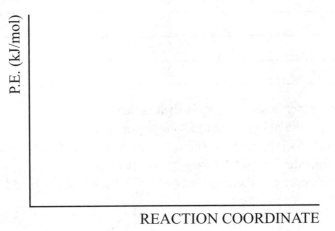

(b) Determine ΔH for the reverse reaction.
(c) What is the potential energy stored in the activated complex? Explain.
(d) What is the activation energy of the reverse reaction? Explain.

3. Student rate data for the reaction $2R(g) + Z_2(g) \rightarrow 2M(g)$

R Pressure (mm Hg)	Z_2 Pressure (mm Hg)	Initial Rate (mm Hg/sec)
1. 400	76	6.25
2. 400	152	25
3. 400	301	101
4. 300	400	165
5. 200	400	110
6. 100	400	55
7. 200	200	?

(a) Which of the above reactants, if either, is **first** order? Explain
(b) Write the rate law for the above reaction. Show your reasoning.
(c) Determine the value of k, the rate constant, for the reaction above and include the units on k.
(d) Determine the initial rate for trial 7. Show your reasoning.
(e) Which graph below describes the reactant order for Reactant R? Explain.

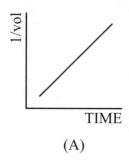
(A)

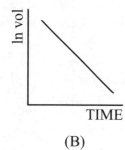
(B)

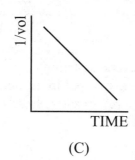
(C)

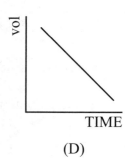
(D)

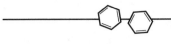

4.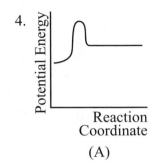

(A)

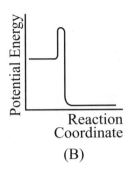

(B)

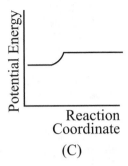

(C)

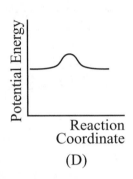

(D)

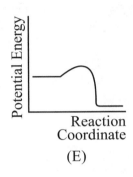

(E)

(a) Which graph above describes a reaction pathway that is exothermic and that has a high activation energy? Explain your choice.

(b) Which graph above most closely depicts the net sum of the reactions that occur in the human body? Justify your choice.

CHEMICAL EQUILIBRIUM

Big Idea 6: Any bond or intermolecular attraction that can be formed can be broken. These two processes are in a dynamic competition, sensitive to initial conditions and external perturbations.

Many chemical reactions proceed to completion with the reactants being converted completely to products as shown in Diagram I below.

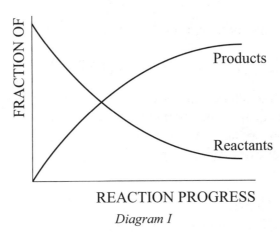

Diagram I

However, a significant number of reactions are reversible and proceed only part way to completion, leaving a mixture of reactants and products in a condition referred to as equilibrium.

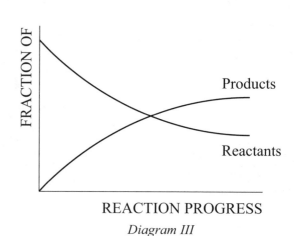

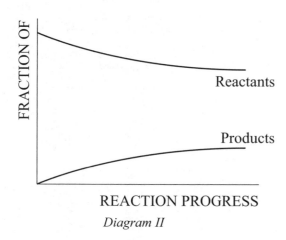

Diagram II

Diagram III

As shown in Diagrams II and III above, the relative quantities of reactants present at equilibrium may be different for different reactions and, for a given reaction, may vary with the reaction conditions.

Equilibrium systems have been known since the early 1800s and have several important characteristics.

1. The equilibrium state can be approached from either reactants or products.
2. Once equilibrium has been reached the concentrations of reactants and products remain constant unless the reaction conditions are changed.
3. At equilibrium the rates of the forward and reverse reactions are equal.

The Mass-Action Expression and the Equilibrium Constant

The law of mass action was proposed early in the study of this topic as a way to describe the relationship between the reactants and products of a reaction. For a reaction represented as;

$$a\,A + b\,B \rightleftharpoons c\,C + d\,D$$

the mass-action expression (reaction quotient, Q) in terms of concentrations is

$$Q_c = [C]^c\,[D]^d / [A]^a\,[B]^b$$

The reaction products (raised to the appropriate powers) are divided by reactants with the exponent for the concentration of each substance equal to the coefficient for that substance in the balanced equation. As the above expressions show, the terms in the balanced equation are multiplied by their coefficients and added to one another but in the equilibrium expression, are raised to the powers of their coefficients and multiplied by one another.

Q can also be expressed in terms of partial pressures (indicated as Q_p). The conversion between Q_c and Q_p will be discussed below. The exponents remain the same during the course of the reaction but the concentrations or pressures of the reaction components change until the system reaches equilibrium, after which they remain constant and Q equals K, the equilibrium constant.

$$K = [C]^c\,[D]^d / [A]^a\,[B]^b$$

The magnitude of K provides an indication of the extent of a reaction at equilibrium, with larger values corresponding to more extensive forward reactions. Thus, Diagram III represents a reaction with a larger value of K than does Diagram II. A comparison of the values of K for a reaction and Q for a set of conditions affords information about the direction the reaction will progress. For example, if $Q < K$, the product/reactant ratio is less than that at equilibrium so the reaction will shift toward products. In contrast, if $Q > K$ the product/reactant ratio is greater than that at equilibrium and the reaction will shift toward the reactants.

Writing Mass-Action Expressions from Chemical Equations

All substances in a chemical equation are included in a mass-action or equilibrium expression if their concentrations are subject to change. Thus, gases and substances in solution would be included, but solids and pure liquids would not be, because their densities, which remain constant with constant temperatures, (and therefore their concentrations) do not change even when their quantities do. Some examples of equations and equilibrium expressions include;

a. $PCl_5(g) \rightleftharpoons PCl_3(g) + Cl_2(g)$ $K_c = [PCl_3][Cl_2]/[PCl_5]$

b. $2\,CO(g) + O_2(g) \rightleftharpoons 2\,CO_2(g)$ $K_c = [CO_2]^2/[CO]^2[O_2]$

c. $HF(aq) \rightleftharpoons H^+(aq) + F^-(aq)$ $K_c = [H^+][F^-]/HF$

d. $C(s) + O_2(g) \rightleftharpoons CO_2(g)$ $K_c = [CO_2]/[O_2]$ C(s) is omitted

e. $2\,HgO(s) \rightleftharpoons 2\,Hg(l) + O_2(g)$ $K_c = [O_2]$ HgO(s) and Hg(l) are omitted

f. $AgI(s) \rightleftharpoons Ag^+(aq) + I^-(aq)$ $K_c = [Ag^+][I^-]$ AgI(s) is omitted

Changing the Form of K to Match Different Forms of an Equation

Chemical equations written in more than one form require different mass-action expressions. For example, equation b. above could be written as

g. $CO(g) + 1/2\,O_2(g) \rightleftharpoons CO_2(g)$ with $K_c = CO_2/[CO][O_2]^{1/2}$

or as the reverse reaction

h. $2\,CO_2(g) \rightleftharpoons 2\,CO(g) + O_2(g)$ with $K_c = [CO]^2[O_2]/[CO_2]^2$

While the equilibrium expression for either of these situations can be obtained from the new form of the equation, it is possible to obtain the new K from the original using the rules below:

1. The K expression for a chemical equation that is multiplied by a numerical factor is obtained by raising the original K expression to that power.
2. The K expression for a reverse reaction is the inverse of the K expression for the original equation.

A third rule about manipulating K expressions comes from the fact that some chemical equations result from the sum of two other equations. Equation d. can be considered the sum of equation g. and equation i. below.

i. $C(s) + 1/2\,O_2\,(g) \rightleftharpoons CO\,(g)$ $K_c = [CO]/[O_2]^{1/2}$

3. The equation for the overall reaction can be obtained by adding those for the other two reactions and the overall K expression is obtained by multiplying the individual Ks.

The fourth rule allows conversions between K_c and K_p for reactions involving gases. After rearranging the Ideal Gas Equation, $PV = nRT$, to $P = [n/V]\,RT$ it can be seen that the pressure equals the concentration multiplied by RT, with $R = 0.0821\ L \cdot atm \cdot mol^{-1} \cdot {}^{\circ}C^{-1}$.

4. In order to convert a K_c expression to a K_p expression, each [ ] must be multiplied by RT, i.e. $K_p = K_c\,(RT)^{\Delta n}$ where Δn represents the difference between the number of moles of gaseous products and gaseous reactants. If the moles of gas are equal, the RT factors cancel and $K_c = K_p$ whereas if the moles differ, K_p and K_c will also differ.

Quantitative Considerations for Gaseous Equilibria

Calculating K Values

When the K expression has been established for a reaction the equilibrium concentrations can be substituted and the numerical value of K can be calculated. As an example, for the reaction; $2\,CO\,(g) + O_2\,(g) \rightleftharpoons 2\,CO_2\,(g)$ at 1400°C the $[CO] = 0.010\ M, [O_2] = 0.0050\ M, [CO_2] = 0.99\ M$.

What is the value of K_c?

$K_c = [CO_2]^2/[CO]^2\,[O_2]$
$K_c = (0.99)^2/(0.010)^2\,(0.0050)$
$K_c = 0.9801/(1.0 \times 10^{-4})(0.0050)$
$K_c = 0.9801/5.0 \times 10^{-7}$
$K_c = 1.96 \times 10^6$

From the equation and K_c above what is the K_c value for the reaction;
$2\,CO_2(g) \rightleftharpoons 2\,CO(g) + O_2(g)$
This equation is the reverse of the one above, so $K_c = 1/1.96 \times 10^6$ or 5.1×10^{-7}

What is the value of K_p for the reaction; $2\,CO(g) + O_2(g) \rightleftharpoons 2\,CO_2(g)$ at 1400°C?

Since $K_p = K_c\,(RT)^{\Delta n}$ and the number of moles of gas changes from 3 to 2, $\Delta n = -1$
$K_p = 1.96 \times 10^6\,(0.0821 \times 1673)^{-1}$
$K_p = 1.43 \times 10^4$

What is the K_c value be for the reaction; $CO(g) + 1/2\,O_2(g) \rightleftharpoons CO_2(g)$

Since this equation is $1/2$ of the original equation, its K_c = the square root of the original K_c. Therefore,
$K_c = (1.96 \times 10^6)^{1/2}$
$K_c = 1.4 \times 10^3$

Using K Values to Calculate Concentrations (or Pressures)

Once the value of K has been determined for a reaction it can be used along with the equilibrium expression to calculate the concentrations of the reaction components at equilibrium. One of the simplest reactions from an equilibrium perspective is one in which a molecule in one isomeric form is converted into another isomeric form such as;

$$H_3C \diagdown \quad CH_3 \diagup$$
$$C=C \rightleftharpoons$$
$$H \diagup \quad H \diagdown$$

$$H_3C \diagdown \quad H \diagup$$
$$C=C$$
$$H \diagup \quad CH_3 \diagdown$$

cis - 2 - butene   trans - 2 - butene

for which K_c = [trans-2-butene]/[cis-2-butene] with a value of 9.6 at 25°C. If 0.50 mole of cis-2-butene is placed in a 2.0 L flask at 25°C, calculate the equilibrium concentrations of the two isomers. The best way to attack such problems is to use a table such as the one below (often referred to as an ICE table or an ICE diagram or ICE box).

	[cis-2-butene]	[trans-2-butene]
Initial	0.25	0
Change	−x	x
Equilibrium	0.25 − x	x

The values in the Equilibrium line of this Table are substituted into the equilibrium expression,
$9.6 = x/(0.25 - x)$
$9.6(0.25 - x) = x$
$2.4 - 9.6x = x$
$2.4 = 10.6\,x$
$x = 0.226$

The results of equilibrium calculations should be checked by substituting the results into the equation and comparing the calculated value of K with the original value as below.

Check:
$K_c = 0.226/(0.25 - 0.226)$
$K_c = 0.226/0.024$
$K_c = 9.4$ (The 0.2 difference between the original and calculated K values is due to rounding of the concentrations.)

As a second example, consider the reaction; $PCl_5(g) \rightleftharpoons PCl_3(g) + Cl_2(g)$, for which $K_c = 4.0$ at 228°C. Calculate the equilibrium concentrations of all species for an initial $[PCl_5] = 0.50$.

	$[PCl_5]$	$[PCl_3]$	$[Cl_2]$
Initial	0.50	0	0
Change	$-x$	x	x
Equilibrium	$0.50 - x$	x	x

$K_c = [PCl_3][Cl_2]/[PCl_5]$
$4.0 = x^2/(0.50 - x)$
$4.0(0.50 - x) = x^2$
$2.0 - 4x = x^2$
$x^2 + 4x - 2 = 0$

This equation cannot be factored simply but can be solved using the quadratic formula; $x = [-b \pm (b^2 - 4ac)^{1/2}]/2a$ where $a = 1$, $b = 4$ and $c = -2$.

Two solutions result, -4.45 (which can be discarded because it makes no chemical sense) and 0.45. When the latter value is substituted for x in $x^2/(0.50 - x)$, the result is 4.05 in agreement with the K_c, 4.0. (Note: use of the quadratic equation will no longer be assessed on AP Chemistry examinations.)

Any equilibrium can be solved in a similar manner although more complex equilibria may require the use of stoichiometry to determine the equilibrium values and approximation methods to solve the more complicated mathematical equations.

For example, to calculate the equilibrium concentrations of all species for the reaction $2\,CO_2(g) \rightleftharpoons 2\,CO(g) + O_2(g)$ with $K_c = 5.1 \times 10^{-7}$, starting with $[CO_2] = 1.0$ M, the ICE box is

	$[CO^2]$	$[CO]$	$[O_2]$
Initial	1.0	0	0
Change	$-x$	x	$0.5\,x$
Equilibrium	$1.0 - x$	x	$0.5\,x$

$K_c = [CO]^2[O_2]/[CO_2]^2$
$5.1 \times 10^{-7} = [x^2][0.5x]/[1.0 - x]$ With a Kc this small, we can assume $x \ll 1.0$
$5.1 \times 10^{-7} = 0.5\,x^3$
$x^3 = 1.02 \times 10^{-6}$
$x = 0.010$

Check:
$K_c = [0.010]^2[0.005]/1.0$
$K_c = 5 \times 10^{-7}$

The approximation that $x \ll 1.0$ was valid, as is typically true for $K < 1 \times 10^{-5}$.

Using K and Q values to Predict the Direction of a Reaction

In the above examples there was no question about the direction of the reaction. With only one substance (the reactant) present the reactant concentration had to decrease (–x) to form products. If all three substances (e.g. $PCl_5(g)$, $PCl_3(g)$ and $Cl_2(g)$) were present the direction of the reaction might be in doubt. For a system with $[PCl_5] = 0.050$ and $[PCl_3] = [Cl_2] = 0.50$, $Q_c = 5.0$ Because $Q > K$ (4.0 above) the reaction would shift toward the reactant as reflected in the ICE box.

	$[PCl_5]$	$[PCl_3]$	$[Cl_2]$
Initial	0.050	0.50	0.50
Change	x	–x	–x
Equilibrium	0.02 + x	0.50 – x	0.50 – x

The solution of the resulting equation gives x = 0.034 and the check gives $K = 4.0$

[NOTE: Although the AP exam may not require solving equations like this, it is likely to ask students to calculate Q values and compare them to K to predict a reaction's direction.]

Factors that Affect the Equilibrium Position: Le Chatelier's Principle

While K values provide a measure of the extent of different reactions, there are a number of ways that the amounts of reactants and products can be affected in a reaction without changing the value of K. For gaseous equilibria these factors include;

a. adding or removing a gaseous reactant or product, (or adding a substance that reacts with a reactant or product to change its concentration),

b. compressing or expanding the system,

c. changing the temperature, although this will also change the K value.

The effect of any of these changes can be predicted on the basis of Le Chatelier's Principle (1884) which can be stated as "If a system at equilibrium is disturbed it will shift in a direction that reduces the effect of the disturbance."

As one example, if PCl_5 is added to the equilibrium; $PCl_5(g) \rightleftharpoons PCl_3(g) + Cl_2(g)$, with $[PCl_5] = 0.016$, $[PCl_3] = [Cl_2] = 0.46$, the reaction will shift to reduce the amount of PCl_5 by forming more PCl_3 and Cl_2. (In terms of Q and K, the addition of more PCl_5 will increase the magnitude of the denominator, causing $Q < K$ and leading to the formation of more PCl_3 and Cl_2. In contrast, if PCl_5 is removed the reaction will shift to offset this change, forming more PCl_5 at the expense of PCl_3 and Cl_2.

NOTE: Adding (or removing) a small amount of solid (or liquid), even if it appears in the balanced equation, does not affect the equilibrium position because it does not appear in the equilibrium expression.

As a second example, consider the reaction; $PCl_5(g) \rightleftharpoons PCl_3(g) + Cl_2(g)$, at equilibrium in a flexible container similar to a piston. If the container is compressed, the equilibrium will shift in a direction to reduce the pressure by decreasing the number of moles of gas. That is, $PCl_3(g)$ and $Cl_2(g)$ will have a greater collision frequency, and will react to form $PCl_5(g)$. (In terms of Q and K, compressing the container will increase the concentrations of all three components by the same amount. However, because $[PCl_3]$ and $[Cl_2]$ are multiplied, the numerator will increase more than the denominator, $Q > K$, and the reaction will shift to form more PCl_5. In contrast, the system will form more PCl_3 and Cl_2 if the container is expanded.

NOTE: Changing the pressure of a system at costant volume by adding an inert gas has no effect on the position of an equilibrium because the inert gas does not appear in the equilibrium expression and the partial pressures of the other gases do not change. On the other hand, if an inert gas is added to a system at constant pressure such that the volume changes it may alter the equilibrium position because the change in volume will cause a change in the partial pressures of the reactants and products.

In order to predict the effects of a temperature change on the position of an equilibrium it is necessary to consider the value of ΔH (chapter 9). For the reaction;

$$PCl_5(g) \rightleftharpoons PCl_3(g) + Cl_2(g) \qquad \Delta H = 87.9 \text{ kJ/mol}$$

Thus, the decomposition of PCl_5 is endothermic, requiring heat to proceed in the forward direction. If the temperature is increased, heat is added to the system and this disturbance can be reduced if the system forms more products. This system would shift in the opposite direction if the temperature is decreased. The opposite changes would occur for an exothermic reaction.

NOTE: In addition to affecting the relative amounts of reactants and products temperature changes also change the value of K. (See the section on K and Thermodynamics below.)

NOTE: The addition of a catalyst to a system at equilibrium has NO effect on the relative amounts of reactants and products. As was pointed out in chapter 7, a catalyst may increase the rate of a chemical reaction and decrease the time needed for the reaction to reach equilibrium. However, because the rates of the forward and reverse reactions are affected equally, there is no change in the equilibrium position.

Aqueous Equilibria

The same principles used for gaseous equilibria also apply to solution equilibria such as acid-base and solubility equilibria except for the effects of pressure (because liquid volumes are not as sensitive to pressure effects as are gases). In chapter 5 water was described as ionizing to give equal concentrations of H^+ and OH^- (1.0×10^{-7} M at 25°C). This is due to the reaction $H_2O(1) \rightleftharpoons H^+(aq) + OH^-(aq)$, for which the equilibrium expression is $K_c = [H^+][OH^-]/[H_2O]$. Since the $[H_2O]$ concentration (55.5 M) does not change appreciably during reactions in aqueous solution, that term is multiplied by K_c to give $K_w = [H^+][OH^-]$ which has a value of 1.0×10^{-14} at 25°C. The $[H^+] = [OH^-]$ values (1.0×10^{-7} M) for pure H_2O result from $(1.0 \times 10^{-14})^{1/2}$ and the inverse relationship between $[H^+]$ and $[OH^-]$ follow from $K_w = [H^+][OH^-]$.

What is the $[OH^-]$ in an aqueous solution with $[H^+] = 5.0 \times 10^{-4}$?

$[H^+][OH^-] = 1.0 \times 10^{-14}$
$[OH^-] = 1.0 \times 10^{-14}/(5.0 \times 10^{-4})$
$[OH^-] = 2.0 \times 10^{-11}$

Acid-Base

There are many ways to raise the $[H^+]$ in aqueous solution above that in pure water. Strong acids such as HCl, HBr, HI, HNO_3, $HClO_4$, and H_2SO_4 ionize completely in H_2O so that the $[H^+]$ equals the calculated molarity of the acid. (In some other solvents it is possible to distinguish among their strengths.) Weak acids, indicated HA, ionize to a smaller degree than strong acids resulting in an equilibrium; $HAx(aq) \rightleftharpoons H^+(aq) + A^-(aq)$ with an equilibrium expression $Ka = [H^+][A^-]/[HA]$. Some weak acids, such as H_2SO_3 and H_3PO_4, possess more than one ionizable H^+ but their successive ionization constants differ sufficiently ($\sim 10^5$) that each ionization can be treated individually. Several weak acids are listed below along with their ionization constants.

Acid	K_1	K_2	K_3
$HC_2H_3O_2$	1.8×10^{-5}		
$HOCl$	2.8×10^{-8}		
H_2SO_3	1.7×10^{-2}	6.0×10^{-8}	
H_3PO_4	7.1×10^{-3}	6.2×10^{-8}	4.5×10^{-13}

The $[H^+]$ for a weak acid can be calculated using an ICE box along with the equilibrium expression and K_a. For a 0.10 M solution of ethanoic (acetic) acid, the ICE box is

	$[HC_2H_3O_2]$	$[H^+]$	$[C_2H_3O_2^-]$
Initial	0.10	0	0
Change	$-x$	x	x
Equilibrium	$0.10 - x$	x	x

From the equilibrium line the equilibrium expression is $1.8 \times 10^{-5} = x^2/(0.10 - x)$. This equation can be solved rigorously by using the quadratic formula as described above but can be simplified by assuming that $x << 0.10$ to give $1.8 \times 10^{-5}(0.10) = x^2$, from which $x = 1.3 \times 10^{-3}$. The x value is 1.3% of the original $[HC_2H_3O_2]$ and the check gives $K = 1.8 \times 10^{-5}$ meaning the approximation was valid. **In general, x (in 0.1 − x) can be neglected if the approximation produces an $[H^+]$ that is less than 5% of the original $[HA]$.**

The approximation is unlikely to be valid for lower [HA]s or larger K_a values. For example, making the same assumption for an initial $[HC_2H_3O_2] = 1.0 \times 10^{-3} M$ would give $[H^+] = 1.3 \times 10^{-4} M$, 13.4% of the original $[HC_2H_3O_2]$. Thus the approximation is not valid. For a 0.10 M $[H_2SO_3]$ with $K_a = 1.7 \times 10^{-2}$, the approximation yields $[H^+] = 0.041 M$, 41% of the original $[H_2SO_3]$!

Hydrated metal ions (described in chapter 5 and chapter 10), especially those with high charges, attract the oxygen atoms of the coordinated water molecules strongly enough that the bond between oxygen and hydrogen breaks to release H^+ ions (a process called hydrolysis). For example, the hexaaquoiron(III) ion, $Fe(H_2O)_6^{3+}$, forms $Fe(H_2O)_5(OH)^{2+} + H^+$ with a K_a of 6.7×10^{-3}, making it a stronger acid than acetic acid.

Solubility Equilibria

Some salts are only slightly soluble in water with solubilities described by an equilibrium expression referred to as K_{sp}. Examples include the following;

$$CaCO_3(s) \rightleftharpoons Ca^{2+}(aq) + CO_3^{2-}(aq) \qquad K_{sp} = [Ca^{2+}][CO^{2-}]$$

$$Ag_2CrO_4(s) \rightleftharpoons 2\,Ag^+(aq) + CrO_4^{-2}(aq) \qquad K_{sp} = [Ag^+]^2[CrO_4^{2-}]$$

$$Mg_3(PO_4)_2(s) \rightleftharpoons 3\,Mg^{2+}(aq) + 2\,PO_4^{3-}(aq) \qquad K_{sp} = [Mg^{2+}]^3[PO_4^{3-}]^2$$

In these examples the reactants are omitted from the K_{sp} expression (because they are solids) and the exponents for the concentrations of the solution species are the coefficients in the balanced equations. The rules for writing K_{sp} expressions are the same as those given for other equilibrium expressions at the beginning of this chapter.

These expressions lead to three types of calculations -

i.   finding the value of K_{sp} from the solubility of a salt,
ii. calculating the solubility from the K_{sp}, and
iii. determining whether a precipitate will form in a solution with specified ion concentrations. Examples of all three types of calculations are given below.

Ksp from solubility

Calculate the K_{sp} for Ag_2CrO_4 if 1.0 L of a saturated solution contains 0.0287 g of Ag_2CrO_4.

$0.0287\,g/331.8 = 8.65 \times 10^{-5}\,mol/L$
$[Ag^+] = 2(8.65 \times 10^{-5})\,M = 1.73 \times 10^{-4}\,M$
$[CrO_4^{2-}] = 8.65 \times 10^{-5}\,M$
$K_{sp} = [Ag^+]^2[CrO_4^{2-}]$
$K_{sp} = (1.73 \times 10^{-4})^2(8.65 \times 10^{-5})$
$K_{sp} = 2.6 \times 10^{-12}$

Solubility from Ksp

If the solubility of a salt is represented as S, the equation to find the solubility from K_{sp} depends on the formula of the compound.

1:1 compounds – Regardless of the formulas or charges of the ions any compound with an MX formula, such as AgCl, $CaCO_3$, or $AlPO_4$, has the same form for K_{sp}. If the solubility of the salt is represented by S, the concentration of each ion will equal S and $K_{sp} = S^2$.

Example: Calculate the molar solubility of $MgCO_3$ from its $K_{sp} = 3.5 \times 10^{-8}$.
$K_{sp} = s^2$
$3.5 \times 10^{-8} = s^2$
$S = (3.5 \times 10^{-8})^{1/2}$
$S = 1.9 \times 10^{-4}\,M$

For 1:2 (or 2:1) compounds – If the solubility of MX_2 (or M_2X) is represented by s, the concentration of one ion will be s and that of the other ion will be 2s. Because $K_{sp} = [M][X]^2$ (or $[M]^2[X]$), $K_{sp} = [2s]^2[s] = 4s^3$. Examples include Ag_2CO_3 and $Mg(OH)_2$.

Example: Find the solubility and the concentrations of each ion in a saturated BaF_2 solution.

$K_{sp} = 3.8 \times 10^{-8}$

$K_{sp} = 4s^3$

$s = (3.8 \times 10^{-8}/4)^{1/3}$

$s = [Ba^{2+}] = 2.1 \times 10^{-3}$

$[F^-] = 2S = 4.2_4 \times 10^{-3}$

Check, $K = (2.1_2 \times 10^{-3})(4.2_4 \times 10^{-3})^2$

$K = 3.8 \times 10^{-8}$

Note: The K_{sp} values in these two examples are very similar but the solubility of BaF_2 is about ten times as large as that of $MgCO_3$ because of the form of the K_{sp} expression. As a general rule, the relative solubilities of compounds can be established by comparing K_{sp} values only if the chemical formulas have the same stoichiometry.

For 1:3 (or 3:1) compounds – With solubility represented as S, the concentration of the single ion will be S and that of the other ion will be 3S. When the ion with the coefficient of 3 is raised to that power and multiplied by s, $K_{sp} = 27s^4$.

The K_{sp} expressions for compounds with more complicated formulas can be found in a similar manner.

Common Ion Effect

When one of the ions that is part of an aqueous equilibrium, either acid-base or solubility, the concentration of the ion of interest changes, as another illustration of Le Chatelier's Principle.

Acid-base Example: Calculate the $[H^+]$ in a 0.10 M solution of ethanoic (acetic) acid containing 0.050 M $C_2H_3O_2^-$. The ICE box ([initial] − [change] = [equilibrium]) is

	$[HC_2H_3O_2]$	$[H^+]$	$[C_2H_3O_2^-]$
Initial	0.10	0	0.050
Change	−x	x	x
Equilibrium	0.10 − x	x	0.050 + x

The K_a expression is $1.8 \times 10^{-5} = [H^+][C_2H_3O_2^-]/[HC_2H_3O_2]$

$1.8 \times 10^{-5} = x(0.050 + x)/(0.10 - x)$

$1.8 \times 10^{-5}(0.10 - x) = x(0.050 + x)$

$1.8 \times 10^{-6} - 1.8 \times 10^{-5}x = 0.050x + x^2$

This quadratic equation can be simplified by assuming that x << 0.050 and 0.10 to give $1.8 \times 10^{-6} = 0.050x$, which makes $x = 3.6 \times 10^{-5}$. The assumption is valid and the $[H^+]$ is much smaller than the value found above (1.3×10^{-3}) without the addition of extra $C_2H_3O_2^-$.

Solubility Example 1: Find the the solubility of BaF_2 and the concentration of fluoride ion in a saturated solution of BaF_2 in which $[Ba^{2+}] = 0.050$ M and compare it with the value in a solution of BaF_2.

$K_{sp} = 3.8 \times 10^{-8}$.

Let s be the solubility of BaF_2.

$[Ba^{2+}] = 0.050 + s$

$[F^-] = 2s$

$3.8 \times 10^{-8} = [Ba^{2+}][F^-]^2$

$3.8 \times 10^{-8} = (0.050 + s)(2s)^2$

Assume $S \ll 0.050$

$3.8 \times 10^{-8} = 0.20s^2$

$S^2 = 3.8 \times 10^{-8}/0.20$

$S^2 = 1.9 \times 10^{-7}$

$S = 4.3_6 \times 10^{-4}$

$[F^-] = 8.7_2 \times 10^{-4}$

Check; $K = 0.050(8.7_2 \times 10^{-4})^2 = 3.8 \times 10^{-8}$

The solubility is less than one-half that calculated above for the solubility of BaF_2 without added Ba^{2+} ions and the $[F^-]$ is approximately one-half as large as that found above.

Solubility Example 2: Find the solubility and the $[Ba^{2+}]$ in a saturated solution of BaF_2 in which $[F^-] = 0.050$ M and compare it with the $[Ba^{2+}]$ in the solution of BaF_2 above.

$3.8 \times 10^{-8} = [Ba^{2+}][F^-]^2$

Let s be the solubility of BaF_2

$[Ba^{2+}] = s$

$[F^-] = 0.050 + 2s$

Assume $2s \ll 0.050$

$3.8 \times 10^{-8} = S(0.050)^2$

$3.8 \times 10^{-8}/(2.5 \times 10^{-3})$

$S = 1.5_2 \times 10^{-5}$

Check; $K = (1.5_2 \times 10^{-5})(2.5 \times 10^{-3})$

$K = 3.8 \times 10^{-8}$

In both examples the solubility is smaller than in the solution with no added ions. Further, the same concentration of F^- ions has a greater effect on the solubility of BaF_2 due to its higher exponent in the K_{sp} expression.

A qualitative discussion of this concept is given below under LeChatelier's Principle.

Determining whether a precipitate will form

It was stated above that the direction of a reaction can be predicted by comparing the value of Q (for instantaneous concentrations or pressures) with the value of K. The same technique can be used to determine whether a precipitate will form when the ions of a slightly soluble salt are present in solution at specified concentrations. Q expressions have the same form as K_{sp} expressions, so that Q values can be calculated by substituting instantaneous ion concentrations. If Q is greater than K_{sp}, the substance will precipitate, whereas if Q is less than K_{sp}, the ions are stable in solution at those concentrations.

Relationships between K and Thermodynamic Quantities $\Delta G°$ and ΔH (chapter 9)

The equilibrium constant, K, and the free energy change, $\Delta G°$ (chapter 9), both provide a measure of the extent of a chemical reaction, so it should not be surprising that a relationship exists between these two terms: $\Delta G° = -RT\ln K$. The negative sign indicates that $\Delta G°$ and K are inversely related and the $\ln K$ term shows that K exhibits a greater range than $\Delta G°$. As shown in the table below, for a reaction at 25°C, a variation in $\Delta G°$ values from large positive to large negative values corresponds to changes in K ranging from very small to very large.

$\Delta G°$, kJ	K	Significance
100	3×10^{-18}	No forward reaction; reverse reaction goes to completion
0	1	Forward and reverse reactions occur to same extent.
−100	3×10^{17}	Forward reaction goes to completion; no reverse reaction

It was mentioned above under Le Chatelier's Principle that the value of ΔH for a reaction affects the position of equilibrium. In addition, ΔH also affects the value of K as expressed in the equation $\ln(K_2/K_1) = \Delta H/R\,[1/T_1 - 1/T_2]$. Although the mathematical aspects of this relationship will not be assessed in the Revised AP Program, they will likely be encountered on other exams. Further, AP students should be aware that, of the factors that can alter the position of an equilibrium, a change in temperature is the only one that also alters the equilibrium constant. As expected, the value of K increases with a temperature increase for $\Delta H > 0$ and decreases with a temperature increase for $\Delta H < 0$.

CHAPTER 8

MULTIPLE-CHOICE QUESTIONS

1. At elevated temperatures ammonium carbamate, NH_2COONH_4, is in equilibrium with NH_3 and CO_2 according to the equation; $NH_2COONH_4(s) \rightleftharpoons 2\,NH_3(g) + CO_2(g)$. What is the equilibrium expression for this reaction?

   (A) $K = 2[NH_3][CO_2]/[NH_2COONH_4]$
   (B) $K = [NH_3]^2[CO_2]/[NH_2COONH_4]$
   (C) $K = 2[NH_3][CO_2]$
   (D) $K = [NH_3]^2[CO_2]$

2. Equilibrium expressions can be written from balanced equations but balanced equations cannot always be inferred from equilibrium expressions. This is due to difficulties

   (A) identifying solids or liquids omitted from K expressions
   (B) distinguishing among reactants and products
   (C) determining the extent of the reaction
   (D) assigning coefficients to reactants

3. The reaction; $2\,SO_2(g) + O_2(g) \rightleftharpoons 2\,SO_3(g)$ has an equilibrium constant of K_1. What is the K value for the reaction; $SO_3(g) \rightleftharpoons SO_2(g) + 1/2\,O_2(g)$?

   (A) $1/2K_1$
   (B) $1/K_1$
   (C) $(1/K_1)^{1/2}$
   (D) $K_1^{1/2}$

4. What is the value for the reaction; $N_2(g) + 2\,O_2(g) \rightleftharpoons N_2O_4(g)$ in terms of the K values for the reactions;

$1/2\,N_2(g) + 1/2\,O_2(g) \rightleftharpoons NO(g)$ K_1
$2\,NO(g) + O_2(g) \rightleftharpoons N_2O_4(g)$ K_2

(A) $K_1 + K_2$
(B) $K_1^2 + K_2$
(C) $2\,K_1 \times K_2$
(D) $K_1^2 \times K_2$

5. The equilibrium; $2\,NO_2(g) \rightleftharpoons N_2O_4(g)$ has $K_c = 4.7$ at 100°C. What is true about the rates of the forward (rate_{for}) and reverse (rate_{rev}) reactions initially and at equilibrium?

	Initial	Equilibrium
(A)	$\text{rate}_{for} > \text{rate}_{rev}$	$\text{rate}_{for} > \text{rate}_{rev}$
(B)	$\text{rate}_{for} > \text{rate}_{rev}$	$\text{rate}_{for} = \text{rate}_{rev}$
(C)	$\text{rate}_{for} = \text{rate}_{rev}$	$\text{rate}_{for} = \text{rate}_{rev}$
(D)	$\text{rate}_{for} < \text{rate}_{rev}$	$\text{rate}_{for} > \text{rate}_{rev}$

6. The reaction, $2\,NO_2(g) \rightleftharpoons N_2O_4(g)$ has $K = 4.7$ at 100°C. What changes will occur as a system in which $[NO_2] = 0.50$ and $[N_2O_4] = 1.50$ approaches equilibrium?

(A) $NO_2(g)$ will form $N_2O_4(g)$ because $Q = 1.5$.
(B) $NO_2(g)$ will form $N_2O_4(g)$ because $Q = 3.0$.
(C) $N_2O_4(g)$ will form $NO_2(g)$ because $Q = 6.0$.
(D) No changes will occur in $[NO_2]$ or $[N_2O_4]$ because the system is at equilibrium.

7. Gaseous ICl (0.20 mol) was added to a 2.0 L flask and allowed to decompose at a high temperature:

$$2\,ICl(g) \rightleftharpoons I_2(g) + Cl_2(g)$$

If the equilibrium [ICl] = 0.060, what is the value of K_c?

(A) 0.11
(B) 0.33
(C) 0.44
(D) 0.67

Questions 8 and 9 should be answered using the following responses.

(A) 2s
(B) s^2
(C) $4s^2$
(D) $4s^3$

8. If the solubility of $MgCO_3$ is represented by s, what is the formula for its K_{sp}?

9. If the solubility of Ag_2CO_3 is represented by s, what is the formula for its K_{sp}?

10. For the reaction, $CO_2(g) + 4 H_2(g) \rightleftharpoons CH_4(g) + 2 H_2O(g)$, $K = 8.2 \times 10^{19}$ at 25 °C. Beginning with 1 M each of $CO_2(g)$ and $H_2(g)$ at 25 °C, which substance will have the highest concentration in an equilibrium mixture?

(A) $CO_2(g)$
(B) $H_2(g)$
(C) $CH_4(g)$
(D) $H_2O(g)$

Questions 11–14 should be answered using the following responses for the water gas reaction,

$$C(s) + H_2O(g) \rightleftharpoons H_2(g) + CO(g) \qquad \Delta H° = 131 \, kJ/mol$$

(A) some $C(s)$ is added.
(B) the temperature is increased.
(C) the container is compressed.
(D) some $H_2O(g)$ is added.

11. Which change will alter the value of the equilibrium constant, K?

12. Which change will increase the quantity of $H_2(g)$ without affecting the value of K?

13. Which change will not affect the position of the equilibrium?

14. Which change will decrease the quantity of $H_2(g)$ at equilibrium?

15. For the reaction,

$$CO_2(g) + 4 H_2(g) \rightleftharpoons CH_4(g) + 2 H_2O(g) \quad \Delta H° = -165 \text{ kJ/mol}$$

Based on Le Chatelier's Principle, under what conditions would the yield of $CH_4(g)$ be maximized?

(A) high P and high T
(B) high P and low T
(C) low P and high T
(D) low P and low T

16. In the drawing below, filled circles represent H^+ ions and open circles represent anions. This diagram best represents a 1 M solution of which acid?

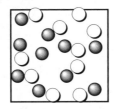

(A) HCl (strong)
(B) HOClO ($K_a = 0.01$)
(C) $HC_2H_3O_2$ ($K_a = 1.8 \times 10^{-5}$)
(D) HOCl ($K_a = 2.9 \times 10^{-8}$)

17. Which quantity is the same for separate 25 mL portions of 1.0 M strong and weak acids ($K_a \sim 1 \times 10^{-5}$)?

(A) initial pH
(B) pH at equivalence point of titration with 1.0 M NaOH
(C) percent ionization
(D) volume of 1.0 M NaOH to reach equivalence point

18. The value of K_w at several temperatures is given in the table below. What conclusion can be drawn on the basis of this information?

T, °C	0	25	45
K_w	1.14×10^{-15}	1.01×10^{-14}	5.48×10^{-14}

(A) Pure water becomes more acidic as the temperature is increased.
(B) The pH of pure water decreases as the temperature is increased.
(C) Pure water becomes more alkaline as the temperature is increased.
(D) The ionization of water is an exothermic process.

19. A 0.50 M solution of an unknown acid has a pH $= 4.0$. Of the following, which is the acid in this solution?

(A) HBr (strong acid)
(B) HF $(K_a = 6.8 \times 10^{-4})$
(C) HOCl? $(K_a = 2.0 \times 10^{-8})$
(D) $C_6H_5OH (K_a = 1.0 \times 10^{-10})$

20. AgBr $(K_{sp} = 5.4 \times 10^{-13})$ Ag$_2$CO$_3$ $(K_{sp} = 8.0 \times 10^{-12})$ AgCl $(K_{sp} = 1.8 \times 10^{-10})$

On the basis of the K_{sp} values above, what is the order of solubility from least soluble to most soluble for these compounds?

(A) AgBr $<$ Ag$_2$CO$_3$ $<$ AgCl
(B) AgBr $<$ AgCl $<$ Ag$_2$CO$_3$
(C) AgCl $<$ Ag$_2$CO$_3$ $<$ AgBr
(D) Ag$_2$CO$_3$ $<$ AgBr $<$ AgCl

21. The solubilities of the following compounds (in moles/L) are; AgBr 7.3×10^{-7}, AgCN 7.7×10^{-9}, AgSCN 1.0×10^{-6}. When these compounds are arranged in order of decreasing K_{sp} values (largest K_{sp} first), what is the correct order?

(A) AgBr $>$ AgCN $>$ AgSCN
(B) AgCN $>$ AgBr $>$ AgSCN
(C) AgCN $>$ AgSCN $>$ AgBr
(D) AgSCN $>$ AgBr $>$ AgCN

22. Magnesium hydroxide, Mg(OH)$_2$, has a $K_{sp} = 6.3 \times 10^{-10}$. The solubility of Mg(OH)$_2$ will be lowest in 1.0 L of which of the following?

(A) 0.10 M HCl
(B) 0.10 M NaOH
(C) 0.10 M MgCl$_2$
(D) pure H$_2$O

23. Of the following compounds, which is(are) substantially more soluble in a strong acid solution than in pure H$_2$O?

(A) AgBr
(B) Ag$_2$CO$_3$
(C) AgNO$_3$
(D) AgI

24. What are the thermodynamic signs for the process shown below?

$$M^{3+}(g) + x\,H_2O(g) \rightarrow M(H_2O)^{3+}(aq)$$

(A) $\Delta H < 0, \Delta S < 0$
(B) $\Delta H < 0, \Delta S > 0$
(C) $\Delta H > 0, \Delta S < 0$
(D) $\Delta H > 0, \Delta S > 0$

25. What is the value of the equilibrium constant, K_p, in terms of $\Delta G°$ and R?

(A) $K_p = \Delta G°/RT$
(B) $K_p = -\Delta G°/RT$
(C) $K_p = e^{\Delta G°/RT}$
(D) $K_p = e^{-\Delta G°/RT}$

26. What value of the equilibrium constant, K, at 25°C corresponds to a large negative value of $\Delta G°$?

(A) large positive value
(B) small positive value
(C) large negative value
(D) small negative value

CHAPTER 8
CONSTRUCTED-RESPONSE QUESTIONS

1. The equation and $\Delta H°$ value for the water gas reaction (WGR) at 25°C are:

$$C(s) + H_2O(g) \rightleftharpoons CO(g) + H_2(g) \qquad \Delta H° = 131 \text{ kJ/mol}$$

and those for the water gas shift reaction (WGSR) are:

$$CO(g) + H_2O(g) \rightleftharpoons CO_2(g) + H_2(g) \qquad \Delta H° = -41 \text{ kJ/mol}$$

(a) Write equilibrium expressions for the;
   i. Water gas reaction
   ii. Water gas shift reaction
   iii. the overall reaction between C(s) and $H_2O(g)$

(b) Will the quantity of H_2 formed in the water gas reaction increase, decrease, or be unchanged by each of the changes below? In each case justify your prediction.
   i. increase in temperature
   ii. increase in pressure

(c) Will the quantity of H_2 formed in the water gas shift reaction increase, decrease, or be unchanged by each of the changes below? In each case justify your answer.
   i. increase in temperature
   ii. increase in pressure

(d) Will the quantity of H_2 formed in the overall reaction increase, decrease, or be unchanged by each of the changes below? In each case justify your prediction.
   i. adding C(s)
   ii. increasing pressure
   iii. increasing temperature

2. At 800 K for the reaction:

$$H_2(g) + I_2(g) \rightleftharpoons 2HI(g) \qquad K_p = 62.5$$

(a) If 0.010 mol of HI are introduced into a 1.0 L flask and heated to 800 K, calculate the pressure of HI(g) before any reaction occurs.

(b) Calculate the pressure of each species when equilibrium is established in (a).

(c) In another experiment, $H_2(g)$, $I_2(g)$ and HI(g) are introduced to a flask to pressures of 0.010 atm, 0.020 atm, and 0.10 atm, respectively. Calculate the value of Q and state whether the reaction is at euilibrium. If it is not at equilibrium, state the direction that it will shift to reach equilibrium.

(d) How will the value of K_c compare with that of K_p at 800 K? Explain.

3. Acetic acid, CH_3COOH, has a $K_a = 1.8 \times 10^{-5}$ at 25°C.

(a) Write an equilibrium expression for the ionization of acetic acid in water.

(b) Calculate the concentrations of all species in a 0.10 M acetic acid solution.

(c) Calculate the $[H^+]$ and pH of 100. mL of 0.10 M acetic acid solution to which 0.0050 mol of sodium acetate has been added.

(d) If the K_a for acetic acid is 9.78×10^{-6} at 100°C, is $\Delta H°$ for the ionization of acetic acid in water a positive or negative value? Explain.

THERMODYNAMICS

New for preparation for the 2014 examination, the AP Chemistry curriculum is presented as six Big Ideas, each separated into multiple Learning Objectives and supported by one or more Science Practices. Big Idea Five is thermochemistry, supported by eighteen Learning Objectives and many Science Practices. BI 5 is stated as "**The laws of thermodynamics describe the essential role of energy and explain and predict the direction of changes of matter**."

The study of thermodynamics includes the laws that deal with the conversion of energy from one form to another. This includes considering energy as expressions of heat or work, the direction of heat transfer, and the potential for energy to perform work. Standard heats of formation, Hess' Law, and calorimetry can be used to calculate changes in enthalpy. Thermodynamics allow prediction of the spontaneity of a process. The concept of Gibbs' free energy and the Gibbs equation link temperature, enthalpy, and entropy.

Thermochemistry

The form of energy that is transferred from a hot object to a cold one when they make contact is called thermal energy q, popularly "heat". The measure of that thermal energy is called temperature and the amount of thermal energy is directly proportional to its thermal energy. The standard unit of this energy is the joule (J); 4.184 J are equivalent to the amount of energy that would raise the temperature of one gram of water by one degree Celsius. The direction of heat transfer is indicated by its sign; a negative sign indicates an exothermic process, where thermal energy is transferred from the process in question to its environs. An endothermic process draws thermal energy from its environs and is indicated by a positive sign. If a system does work (in chemistry, usually $P\Delta V$ or expansion against the surroundings), its internal energy is decreased. When work is done on a system, the opposite occurs and internal energy increases.

If a chemical reaction happens at constant pressure, the thermal energy change is the enthalpy change q is called ΔH. Examples include the heat of combustion (or enthalpy of combustion), heat of fusion, and heat of vaporization. The heat of formation (or standard molar enthalpy of formation) ΔH_f is the enthalpy change with the formation of one mole of a substance from its elemental forms, all under standard conditions of 298 K and 1 atm. Enthalpies of formation for products and reactants can be used to calculate the change in enthalpy by using Hess' Law: $\Delta H_{reaction} = \sum \Delta H_{f(products)} - \sum \Delta H_{f(reactants)}$.

Example: Heating/cooling curve

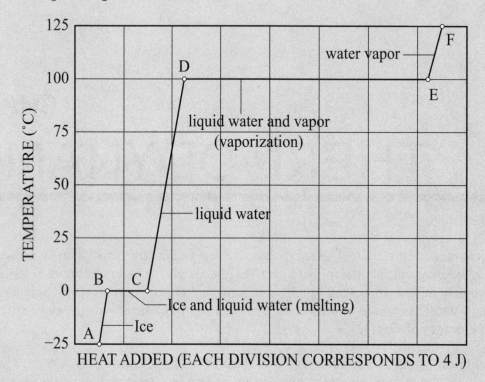

How much heat would be required to change 25.0 grams of ice at $-10.0°C$ to steam at $125.0°C$?

Solution: This problem requires five separate calculations before reaching a grand total. Three steps examine a temperature change within a phase ($q = m\,c\,\Delta T$) and two steps consider addition of heat to change phase without changing temperature ($q = m\,H_{fusion}$ or $q = m\,H_{vaporization}$).

1. To change temperature within the solid (ice) phase:
   $q = m\,c\,\Delta T = (25.0\,g)(2.09\,J/g°C)(10.0°C) = 522.5\,J$
2. To change phase from solid to liquid without changing temperature:
   $q = m\,H_{fusion} = (25.0\,g)(333.5\,J/g) = 8338.0\,J$
3. To change temperature within the liquid phase:
   $q = m\,c\,\Delta T = (25.0\,g)(4.184\,J/g°C)(100°C) = 10{,}460\,J$
4. To change phase from liquid to gas without changing temperature:
   $q = m\,H_{vaporization} = (25.0\,g)(2256\,J/g) = 56{,}465.0\,J$
5. To change temperature within the gaseous phase:
   $q = m\,c\,\Delta T = (25.0\,g)(2.03\,J/g°C)(25°C) = 1268.8\,J$

Total $= (522.5\,J) + (8338.0\,J) + (10{,}460\,J) + (56{,}465.0\,J) + (1268.8\,J) = 77{,}054\,J = 7.71\,kJ$

Hess' Law may also be used with a series of equations that lead to an overall equation. If a reaction can be expressed as the sum of series of several steps including other reactions, then the enthalpy change for the overall reaction is also the sum of the enthalpies of the stepwise reactions.

Example: Hess' Law calculation

Given these reactions

$$S(s) + O_2(g) \rightarrow SO_2(g) \qquad \Delta H° = -296.8 \text{ kJ}$$
$$2\,SO_2(g) + O_2(g) \rightarrow 2\,SO_3(g) \qquad \Delta H° = -197.0 \text{ kJ}$$

Calculate the heat of reaction for this reaction

$$S(s) + 1.5\,O_2(g) \rightarrow SO_3(g) \qquad \Delta H° = ?$$

Solution: Keep the formation reaction for SO_2 as is. Multiply the second reaction by one-half, including the $\Delta H°$ value. When the two reactions are added together, they total the formation reaction for sulfur trioxide. $\Delta H° = (-296.8) + (-98.5) = -395.3 \text{ kJ}$

The art of determining the amount of thermal energy transferred in a process by measuring its change in temperature is called calorimetry. The generic equation to describe this is $q = m\,c\,\Delta T$, where q means the thermal energy absorbed; m is the mass of the object in grams; c is the specific heat capacity of the material, in $J\,g^{-1}°C^{-1}$; ΔT represents the change in temperature, calculated by subtracting the initial temperature from the final temperature. If a calorimeter, a device used to measure changes in thermal energy, is used, its heat capacity must also be considered: $q = C_{calorimeter}\,\Delta T$, where $C_{calorimeter}$ is the amount of thermal energy required to change the temperature of the device by one degree Celsius.

Example: Calorimeter problem

If a 10.0 gram copper nail is transferred from a boiling water bath to 50.0 mL of water at 22°C in a coffee-cup calorimeter, what will be the final temperature of the system? The specific heat of copper is 0.384 J/g°C and that of water is 4.184 J/g°C.

Solution: Heat lost by the copper must equal the heat gained by the water, assuming no loss of heat to the calorimeter or the surroundings.

$$q_{\text{lost by Cu}} = q_{\text{gained by water}}$$
$$m\,c\,\Delta T = m\,c\,\Delta T$$
$$(10.0\,g)(0.384\,J/g°C)(100 - T_f) = (50.0\,g)(4.184\,J/g°C)(T_f - 22)$$
$$T_f = 23.4°C$$

Three Laws of Thermodynamics

Chemical thermodynamics involves the study of energy transfers that occur with chemical changes, governed by three basic tenets:

First Law

Energy in the universe is finite and constant ($\Delta E_{universe} = \Delta E_{surroundings} + \Delta E_{system} = 0$). It can be expressed either as heat or as work ($E = q + w$). It is possible to convert energy between heat and work.

Second Law

While the First Law indicates that energy can be converted from heat to work and vice versa, the Second Law indicates that this cannot be done with 100% efficiency. In other words, energy lost to the surroundings increases the entropy of those surroundings. In any spontaneous process, the total entropy change of the universe is positive ($\Delta S_{universe} > 0$).

Third Law

In order to assign numerical values to ΔS, there must be a baseline value for S. This can be stated in this fashion: as the absolute temperature approaches zero, the entropy of a perfect crystalline solid approaches zero. Evaluating the change in entropy as one mole of a substance then moves to standard conditions (1 atm pressure and 298 K temperature) gives the standard molar entropy ($\Delta S°$). Entropy changes in a chemical reaction may be calculated using tabulated thermodynamic values: $\Delta S_{reaction} = \sum \Delta S_{f(products)} - \sum \Delta S_{f(reactants)}$. Indications of increasing entropy (that is, $\Delta S > 0$) include these factors:

1. A move to a more disordered phase (entropy of solid < liquid < << gas) shows an increase in entropy.

2. A solution formed when a solid or liquid solute dissociates into a liquid solvent shows increased entropy. However, forcing a chaotic gaseous solute into the relative order of a liquid solvent decreases entropy.

3. Increasing the number of electrons or atoms shows a greater number of possible positions so entropy increases.

4. Increasing delocalization of electrons means greater entropy. Transfer of electrons to form ions allows an ionic bond to form and the electrons stay permanently with their new nuclei. A covalent bond shares electrons between two nuclei. Certain resonance structures actually imply delocalization of electrons among or around a molecule or polyatomic ion. Metallic bonding shares valence electrons among many nuclei. Entropy increases from ionic to covalent to metallic bonds as a result.

5. Weaker bonds and increased softness imply greater entropy.

6. Increasing chemical complexity means increasing entropy.

A change in a system that will occur without any outside influence is called a spontaneous change, favored by increased entropy and an exothermic process. Standard molar enthalpies of formation and standard molar entropies can be linked via the free energy change ΔG in the Gibbs' equation: $\Delta G = \Delta H - T\Delta S$. The standard molar free energies of formation $\Delta G°_f$ can be used to calculate $\Delta G°$ in a Hess' Law like process ($\Delta G_{reaction} = \sum \Delta G_{f(products)} - \sum \Delta G_{f(reactants)}$), or they can be calculated using values of $\Delta H°$ and $\Delta S°$: $\Delta G° = \Delta H° - T\Delta S°$.

Gibbs free energy change and changes in enthalpy and entropy

ΔG	ΔH	ΔS	Comment
(−)	(−)	(+)	Spontaneous at any T
Become (−) at high T	(+)	(+)	Spontaneous at high enough T, not at low T
(−) at low T but (+) at high T	(−)	(−)	Become non-spontaneous at high T, spontaneous at low T
Always (+)	(+)	(−)	Never spontaneous (reverse is always spontaneous)

A reaction may well take place under non-standard conditions with concentrations other than 1 *M*, temperatures other than 298 K, or pressures other than 1 atm. If that is the case, then $\Delta G = \Delta G° + RT \ln Q$ where $R = 8.3145$ J K^{-1} and Q is the trial equilibrium quotient, the ratio of products to reactants that resembles the equilibrium constant *K*. If a reaction has attained equilibrium, then $Q = K$ and $\Delta G = 0$, so $\Delta G = -RT \ln K$.

Example:

For some reaction, $\Delta H°$ is −255 kJ mol^{-1} while $\Delta S°$ is 211 J K^{-1}. At which temperature does ΔG become −350 kJ mol^{-1}?

Solution:
$$\Delta G° = \Delta H° - T\Delta S°$$
$$(-350) = (-255) - x(0.211)$$
$$x = 450 \text{ K}$$

The link between free energy and cell potential is discussed in the chapter on electrochemistry but it is useful to review this equation:

$$\Delta G° = -nFE°$$

where E° is the standard cell potential, F = Faraday's constant (96,485 C mol^{-1}), and n is the number of moles of electrons transferred in the oxidation-reduction process.

Example:

Use a Table of Standard Reduction Potentials to calculate $\Delta G°$ for the reaction

$$2\,Br^-(aq) + I_2(s) \rightarrow Br_2(l) + 2\,I^-(aq)$$

Solution:

$$E°_{red} + E°_{ox} = E°_{cell}$$
$$(+0.53\ V) + (-1.07\ V) = -0.54\ V$$
$$\Delta G° = -nFE°$$
$$= -(2\ mol\ e^-)(96{,}485\ C\ mol^{-1})(-0.54\ J\ C^{-1})$$
$$= +104\ kJ$$

Since the voltage is negative (non-spontaneous), one would expect $\Delta G°$ to have a positive value (non-spontaneous).

MULTIPLE-CHOICE QUESTIONS

1. A reaction is non-spontaneous at any temperature when

   (A) ΔH is positive and ΔS is positive
   (B) ΔH is positive and ΔS is negative
   (C) ΔH is negative and ΔS is positive
   (D) ΔH is negative and ΔS is negative

2. A reaction with positive values for both ΔH and ΔS is spontaneous

   (A) At any temperature
   (B) At high temperature only
   (C) At low temperature only
   (D) At no temperature whatsoever

3. At standard temperature, liquid water vaporizes to become water vapor. The thermodynamic values ΔH and ΔS must be, respectively

   (A) Positive, positive
   (B) Positive, negative
   (C) Negative, positive
   (D) Negative, negative

4. A 30. mL sample of distilled water at 10°C is added to a 50. mL sample of the same water at 50°C in a coffee-cup calorimeter. The final temperature of the mixture is closest to

   (A) 10°C
   (B) 20°C
   (C) 30°C
   (D) 60°C

5. Addition of 50. J to a 10.0 g sample of a metal will cause the temperature of the metal to rise from 25°C to 35°C. The specific heat c of the metal is closest to

(A) 5.0×10^{-4} J/g °C
(B) 0.50 J/(g °C)
(C) 2.5 J/(g °C)
(D) 4.2 J/(g °C)

6. If 7500 J were to be added to a 25 mL sample of water at 25°C, the water would

(A) Freeze
(B) Warm slightly
(C) Warm considerably
(D) Boil

7. Natural gas, a significant source of energy for heat of electricity, is comprised mostly of

(A) Butane
(B) Methane
(C) Octane
(D) Propane

8. The endothermic process among the following is

(A) Natural gas is combusted in a Bunsen burner.
(B) Water vapor condenses on the outside of a glass of iced tea.
(C) A cup of hot water cools as a tea bag brews.
(D) An ice cube melts on a countertop.

9. In a commercial chemical cold pack, an inner pouch containing water is broken and the water is allowed to mix with a sample of solid ammonium nitrate. The signs of the values for ΔH and ΔS for the dissociation reaction must be, respectively

(A) Positive, positive
(B) Positive, negative
(C) Negative, positive
(D) Negative, negative

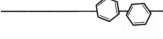
10. Of the following reactions occurring at 25°C, which one involves the greatest increase in entropy?

(A) $Pb^{2+}(aq) + 2\,Cl^-(aq) \rightarrow PbCl_2(s)$
(B) $CO_2(s) \rightarrow CO_2(g)$
(C) $H_2(g) + Cl_2(g) \rightarrow 2\,HCl(g)$
(D) $H_2O(s) \rightarrow H_2O(l)$

11. For some reaction, $\Delta H° = +\,50$ kJ and $\Delta S° = +40$ J/K. The reaction will be spontaneous

(A) At all temperatures
(B) At no temperature
(C) When T $>$ 1250 K
(D) When T $<$ 1250 K

12. The Third Law of Thermodynamics indicates that the

(A) enthalpy of the universe is constant
(B) entropy of the universe increases
(C) sum of the entropies of the system plus surroundings is zero
(D) entropy of a perfectly ordered pure crystal is zero at absolute zero

13. The First Law of Thermodynamics indicates that

(A) Work is force exerted over a distance.
(B) Energy in the universe is finite.
(C) An increase in disorder is part of any spontaneous process.
(D) Work is a state function.

14. The entropy of the universe is

(A) always zero
(B) always constant
(C) always increasing
(D) always decreasing

15. A process which causes a decrease in the entropy is

(A) condensation of steam to form liquid water
(B) vaporization of liquid water to form steam
(C) dissociation of solid sodium chloride into aqueous sodium cations and chloride anions
(D) sublimation of snow to water vapor

16. The maximum work that can be accomplished by a system on its surroundings is

    (A) ΔG
    (B) ΔH
    (C) ΔS
    (D) $T\Delta S$

17. Which of the following is correct about the equilibrium constant K if $\Delta G < 0$?

    (A) K is zero
    (B) K is less than 1
    (C) K is equal to 1
    (D) K is greater than 1

18. Butane combusts in the atmosphere and releases heat:

$$2\,C_4H_{10}(g) + 13\,O_2(g) \rightarrow 8\,CO_2(g) + 10\,H_2O(g)$$

    The signs of the values for ΔG, ΔH, and ΔS for this reaction would be

    (A) $-, +, +$
    (B) $+, -, -$
    (C) $-, -, +$
    (D) $+, +, -$

19. Which of the following has a value for its standard enthalpy of formation which is less than zero?

    (A) $Hg(l)$
    (B) $Mg(s)$
    (C) $C(graphite)$
    (D) $CO_2(g)$

20. Which statement about Hess' Law is *incorrect*?

    (A) The overall value of ΔH for a reaction is the same whether it is developed in a single step of in a series of steps.
    (B) The enthalpy of a reaction is a state function which depends only on its initial and final states.
    (C) All heats of formation in a series of chemical reactions must cancel.
    (D) The heat of formation of any element in its normal state under standard conditions is zero.

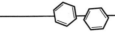

21. For a spontaneous exothermic reaction, what must be true about the sign of ΔS?

(A) $\Delta S < 0$
(B) $\Delta S = 0$
(C) $\Delta S > 0$
(D) Depending on the temperature, ΔS could be negative or positive.

22. Which of the following forms would have the greatest standard molar entropy?

(A) $H_2(g)$
(B) $H_2(l)$
(C) $H_2O(g)$
(D) $H_2O(l)$

23. For which of the following processes will ΔS be negative?

(A) $PbCl_2(s) \rightarrow Pb^{2+}(aq) + 2\,Cl^-(aq)$
(B) $MgO(s) + CO_2(g) \rightarrow MgCO_3(s)$
(C) $CO_2(aq) \rightarrow CO_2(g)$
(D) $C_5H_{12}(l) + 8\,O_2(g) \rightarrow 5\,CO_2(g) + 6\,H_2O(g)$

24. The substance with the smallest value for $S°$ is

(A) $AlCl_3$
(B) $MgCl_2$
(C) $NaCl$
(D) $SnCl_4$

25. As a car battery discharges,

(A) ΔH increases
(B) ΔH decreases
(C) ΔH remains the same
(D) ΔG increases

CHAPTER 9
CONSTRUCTED-RESPONSE QUESTIONS

1. $H_2(g) + I_2(s) \rightarrow 2 HI(g)$

Substance	$\Delta H(kJ\ mol^{-1})$	$\Delta S(J\ mol^{-1}K^{-1})$
$H_2(g)$	0.0	130.6
$I_2(s)$	0.0	116.1
$HI(g)$	26.0	206.0

Use the values in the table above to calculate the following:

(a) $\Delta H°$

(b) $\Delta S°$

(c) $\Delta G°$

(d) K_{eq}

2. Consider the phase change of ice to liquid water: $H_2O(s) \rightleftharpoons H_2O(l)$

(a) If the molar heat of fusion for water is 6.01 kJ mol^{-1}, how many joules are required to melt 1 gram of ice at 273 K?

(b) What is the change in free energy, ΔG, for this process?

(c) What is the entropy change when 1 gram of ice melts at 273 K?

3. Answer the following questions about hydrides of boron. Boron hydrides have large heats of combustion and have been candidates for selection as rocket fuel.

   (a) The standard heat of formation (ΔH_f) of B_5H_9 is +62.8 kJ. Write the balanced reaction that corresponds to this formation.

   (b) B_5H_9 gas combusts in excess oxygen gas to form solid B_2O_3 and liquid water.

       i. Write a balanced equation to describe this process.
       ii. Use the table of heats of formation to calculate the heat of combustion per mole of $B_5H_9(s)$.

Substance	$B_5H_9(g)$	$O_2(g)$	$B_2O_3(s)$	$H_2O(l)$
ΔH_f° (kJ/mol)	+62.8	0	−1264	−285.8

   (c) Gaseous diborane, B_2H_6, was also studied for possible use as a rocket fuel.

       i. Write the balanced equation for the formation of diboron.
       ii. Use the following reactions to calculate the heat of formation of diboron.

$$B_2H_6(g) + 3\,O_2(g) \rightarrow B_2O_3(s) + 3\,H_2O(g) \qquad \Delta H = -2035 \text{ kJ}$$
$$2\,B(s) + 1.5\,O_2(g) \rightarrow B_2O_3(s) \qquad \Delta H = -1273 \text{ kJ}$$
$$H_2(g) + 0.5\,O_2(g) \rightarrow H_2O(l) \qquad \Delta H = -286 \text{ kJ}$$
$$H_2O(l) \rightarrow H_2O(g) \qquad \Delta H = +44 \text{ kJ}$$

4. Answer the following questions concerning the combustion of butane.

(a) Write a balanced equation to describe the combustion of butane in excess oxygen.

(b) Use the table of bond energies to calculate $\Delta H_{combustion}$ of butane gas.

Bond	C-C	C-H	C=O	O-H	O=O
kJ/mol	348	413	728	463	485

CHAPTER 10
ACIDS AND BASES

When we begin an investigation of acids and bases, the ideas depend upon in which century we investigate the topic. In the 19th Century, chemists searching for patterns in the behaviors of acids and bases listed behavioral definitions of each, which one typically studies in earlier courses.

Behavioral Definitions

Acids	Bases
Taste sour	Taste bitter
Sting in open cuts	Feel slippery
Turn blue litmus red	Turn red litmus blue
Solution will conduct an electrical current	Solution will conduct an electrical current
React with many metals to liberate H_2	Can neutralize acids

CONCEPTUAL MODELS

I. Then Svante' **Arrhenius**, the Swedish chemist, began to look for their *chemical* similarities leading to the behaviors cited above, and developed one of the earliest **conceptual models** for acids and bases, based upon these chemical similarities and differences.

    a.   **acids** – release H^+ ions in aqueous solutions
         bases – release OH^- ions in aqueous solutions

b. **water** – because pure water did not exhibit any of the behaviors of either category, that is, it did not conduct an electric current, tasted neither sour nor bitter, and did not cause the color of litmus paper to change, etc., Arrhenius declared water to be *neither* an acid nor a base.

c. **neutralization** – was described by Arrhenius as a reaction between an acid and a base to produce a salt (an ionic compound) and water.

d. **Examples** – One of the most frequently cited examples of an Arrhenius acid-base reaction is the one between HCl and NaOH solutions. $HCl(aq) + NaOH(aq) \rightarrow NaCl(aq) + HOH$. (The latter product is more often recognized as H_2O). Other examples include $HNO_3(aq) + KOH(aq) \rightarrow KNO_3(aq) + H_2O$ (the salt) as well as $2LiOH(aq) + H_2SO_44(aq) \rightarrow 2H_2O + Li_2SO_4(aq)$ (the salt).

All of this information has likely been studied in a previous chemistry course.

II. The next significant conceptual model was developed by two chemists, J.N. Brønsted and T.M. Lowry working independently around 1923 and in separate countries. This model is currently known as the **Brønsted–Lowry theory** of acids and bases (frequently shortened to the Bronsted theory). With this theory, definitions include:

a. **acids** – described as proton donors
   bases – described as proton acceptors.

b. **water** – because water is capable of donating or accepting a proton (H^+), water is now classified as *either* an acid or a base, depending upon its chemical environment. [Note that in aqueous solutions, the proton (H^+) will bond to a water molecule and form the hydronium ion, $H3O^+(aq)$].

c. **neutralization** – now defined as the reaction between an acid and a base to produce a conjugate (new) acid and a conjugate (new) base. The acid definition here is fundamentally the same as an Arrhenius acid, but the Bronsted-Lowry model greatly expands the base model far beyond the OH^- ion.

d. **Examples** –

$NH_3(aq) +$	$HCl(aq) \rightarrow$	$NH_4^+(aq) +$	$Cl^-(aq)$
proton acceptor	proton donor	new proton donor	new proton acceptor
(base)	(acid)	(conjugate acid)	(conjugate base)

Note the *absence* of OH^- and water (as a product) in this reaction, although in its net ionic equation form, this reaction could be written as

$$NH_3(aq) + H_3O^+(aq) \rightarrow \qquad NH_4^+(aq) + H_2O(l)$$
$$\text{conjugate acid} \qquad \text{conjugate base}$$

Other reactions involving proton transfers include equimolar amounts of

$CO_3^{2-}(aq) +$	$NH_4^+(aq) \rightarrow$	$HCO_3^-(aq) +$	$NH_3(aq)$
proton acceptor	proton donor	new proton donor	new proton acceptor
(base)	(acid)	(conjugate acid)	(conjugate base)

This theory illustrates how some substances can act as either acids or bases, depending upon the chemical system. Substances capable of donating or accepting a proton (H^+) are called **amphiprotic** and, and examples, besides water, include ions such as HCO_3^-, HS^- HSO_4^-, etc. This capability of neutralizing either acids or bases is the reason baking soda, $NaHCO_3$ is so prevalent in chemistry fume hoods. With an acid spill, the baking soda reaction is represented by the equation:

$$NaHCO_3(s) + H^+(aq) \rightarrow Na^+(aq) + H_2CO_3 \rightarrow H_2O + CO_2(g)$$

proton acceptor

(base)

However, if a base is spilled, the HCO_3^- ion is capable of furnishing a proton (H^+) according to the equation

$$NaHCO_3(s) + \qquad OH^-(aq) \rightarrow \qquad Na^+(aq) + \qquad H_2O(l) + CO_3^{2-}(aq)$$

proton donor (conjugate acid) (conjugate base)

(acid)

Other examples of acids and their conjugate bases include

Acid	Conjugate Base
HNO_3 (nitric acid)	NO_3^-
HF (hydrofluoric acid)	F^-
HCN (hydrocyanic acid)	CN^-
CH_3COOH (acetic acid)	CH_3COO^-
Also written as ($HC_2H_3O_2$)	($C_2H_3O_2^-$) acetate the old way
H_2O	OH^-

Other examples of bases and their conjugate acids include

Base	Conjugate Acid
NH_3	NH_4^+
OH^-	H_2O
O^{2-}	OH^-

A term that is sometimes confused with amphiprotic is **amphoteric**. An amphoteric compound is a hydroxide-bearing compound capable of *neutralizing either an acid or base*. Two of the more common examples of such behavior are $Al(OH)_3$ and $Zn(OH)_2$. One can readily see that the hydroxide ions in both compounds make them capable of neutralizing acids

$$Al(OH)_3(s) + 3H_3O^+(aq) \rightarrow Al^{3+}(aq) + 3H_2O(l)$$

Their ability to neutralize bases stems from their ability to form complex ion structures with the hydroxide ion.

$$Al(OH)_3(s) + OH^-(aq) \rightarrow Al(OH)_4^-(aq) \qquad Zn(OH)_2(s) + 2OH^-(aq) \rightarrow Zn(OH)_4^{2-}(aq)$$

III. A third model, the **Lewis model of acids and bases**, is another useful, still broader model for explaining some acid-base behaviors. This model has been dropped from the recent revision of the AP Chemistry, but is so significant, particularly in organic chemistry, that the authors feel it merits a brief discussion here. The definitions here include classification as acids or base by valence electron structures and makes no specific reference to H^+ ions nor proton donors. It is said that, when it comes to acid-base reactions, "Bronsted freed us from water; Lewis freed us from hydrogen."

a.   **Acids** – defined as an **electron pair acceptor**. This means the acids need to contain an empty electron orbital.

b.   **Bases** – defined as an **electron pair donor**. This means there needs to be at least one pair of non-bonded (lone pair) electrons on the atom or ion in order donate(share) this pair with another substance.

c.   **Neutralization** – described as the reaction of an acid and a base to produce a new substance that contains a new (coordinate) covalent bond.

d.   **Examples** –

1. The conventional Arrhenius acid-base net ionic reaction for a strong acid and a strong base is still covered with this model $H^+ + OH^- \rightarrow H_2O$ because the H^+ ion has the empty 1s orbital and the $:OH^-$ ion contains several non-bonded electron pairs. A covalent bond arises (H:OH) in which the OH^- furnishes the *pair* of electrons to be shared with the incoming H^+.

2. Lewis acid base reaction can typically be predicted when the central atom on one substance is from the III (a). Family and the central atom from another substance is from the VA Family. For example, when BCl_3 (with 3 valence electrons on boron and an empty orbital) is reacted with NH_3, the N atom furnishes the electron pair to be shared with B, resulting in the equation
$$BCl_3 + :NH_3 \rightarrow Cl_3B:NH_3$$
with BCl_3 serving as the acid (the electron pair acceptor) and NH_3 (the electron pair donor) serving as the base. Note the absence of any H^+ in BCl_3, the acid.

3. The amphoteric nature of $Al(OH)_3$ discussed earlier in this chapter can be explained with the Lewis model as well, $Al(OH)_3(s) + OH^-(aq) \rightarrow Al(OH)_4^-(aq)$ with the empty orbital on $Al(OH)_3$ (the acid)and the non-bonded pairs on the OH^- ion (the base). Arrhenius would never have conceived of $Al(OH)_3$ serving as an acid!

THE pH SCALE

The development of the quantitative pH scale was discussed in an earlier chapter on Solutions, but to briefly re-visit the mathematics of acid-base chemistry, we begin with the notion that every aqueous solution is either acidic, basic or neutral. Using brackets to denote molar concentrations,

neutral solution $[H_3O^+] = [OH^-]$

acidic solution $[H_3O^+] > [OH^-]$

basic solution $[H_3O^+] < [OH^-]$

The pH scale is a mathematically convenient way of expressing [H$^+$] or [OH$^-$] concentrations for dilute solutions and can be thought of as the (base 10) power of [H$^+$].

For the ionization/dissociation of water, the equation is $2H_2O \Leftrightarrow H_3O^+$ and OH^- where the [H$_3$O$^+$] at 25.0 C = 1×10^{-7}M. With a 1:1 relationship between [H$_3$O$^+$] and [OH$^-$], the [OH$^-$] is also = 1×10^{-7}M. The Keq expression (usually written as Kw = [H$_3$O$^+$][OH$^-$] = $(1 \times 10^{-7})^2 = 1 \times 10^{-14}$.

The **pH** is defined as the $-\log[\mathbf{H_3O^+}]$ and the **pOH** is defined as the $-\mathbf{log\ of}$ [**OH**$^-$]. As shown in the solutions chapter of this book, the **pH + pOH = 14** at 25°C, (as in Keq = 10^{-14}). If the pH is known, the [**H$_3$O$^+$**] = $\mathbf{10^{-pH}}$ and the **pOH** = $\mathbf{10^{-pOH}}$.

Examples: If the [H$^+$] = 1.0×10^{-4}, the pH is $-\log[10^{-4}] = 4.00$. If the [H$^+$] = 2.0×10^{-4}, the pH is $-\log[2 \times 10^{-4}] = 3.70$. The significant digits issue show up in the decimal places. The number of significant digits is based upon the number of decimal places used. The pH of 3.70 has 2 significant digits.

If the pH is known, the [H$^+$] can be determined as follows. If the pH = 3.0, the [H$^+$] = 10^{-3} or 1×10^{-3}. If the pH = 2.30, the [H$^+$] = $10^{-2.3}$, but in chemistry, we report values using only whole number exponents. Using a calculator, the numerical value of $10^{-2.3}$ becomes 5.0×10^{-3}.

WEAK ACIDS AND BASES

Most textbooks list 6-7 aqueous solutions as strong acids. These include $HClO_4$, HNO_3, HI, HBr, HCl, H_2SO_4 and sometimes $HClO_3$. In aqueous solution, these acids ionize to produce the hydrated proton, most frequently known as the hydronium ion, and commonly represented as H_3O^+. For the purposes of AP Chemistry, all other acids can be considered weak acids. With bases, the hydroxides of the IA and IIA metal ions (NaOH, KOH, $Sr(OH)_2$, etc. are generally considered strong bases which readily produce OH^- ions in aqueous solutions. For all practical purposes, these compounds are ones which ionize to 100% in water.

When acids or bases ionize to a weaker extent and detectable quantities of the reactant remain, we need to use an equilibrium set-up to determine the [H$_3$O$^+$] or [OH$^-$]. The equilibrium constants (Keq) are then represented as Ka or Kb for weak acids or weak bases. The general form for the dissociation becomes

$HX + H_2O \longleftrightarrow H_3O^+ + X^-$. The equilibrium set-up becomes Ka = $[H_3O^+][X^-]/[HX]$.

For a weak base like NH_3, the equation becomes $NH_3 + H_2O \longleftrightarrow NH_4^+ + OH^-$, and the equilibrium set-up becomes Kb = $[NH_4^+][OH^-]/[NH_3]$.

Example 1

Determine the pH of a 0.20M solution of HCN if the Ka of HCN is 1.0×10^{-10}. The equation for the aqueous solution is written $HCN + H_2O \longleftrightarrow H_3O + + CN^-$. And the equilibrium expression becomes $Ka = [H_3O^+][CN^-]/HCN$.

We do not know the $[H_3O^+]$, so let $x = [H_3O^+]$. Therefore, with $HCN + H_2O \longleftrightarrow H_3O^+ + CN^-$, the equilibrium concentrations become $0.20 - x$ x x and the equilibrium expression set-up becomes $Ka = 1 \times 10^{-10} = [x][x]/0.20 - x$. The initial assumption with the [HCN] is, that the % ionization is less than 5%, and therefore, mathematically negligible, so that $[0.20 - x]$ becomes $\approx [0.20]$. The set-up is now $1 \times 10^{-10} = [x][x]/0.20$, and upon solving for x, $x = [H_3O^+] = 4.47 \times 10^{-6}$. The last step is converting the $[H_3O^+]$ to a pH, (a step which students frequently neglect to complete on AP exams), and so the $pH = -\log[H_3O^+]$ becomes $-\log[4.47 \times 10^{-6}] = $ **pH = 5.35**. We also see that our original assumption that $[0.20 - x]$ for the $[HCN] \approx [0.20]$ was a valid assumption, because $[0.20 - 4.47 \times 10^{-6}]$ is indeed $\approx [0.20]$. When the value for the $[H_3O^+]$ is $\geq 5\%$, the quadratic equation is needed to solve for x. While individual teachers may choose to provide students with this experience, this is generally not the position of AP Chemistry, and students can reasonably expect that Constructed Response questions in Part II of the exam will NOT require using the quadratic equation for determining the $[H_3O^+]$.

EXAMPLE 2

Determine the pH of a 0.10 M solution of NH_3 if the Kb of NH_3 is 1.8×10^{-5}. The equation for the aqueous solution is written $NH_3 + H_2O \longleftrightarrow NH_4^+ + OH^-$, and the K_b expression $= [NH_4^+][OH^-]/[NH_3]$. Once again we do not know how much of the OH forms, so we let $x = [OH^-]$. Using the same approach used with the Ka set-up above, the equilibrium set-up becomes

$$K_b = 1.8 \times 10^{-5} = [x][x]/[0.10 - x]$$

Again, assuming $[0.10 - x] \approx [0.10]$ $x = [OH^-] = 1.34 \times 10^{-3}$, and the $pOH = -\log[OH-] = -\log[1.34 \times 10^{-3}] = 2.87$. The pH + pOH = 14.00, so the **pH = 11.13**, which is indeed indicative of a basic solution.

HYDROLYSIS

Hydrolysis is the reaction of a compound with water to produce an acidic or basic solution. In addition to our conventional acids and bases, we find when certain ionic compounds are dissolved in water, the resulting solution is no longer neutral: it may be acidic or basic, depending upon the compound. When we look for patterns and regularities here, we discover that metallic cations from the IA and IIa like Na^+, K^+ Ba^{2+} do not undergo hydrolysis to any appreciable extent, but metallic cations from the IIIA and transition metals frequently do (Al^{3+}, Cu^{2+}, Fe^{3+} etc). With nonmetallic anions, ions like Cl^-, Br^-, NO_3^-, ClO_4^- (conjugate bases associated with *strong* acids), do not react with water to any appreciable extent, but those anions (conjugate bases) associated with weak acids do.

Net ionic equations for these hydrolysis reactions include the following:

$$NaCN(s) + H_2O \longleftrightarrow HCN + Na^+(aq) + OH^-(aq)$$

and this solution would become basic, which we could (HOH) verify by adding a drop of phenolphthalein (pink color appears in solution) or a strip of litmus paper and noting a blue color. Another example would be: $S^{2-}(aq) + H_2O \longleftrightarrow HS^-(aq) + OH^-(aq)$.

For the metallic ions such as an aqueous Al^{3+}, that does not appear to contain a H+ ion, it is more difficult to "see" why it would produce an acidic solution. Clearly the Arrhenius model cannot explain this reaction. However, the Bronsted-Lowry model does afford us an explanation. The reaction first involves the hydration of the aluminum ion to form the hydrated $Al(H_2O)_6^{3+}(aq)$ and then the loss of an H^+ to a water molecule

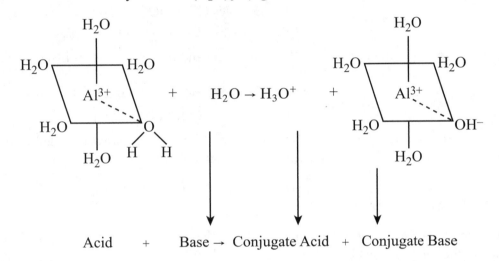

Acid   +   Base → Conjugate Acid   +   Conjugate Base

The stronger the charge on the central metallic ion, the greater its attraction to the O atoms in water, and the weaker the O ← H bond (in the complex ion) becomes. Hence this H is more susceptible to transfer to a water molecule not in the complex ion, and accounts for the presence of H_3O^+ ions in the solution of aluminum ions. However, this ability of an aluminum ion to surround itself with 6 H_2O molecules accounts for its usefulness in underarm antiperspirants and also explains why buffers are frequently added to them as well to avoid the under arm region becoming too acidic.

BUFFERS

A buffer solution is one that resists changes in pH upon the addition of small amounts of acid, base or water. It typically consists of a weak acid and its salt or a weak base and its salt (conjugate acid), depending upon the pH region to be maintained. Human blood needs to maintain a pH between 7.2-7.5 to carry out all the reactions and transport mechanism required of it. A frequent cause of goldfish dying in a goldfish bowl is failure to maintain the proper pH.

How do buffers work? Consider the commonly cited acetic acid (ethanoic acid) and its salt, sodium acetate and the simplified dissociation equation:

$$CH_3COOH \longleftrightarrow H^+(aq) + CH_3COO^-(aq)$$

The K_a expression is $\dfrac{[H^+][CH_3COO^-]}{[CH_3COOH]} = 1.8 \times 10^{-5}$. To determine the pH of 500 ml of a 0.10 M solution of acetic acid, we let x = $[H^+] = [CH_3COO^-]$ and the set up becomes $1.8 \times 10^{-5} = (x)(x)/\approx 0.10$, the value of x (which is the $[H^+]$) = 1.34×10^{-3} M, and the pH = 2.87.

To buffer the solution, we take a 500 mL of a fresh sample of 0.10 acetic acid and add .05 moles of sodium acetate (CH$_3$COONa), to the mixture, there are now = moles of CH$_3$COOH and CH$_3$COO$^-$ present, available to react with small additions of H$^+$ (which can react with the CH$_3$COO$^-$) or OH$^-$ (which can react with the CH$_3$COOH),

$$1.8 \times 10^{-5} = \frac{[H^+][0.05 \text{ moles } CH_3COO^- / 0.500L]}{[.05 \text{ moles } CH_3COOH / 0.500 \text{ L}]}$$

Because the moles of acetate ion and acetic acid are the same and the volume term is the same

$$1.8 \times 10^{-5} = \frac{[H^+]\left[0.05 \cancel{\text{ moles } CH_3COO^-} / 0 \cdot 500L\right]}{[.05 \cancel{\text{ moles } CH_3COOH} / 0.500 \text{ L}]}$$

The [H+] is = 1.8×10^{-5} and the pH = 4.74. Now if 25 mL of *water is added* is added to this acetic acid-acetate ion buffer solution, we can set it up without complicated math:

$$1.8 \times 10^{-5} = \frac{[H^+][\text{moles } CH_3COO^- / \cancel{0.525L}]}{[\text{moles } CH_3COOH / \cancel{0.525L}]}$$

The moles of acetate ion and acetic acid remain the same as they were at the beginning, and the **new volume** term cancels out, so the [H$^+$] remains 1.8×10^{-5} and the pH I still = 4.74.

Now consider a fresh sample of the buffer containing 0.05 moles of acetic acid and 0.05 moles of acetate ion, and add 0.004 more moles of sodium acetate, CH$_3$COONa. To determine the pH of this solution, we start with the original set-up and add in the 0.004 moles of acetate ion.

$$1.8 \times 10^{-5} = \frac{[H^+][0.05 \text{ moles } CH_3COO^- / 0.500 \text{ L}]}{[.05 \text{ moles } CH_3COOH / 0.500 \text{ L}]} \rightarrow \frac{[H^+][0.054 \text{ moles } CH_3COO^- / 0.500 \text{ L}]}{[.05 \text{ moles } CH_3COOH / 0.500 \text{ L}]}$$

The [H$^+$] becomes 1.67×10^{-5} and the pH = 4.78, only slightly changed from the original 4.74; the buffer contents did indeed prevent a significant change in pH.

If we add 0.004 moles of H$^+$ to an original sample of the buffer, the H$^+$ will react with acetate ions, forming more acetic acid. The set-up becomes

$$1.8 \times 10^{-5} = \frac{[H^+][0.05 \text{ moles } CH_3COO^- / 0.500 \text{ L}]}{[.05 \text{ moles } CH_3COOH / 0.500 \text{ L}]} \rightarrow \frac{[H^+][0.054 \text{ moles } CH_3COO^- / \cancel{0.500} \text{ L}]}{[.05 \text{ moles } CH_3COOH / \cancel{0.500} \text{ L}]}$$

and the new [H$^+$] is 2.11×10^{-5} M; the pH = 4.68, which is less than 0.1 pH unit difference from the original pH = 4.74. Again, the buffering contents prevented a significant change in pH.

There are limits to the buffering capacities, but when the mole ratios of acetate ion to acetic acid change no more than by 50% of the original ratios, the pH seldom varies more than a few tenths. Ratio changes larger than by 50% of the original ratios are generally beyond the scope of the new AP Chemistry curriculum.

TITRATION CURVES

Titration curves take two general shapes: they move upwards if a base is added to an acid, and downwards if acid is added to a base. Whether the change in pH is gradual (such as with a weak acid with strong base) or the pH rises sharply (strong acid-strong base), there are two regions which are particularly useful in determining the molar mass and the Ka or Kb of the original (often an "unknown" substance to be titrated.

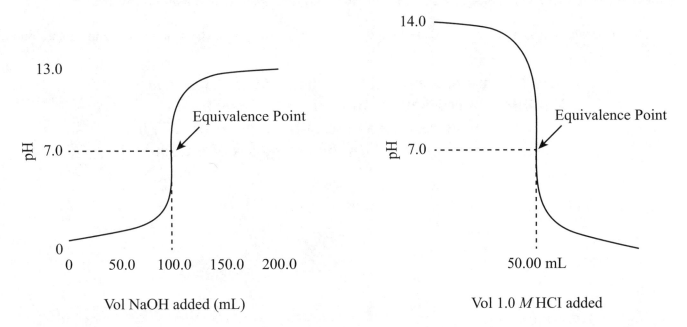

For simplicity, the focus will be on a monoprotic unknown acid. At the equivalence point, there are equivalent number of moles of the added base ant the unknown acid.

Given: A 0.500 g samole of HX, an unknown monoprotic acid which requires 31.25 mL of 0.100M NaOH. What is the molar mass of HX? What is the Ka for HX?

At the equivalence pt., the moles of NaOH added $= .100$ moles/L $\times 0.03125$ L $= 0.003125$ moles $OH^- = 0.003125$ moles of HX. The **molar mass**, grams per mole, can now be calculated: 0.500 g/ 0.003125 moles = **160 g/mole**.

To determine the Ka for the unknown weak acid, any point along the titration curve could be used, because it is an equilibrium **constant**, but a point that is often selected is the half-way point (halfway to the end point)in the titration curve. Here, half of the initial HX acid has been converted to X^-, and half remains, so the set up for determination for the Ka is

$$Ka = \frac{[H^+][X^-]}{[HX]} = \frac{[H^+]\left[\frac{1}{2} \text{ the original \# moles HX} \Big/ \text{volume}\right]}{\left[\frac{1}{2}\text{the original \# moles HX} \Big/ \text{volume}\right]}$$

Once the cancellations are made, all that remains in the above expression is Ka $= [H^+]$ or pKa = pH. The pH can be read off the titration curve at the halfway point and the Ka determined using that pH.

If the unknown acid is diprotic (H_2X), the Ka_2 calculation could be determined by selecting the point halfway between the first equivalence point and the second one.

The topic of acids and bases is indeed, a large one, and we have chosen to present condensed summaries of the salient topics. Further developments of the topics contained in this chapter can be found in the chapters of the common college textbooks, and one finds the material is frequently divided into two chapters.

The ideas summarized in chapter 10 are linked to the revised AP Chemistry Curriculum and can be found under

BIG IDEA # 6, Essential Knowledge 6C.1. Chemical Equilibrium reasoning can be used to describe the proton transfer reactions of acid-base chemistry." This topic is further broken into the categories of 6.C1.a through h1.

MULTIPLE-CHOICE QUESTIONS

1. The pH of a 0.0001 M HNO_3 solution is

   (A) 4
   (B) 3
   (C) 2
   (D) 1

2. Which property is not typically associated with basic solutions?

   (A) Feel slippery
   (B) React with metals to produce H_2 gas
   (C) Have a pH above 7.0
   (D) React with solutions containing CO_3^{2-} ions

Questions 3–5: Use the answers below to answer questions 2–5.

   (A) Br^- (aq)
   (B) S^{2-} (aq)
   (C) NH_4^+ (aq)
   (D) HI (aq)

3. Would be classified as the conjugate acid of a weak base.

4. Would be classified as the conjugate base of a strong acid.

5. Would be classified as weak acid.

6. A 1.0 L solution contains equimolar amounts of NH_4Cl and NH_3. 10 mL of water is added to the solution. Which statement describes the effect of the added water?

(A) The pH increases.
(B) The pH decreases.
(C) The pH remains unchanged.
(D) The molar concentration of the NH_3 increases.

Questions 7-9: Select from the answers below for questions 7–9.

(A) the number of moles present per liter
(B) the molality of the solution
(C) the extent of the dissociation of the electrolytes
(D) inter-ionic attractions

7. Which of the above is most closely related to the distinction between strong acids and weak acids?

8. Which of the above is most closely related to the distinction between concentrated and dilute acid solutions?

9. Which of the above accounts for a pH of 2 for $0.01M$ HCl, but a pH 0f 4 for $0.0001\ M$ HCl?

10. What is the pH of a solution made by adding 200 ml of distilled water to 100 ml of $0.0030\ M\ HNO_3$? (Assume volumes are additive.)

(A) 3.0
(B) 2.7
(C) 2.0
(D) 1.0

Questions 11-13: Choose from the answers below to answer questions 11–13.

(A) KOH
(B) $NaHSO_4$
(C) C_2H_5OH
(D) NH_3

11. Which of the above aqueous solutions is an example of a Bronsted-Lowry acid?

12. Which of the above aqueous solutions would be classified as neither a Bronsted-Lowry acid nor a base?

13. Which of the above 0.1M aqueous solutions would have the highest pH?

14. A student pipettes 25.00 mL samples of HCl solution into separate Erlenmeyer flasks, dilutes the acid with 20 mL of distilled water and adds 3 drops of phenolphthalein to each flask. The solutions are titrated with NaOH from a buret until a pale pink color persists. The following data are recorded.

Volumes of NaOH solution added

Trial #1   32.25 mL
Trial #2   33.50 mL
Trial #3   33.49 mL
Trial #4   33.51 mL

Which statement below is the most probably explanation for the student's results?

(A) The student added too little phenolphthalein to the first solution.
(B) A different amount of water was added to the first flask.
(C) The buret was not rinsed with NaOH solution before filling.
(D) The pipet was not rinsed with HCl before filling

Questions 15–17: Choose from the answers below to answer questions 15–17.

Consider 100 mL of each solution,

(A) 0.1 M NaOH
(B) 0.2 M NaCl
(C) 0.1 M NaC$_2$H$_3$O$_2$
(D) 0.1 M AlCl$_3$

15. Which solution would be expected to have the lowest pH?

16. Which solution would have a pH closest to pH = 8.2?

17. Which solution pH will remain the same if 50 mL of distilled water is added to each solution?

_____

18. Which statement is true?

(A) The outer limits of the pH scale are 0 and 14.
(B) The weaker the acid, the more strongly its salts hydrolyze.
(C) The pH of a neutral solution is always 7.
(D) A solution of HNO$_3$ can be made basic if enough water is added.

19. If the dissociation of water, $H_2O \Leftrightarrow H^+ + OH^-$ is endothermic, and some room temperature water is heated to boiling, which of the following is true?

   (A) The pH will be 7; the solution will be acidic.
   (B) The pH will be greater than 7, but the solution will be neutral.
   (C) The pH will be less than 7, but the solution will be neutral.
   (D) The pH will be less than 7; the pOH will be less than 7, and the solution will be acidic.

QuestionS 20–21:

   (A) Spectrophotometric (color) analysis
   (B) Mass spectroscopy analysis
   (C) Photon emission spectroscopy (PES)
   (D) Titration with a pH meter (probe)

20. Which method would most likely be used to determine the molar mass of an unknown solid monoprotic acid?

21. Which method would most likely be used to determine the wavelength of maximum absorbance for an aqueous $CuSO_4$ solution?

22. A 20.0 mL sample of a weak acid, HX is titrated to the endpoint and requires 50.0 mL of a 0.050 M KOH solution. After the addition of the first 30.0 mL of KOH, the pH of the solution is = 5.00. What is the dissociation constant, K_a, for this weak acid, HX?

   (A) 1.5×10^{-5}
   (B) 2.0×10^{-6}
   (C) 3.0×10^{-6}
   (D) 6.7×10^{-6}

Questions 23–24: Select from the answers below to answer questions 23–24.

   (A) 0.0
   (B) 1.0
   (C) 2.0
   (D) 12

23. The pH of a 1.0 M solution of HI

24. The pH of a 0.01 M solution of KOH

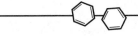

25. Which equation below illustrates amphoteric behavior of $Al(OH)_3$?

(A) $Al^{3+}(aq) + 6H_2O(l) \rightarrow Al(H_2O)_6^{3+}(aq)$

(B) $Al(H_2O)_6^{3+}(aq) + H_2O(l) \rightarrow H_3O^+(aq) + Al(H_2O)_5OH^{2+}(aq)$

(C) $Al(OH)_3(s) \rightarrow Al^{3+}(aq) + 3OH^-(aq)$

(D) $Al(OH)_3(s) + OH^-(aq) \rightarrow Al(OH)_4^-(aq)$

CHAPTER 10

CONSTRUCTED-RESPONSE QUESTIONS

1. A new, solid weak acid, HY, is synthesized. A titration of 0.426 g of HY requires 30.00 mL of 0.10 M KOH solution to reach the equivalence point.

   (a) Write the dissociation equation for HY in water and its equilibrium expression (Ka)
   (b) Write the net ionic equation for the titration reaction.
   (c) Calculate the molar mass of HY. (Please show your set-ups.)
   (d) After 6.00 mL of the base is added, the pH of the solution is 5.00. What is the value for the Ka of HY?
   (e) What is the value of K_b for the Y^- ion?
   (f) At the equivalence point of the reaction, will the solution be acidic, basic or neutral? Write an equation to support your conclusion.
   (g) Calculate the pH of the solution at the equivalence point.

2. The acid dissociation constant, K_a, is 1×10^{-5} for a monoprotic mystery acid, HMyst. What is the percent dissociation of a 0.10 M HMyst?

3. A student is provided a tray containing a clear solution of white vinegar, the indicator phenolphthalein, a pH meter and a solution of 0.2 M NaOH and is asked determine the per cent of acetic acid, $HC_2H_3O_2$, in the solution. Describe/design an experiment and show the mathematical set-up for determining the percent (by volume) of the acetic acid in the vinegar. (Assume the density of the vinegar is essentially the same as the density of water.)

4. Write the formula of the conjugate acid of each Bronsted-Lowry base

    <u>Base</u>   <u>Conjugate Acid</u>

(a) H_2O

(b) NH_2^-

(c) OH^-

(d) HSO_3^-

ELECTROCHEMISTRY

Oxidation-reduction (redox) reactions can occur in gases, as illustrated by the formation of gaseous cations and anions (Chapter 1), in solids, as in many commercial batteries (described below), but are also commonly encountered in aqueous solutions. They were discussed briefly in Chapter 5 along with acid-base and precipitation reactions where the emphasis was on identifying each type of reaction and distinguishing them from the other two types. The discussion here will extend the earlier material to emphasize methods of balancing such equations and using them in electrochemical cells and titrations. As was mentioned in chapter 5, a redox process can be identified by a transfer of electrons or by a change in oxidation number. The substance that loses electrons (or shows an increase in its positive oxidation number, ON) undergoes oxidation and the substance that gains electrons (shows a decrease in ON) undergoes reduction. (Substances that lose electrons are called reducing agents, because they donate those electrons to other chemicals while substances that gain electrons, by removing them from other substances, are called oxidizing agents. Although these terms will not be encountered in AP exams they are commonly encountered in most other chemistry courses and exams.)

Balancing oxidation reduction reactions

The first principle of balancing redox equations is that the number of electrons lost must equal the number gained. This balancing process can be achieved by means of the oxidation number method or the ion electron (half-reaction) method.

Oxidation number method Rules for assigning oxidation numbers to atoms in compounds and/or ions were given in chapter 5 and will be used here without further review. (Anyone wishing to review those rules should consult that chapter.) The technique of balancing a redox reaction using oxidation numbers can be illustrated by the reaction of copper metal with nitrate ions in acid solution.

$$Cu + H^+ + NO_3^- \rightarrow Cu^{2+} + NO + H_2O$$

The ON of copper changes from zero (in the element) to +2 (in the ion) while the ON of nitrogen changes from +5 (in NO_3^-) to +2 (in NO). Since Cu loses two electrons and NO_3^- gains three electrons, three Cu atoms are needed for every two NO_3^- in order to balance the number of electrons gained and lost.

$$0 \xrightarrow{\quad 2(-2\,e^-) = 6\,e^-\ \text{lost}\quad} +2$$

$$+5 \xrightarrow{\qquad\qquad} +2$$
$$2(+3\,e^-) = 6\,e^-\ \text{gained}$$

$$3\,Cu + 8\,H^+ + 2\,NO_3 \xrightarrow{\qquad\qquad} 3\,Cu^{2+} + 2\,NO + 4\,H_2O$$

Once the electrons lost and gained have been balanced by multiplying the atoms / ions appropriately, eight H^+ ions must be added to balance the +6 charge of the three Cu^{2+} ions and react with four oxygen atoms lost by the three NO_3^- ions to give four H_2Os. This method can be used with complete equations as above or by breaking such an equation into half reactions then recombining them after multiplying each by the factors needed to equalize the number of electrons lost and gained.

Ion-electron (half-reaction) Method

Redox processes can be divided into half-reactions, where each half-reaction involves only one chemical species in its oxidized and reduced forms along with the number of electrons, H^+ ions, and H_2O molecules needed to balance the charge and atoms. Balanced half-reactions can be added to give the overall reaction. Half-reactions can be balanced easily by inspection if only electrons are needed and H^+ and H_2O are not involved.

Oxidation half-reactions	Reduction half-reactions
$Zn(s) \rightarrow Zn^{2+}(aq) + 2\,e^-$	$Cl_2(g) + 2\,e^- \rightarrow 2\,Cl^-(aq)$
$Fe^{2+}(aq) \rightarrow Fe^{3+}(aq) + e^-$	$Cu^{2+}(aq) + 2\,e^- \rightarrow Cu(s)$

Although half-reactions that contain oxy-ions may be balanced by inspection as well, it is preferable to have a standard step-wise approach. One such method (called the ion electron method) is illustrated by the following examples:

1. reduction of NO_3^- ions to NO in acid solution.
   step 1: add H_2O to the side of the half-reaction that lacks oxygen.
   $$NO_3^- \rightarrow NO + 2\,H_2O$$
   step 2: balance H^+
   $$NO_3^- + 4\,H^+ \rightarrow NO + 2\,H_2O$$
   step 3: balance by adding electrons as necessary.
   $$NO_3^- + 4\,H^+ + 3\,e^- \rightarrow NO + 2\,H_2O$$
   step 4: check to see that all the atoms and charges are balanced.

2. oxidation of aqueous Mn^{2+} ions to permanganate (MnO_4^-)
   step 1: add H_2O to the side of the equation that lacks oxygen.
   $$Mn^{2+} + 4\,H_2O \rightarrow MnO_4^-$$
   step 2: balance hydrogen with H^+ ions.
   $$Mn^{2+} + 4\,H_2O \rightarrow MnO_4^- + 8\,H^+$$
   step 3: balance by adding electrons as necessary.
   $$Mn^{2+} + 4\,H_2O \rightarrow MnO_4^- + 8\,H^+ + 5\,e^-$$

NOTE: When balancing half-reactions it is not necessary that the charges on the two sides of the equation are zero as in the first example but only that they are equal as in example 2.

The same principles can be used to balance half reactions in alkaline solution with a slight change, illustrated by the oxidation of Cl_2 to form ClO_3^-.

   step 1: balance the atoms undergoing oxidation (or reduction).
   $$Cl_2 \rightarrow 2\,ClO_3^-$$
   step 2: add twice as many OH^- ions as needed to balance the oxygen atoms.
   $$Cl^2 + 12\,OH^- \rightarrow 2\,ClO_3^-$$
   step 3: balance extra H and O with H_2O.
   $$Cl_2 + 12\,OH^- \rightarrow 2\,ClO_3^- + 6\,H_2O$$
   step 4: balance charge using electrons.
   $$Cl_2 + 12\,OH^- \rightarrow 2\,ClO_3^- + 6\,H_2O + 10\,e^-$$
   step 5: check that all atoms and charges balance.

Balanced oxidation and reduction half-reactions can be added after multiplying each by appropriate factors so that the electrons lost and gained cancel. In addition, any chemical species appearing on both sides of the equation (e.g. H^+ or H_2O) are cancelled. For example, Cl_2 can undergo reduction to form Cl^- as shown below

$$Cl_2 + 2\,e^- \rightarrow 2\,Cl^-$$

If this reduction of Cl_2 (multiplied by 5 to give 10 e^-)

$$5\,(Cl_2 + 2\,e^- \rightarrow 2\,Cl^-)$$

is paired with the oxidation half-reaction above the overall equation is

$$6\,Cl_2 + 12\,OH^- \rightarrow 2\,ClO_3^- + 10\,Cl^- + 6\,H_2O$$

This process, in which one substance undergoes both oxidation and reduction, is referred to as disproportionation (or autooxidation-reduction).

Spontaneous reactions

As discussed in chapter nine spontaneous reactions are ones which occur without a net addition of energy from an outside source such as the examples below.

1. When a piece of zinc metal is placed in a solution of copper(II) ions the surface of the zinc darkens, eventually turning the color of copper metal as the zinc metal undergoes oxidation to replace the Cu(II) ions in solution which become reduced to copper metal. The above observations can be represented by the equation.

$$Zn(s) + Cu^{2+}(aq) \rightarrow Zn^{2+}(aq) + Cu(s)$$

2. If a piece of copper metal is placed in a colorless aqueous silver ion solution, silver metal is deposited and the solution turns blue as silver ions become reduced while the copper metal undergoes oxidation. The corresponding equation is

$$Cu(s) + 2\,Ag^+(aq) \rightarrow 2\,Ag(s) + Cu^{2+}(aq)$$

In one of these reactions copper(II) ions undergo reduction while in the other copper metal undergoes oxidation. It is possible to account for these observations and to predict whether other oxidation-reduction reactions will occur spontaneously by referring to a table of standard reduction potentials such as the one given below.

Standard Reduction Potentials

The half-reactions in this table refer to the voltages obtained under the standard conditions of 25°C, 1.0 M concentrations for ions, 1 atmosphere pressure for gases and are listed in order of decreasing tendency for the reduction reactions to occur. Because the potential for a single half-reaction can not be measured, the half-reaction

$$2\,H_3O^+(aq) + 2\,e^- \rightarrow H_2(g) + 2\,H_2O(l)$$

with an assigned value of 0.00 V, is used as a reference for other values.

The reduction of $F_2(g)$, with an SRP of 2.87 V, has a greater tendency to occur than do any of the species listed below it on the left side of the table (all of which have lower E° values). In a similar manner the reduced species (on the right) at the bottom of the table have a greater tendency to undergo oxidation than the species above them because the potentials for their oxidation reactions (the reverse of the SRP) are more positive than those for any reduced species above them. Thus, Ag^+ ions undergo reduction more readily than Cu^{2+} ions and Cu metal undergoes oxidation more readily than Ag metal. Similarly, Cu^{2+} ions undergo reduction more readily than Zn^{2+} ions and Zn metal undergoes oxidation more readily than Cu metal. The results are the reactions discussed above

$$Cu(s) + 2\,Ag^+(aq) \rightarrow Cu^{2+}(aq) + 2\,Ag(s)$$
$$Zn(s) + Cu^{2+}(aq) \rightarrow Zn^{2+}(aq) + Cu(s)$$

Standard Reduction Potentials in Aqueous Solution at 25°C

Reduction Half-Reaction		$E°$ (V)
$F_2(g) + 2\,e^-$	$\rightarrow 2\,F^-(aq)$	$+2.87$
$H_2O_2(aq) + 2\,H_3O^+(aq) + 2\,e^-$	$\rightarrow 4\,H_2O(l)$	$+1.77$
$PbO_2(s) + SO_4^{2-}(aq) + 4\,H_3O^+(aq) + 2\,e^-$	$\rightarrow PbSO_4(s) + 6\,H_2O(l)$	$+1.685$
$MnO_4^-(aq) + 8\,H_3O^+(aq) + 5\,e^-$	$\rightarrow Mn^{2+}(aq) + 12\,H_2O(l)$	$+1.52$
$Au^{3+}(aq) + 3\,e^-$	$\rightarrow Au(s)$	$+1.50$
$Cl_2(g) + 2\,e^-$	$\rightarrow 2\,Cl^-(aq)$	$+1.360$
$Cr_2O_7^{2-}(aq) + 14\,H_3O^+(aq) + 6\,e^-$	$\rightarrow 2\,Cr^{3+}(aq) + 21\,H_2O(l)$	$+1.33$
$O_2(g) + 4\,H_3O^+(aq) + 4\,e^-$	$\rightarrow 6\,H_2O(l)$	$+1.229$
$Br_2(l) + 2\,e^-$	$\rightarrow 2\,Br^-(aq)$	$+1.08$
$NO_3^-(aq) + 4\,H_3O^+(aq) + 3\,e^-$	$\rightarrow NO(g) + 6\,H_2O(l)$	$+0.96$
$OCl^-(aq) + H_2O(l) + 2\,e^-$	$\rightarrow Cl^-(aq) + 2\,OH^-(aq)$	$+0.89$
$Hg^{2+}(aq) + 2\,e^-$	$\rightarrow Hg(l)$	$+0.855$
$Ag^+(aq) + e^-$	$\rightarrow Ag(s)$	$+0.80$
$Hg_2^{2+}(aq) + 2\,e^-$	$\rightarrow 2\,Hg(l)$	$+0.789$
$Fe^{3+}(aq) + e^-$	$\rightarrow Fe^{2+}(aq)$	$+0.771$
$I_2(s) + 2\,e^-$	$\rightarrow 2\,I^-(aq)$	$+0.535$
$O_2(g) + 2\,H_2O(l) + 4\,e^-$	$\rightarrow 4\,OH^-(aq)$	$+0.40$
$Cu^{2+}(aq) + 2\,e^-$	$\rightarrow Cu(s)$	$+0.337$
$Sn^{4+}(aq) + 2\,e^-$	$\rightarrow Sn^{2+}(aq)$	$+0.15$
$2\,H_3O^+(aq) + 2\,e^-$	$\rightarrow H_2(g) + 2\,H_2O(l)$	0.00
$Sn^{2+}(aq) + 2\,e^-$	$\rightarrow Sn(s)$	-0.14
$Ni^{2+}(aq) + 2\,e^-$	$\rightarrow Ni(s)$	-0.25
$V^{3+}(aq) + e^-$	$\rightarrow V^{2+}(aq)$	-0.255
$PbSO_4(s) + 2\,e^-$	$\rightarrow Pb(s) + SO_4^{2-}(aq)$	-0.356
$Cd^{2+}(aq) + 2\,e^-$	$\rightarrow Cd(s)$	-0.40
$Fe^{2+}(aq) + 2\,e^-$	$\rightarrow Fe(s)$	-0.44
$Zn^{2+}(aq) + 2\,e^-$	$\rightarrow Zn(s)$	-0.763
$2\,H_2O(l) + 2\,e^-$	$\rightarrow H_2(g) + 2\,OH^-(aq)$	-0.8277
$Al^{3+}(aq) + 3\,e^-$	$\rightarrow Al(s)$	-1.66
$Mg^{2+}(aq) + 2\,e^-$	$\rightarrow Mg(s)$	-2.37
$Na^+(aq) + e^-$	$\rightarrow Na(s)$	-2.714
$K^+(aq) + e^-$	$\rightarrow K(s)$	-2.925
$Li^+(aq) + e^-$	$\rightarrow Li(s)$	-3.045

Using Standard Reduction Potentials (SRPs)

In addition to being useful for predicting whether an oxidation or reduction half-reaction is more likely to occur than another, SRPs can be used to determine the spontaneity of an overall redox reaction. Because oxidation and reduction are complementary processes one cannot occur without the other. Therefore, reduction and oxidation half-reactions are added to one another. The SRP for the reduction half-reaction and that for the oxidation half-reaction are added after changing the sign of the second SRP because the reversal of this half-reaction.

If this calculation results in a positive value the reaction is spontaneous while if it is negative the reaction as written is non-spontaneous and the reverse reaction, with a positive value, would be spontaneous. The spontaneity of the two examples discussed above is confirmed by these calculations. First, for the reaction of $Cu^{2+}(aq)$ and $Zn(s)$,

$$Cu^{2+}(aq) + 2\,e^- \rightarrow Cu(s) \quad +0.34\ \text{V}$$
$$Zn(s) \rightarrow Zn^{2+}(aq) + 2\,e^- \quad \underline{+0.76\ \text{V}}$$
$$+1.10\text{V}$$

Because the oxidation and reduction half-reactions both have positive potentials the total must be positive. Since each half-reaction involves two electrons the electron loss and gain are equal and the electrons can be cancelled. For the reaction between $Ag^+(aq)$ and $Cu(s)$ the $Ag^+(aq) + e^- \rightarrow Ag(s)$, with $E° = +0.80$ V (the more positive SRP) is the reduction half-reaction and $Cu(s) \rightarrow Cu^{2+}(aq) + 2\,e^-$ with $E°_{ox} = -0.34$ is the oxidation half-reaction.

$$2\left[Ag^+(aq) + e^- \rightarrow Ag(s)\right] \quad +0.80\ \text{V}$$
$$Cu(s) \rightarrow Cu^{2+}(aq) + 2\,e^- \quad \underline{-0.34\ \text{V}}$$
$$+0.46\ \text{V}$$

Once again the potential is positive and this reaction is spontaneous. It is important to point out that while the $Ag^+(aq)$ / $Ag(s)$ half-reaction must be multiplied by 2 to cancel out the electrons lost and gained the value of the potential is **NOT** multiplied because the potential is an intensive property that does not depend on the number of electrons. However, it will be seen below that the number of electrons transferred during a reaction is important in the calculation of $\Delta G°$, which is an extensive property. The transfer of electrons during redox reactions provides the basis for electrochemistry.

Electrochemical Cells

There are two types of electrochemical cells:

Voltaic (also called galvanic) cells are ones in which chemical energy, such as that available from a spontaneous redox reaction, is converted into electrical energy.

Electrolytic cells are those in which an electric current is used to force a non-spontaneous reaction to occur. They will be discussed below.

Voltaic cells are constructed by separating the two half-reactions of a spontaneous reaction from one another. The electrons released by the substance that undergoes oxidation travel through a wire (where they may be used to do work) to the substance that undergoes reduction rather than being transferred directly between them. Direct contact is prevented with a porous barrier, such as a salt bridge, which allows ions to pass but prevents the components from reacting directly. The electrode where oxidation occurs (i.e. where electrons are lost) is known as the anode and that where reduction occurs (i.e. electrons are gained) is called the cathode. These labels can be remembered by recalling that anode and oxidation both begin with vowels while cathode and reduction start with consonants and by using this mnemonic: LEO (the lion) goes (GER) where LEO refers to "Loss of Electrons is Oxidation" and GER represents "Gain of Electrons is Reduction."

If the two half-reactions

$$Zn(s) \rightarrow Zn^{2+}(aq) + 2\,e^- \qquad\qquad Cu^{2+}(aq) + 2\,e^- \rightarrow Cu(s)$$

are separated from one another as described above in a voltaic cell this spontaneous reaction still occurs but the electrons flow through the external circuit producing an electric current rather than going directly from the zinc metal to copper(II) ions.

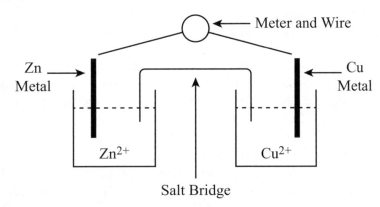

The concentration of Zn^{2+} ions in the anode compartment increases as the Zn metal undergoes oxidation and the concentration of Cu^{2+} ions in the cathode compartment decreases as they undergo reduction. This inbalance would cause the redox reaction to stop very quickly were it not for the presence of the salt bridge. This porous barrier allows cations to diffuse from the anode compartment to the cathode compartment and anions to diffuse in the opposite direction so that each of the compartments remains electrically neutral.

As the reaction proceeds the mass of the zinc electrode decreases and zinc ions go into solution while the mass of the copper electrode increases due to the deposition of copper atoms from the reduction of copper(II) ions from solution. If the cell continues to run for a sufficient period of time the blue color of the copper(II) solution will fade and the zinc electrode may eventually disappear, depending on the concentration of the copper(II) solution and the size of the zinc electrode.

Standard Cell Notation

While the drawing above depicts the structure of the copper/zinc voltaic cell chemists have developed a short-hand system to represent the pertinent features of this cell.

$$Zn\,|\,Zn^{2+}(aq)\,||\,Cu^{2+}(aq)\,|\,Cu$$

In this representation the substance that undergoes oxidation is listed on the left while the substance that becomes reduced is on the right. The single vertical lines (|) represent phase boundaries such as that between zinc metal and aqueous zinc(II) ions and the double vertical lines (‖) represent the salt bridge. As a second example, $H_2(g)$ reacts with $Ag^+(aq)$ to form $Ag(s)$ and $H_3O^+(aq)$ according to the equation.

$$H_2(g) + 2\,Ag^+(aq) + 2\,H_2O(l) \rightarrow 2\,Ag(s) + 2\,H_3O^+(aq)$$

for which the cell notation is

$$Pt \,|\, H_2(g) \,|\, H_3O^+(aq) \,\|\, Ag^+(aq) \,|\, Ag$$

The Pt represents an inert platinum electrode that is required to provide electrical contact between the solution and the external circuit.

Effect of Concentration and Pressure Changes

The potentials for individual half-reactions and voltaic cells can be changed by varying the concentrations of dissolved species and/or the pressures of gases that take part in those reactions. LeChatelier's Principle (chapter 8) can be used to make predictions about these changes, as illustrated by the following examples.

1) The potential of +0.337 V for the half-reaction $Cu^{2+}(aq) + 2\,e^- \rightarrow Cu(s)$ will increase if the $[Cu^{2+}]$ is raised (which would push the equilibrium to the right) and decrease if it is lowered. No changes will occur if the quantity of $Cu(s)$ is changed because the concentration of a solid does not change with its mass.

2) The potential of +1.360 V for the half-reaction $Cl_2(g) + 2\,e^- \rightarrow 2\,Cl^-(aq)$ will be increased by raising the pressure of $Cl_2(g)$ or decreasing the concentration of $Cl^-(aq)$, as both changes would shift the equilibrium to the right. Conversely, the potential will be lowered if the pressure of $Cl_2(g)$ is decreased or the concentration of $Cl^-(aq)$ is increased.

Nernst Equation

Quantitative predictions of these effects can be made by using the Nernst Equation:
$E = E° − (RT/nF) \ln [\text{products}]/[\text{reactants}]$, where

$$RT/nF = (8.314\,\text{J}\cdot\text{mol}^{-1}\cdot\text{K}^{-1})(298\,\text{K})/n\,(96500\,\text{J}\cdot\text{mol}^{-1}\text{V}^{-1})$$
$$= (0.0257/n)\,\text{V}.$$

The Nernst equation can be applied to either half-reactions or complete ones. Although this relationship is not required in the redesigned AP curriculum, it is a part of most college / university courses as well as many other exam activities so it is included here.

For the case of $Cu^{2+}(aq) + 2\,e^- \rightarrow Cu(s)$, if the $[Cu^{2+}]$ is changed to 5.0 M, the E for this half-reaction would be given by

$$E = 0.337 − (0.0257/2) \ln 1/5$$
$$E = 0.337 − (0.01285)(−1.609)$$
$$E = 0.337 + 0.021$$
$$E = 0.358\,\text{V}$$

For the $Cl_2(g) + 2e^- \rightarrow 2Cl^-(aq)$ half-reaction both the reactant and product can be altered. If the Cl_2 pressure is increased to 3.0 atm and the [Cl$^-$] is decreased to 0.10 M,

$E = 1.360 - (0.0257/2) \ln[(0.10)^2/3.0]$
$E = 1.360 - (0.01285) \ln[(0.010)/3]$
$E = 1.360 - (0.01285)(-5.70)$
$E = 1.360 + 0.073$
$E = 1.433$ V

In this example, the Cl_2 pressure appears in the denominator because it is a reactant and the product [Cl$^-$] in the numerator is squared as expected for its coefficient of two in the equation.

The effects of concentration differences are especially important in biology. For example, cells in the human body exhibit a membrane potential due to the concentration differences shown in the table below. These potentials are important in the function of many organs in the body including the heart, kidneys, and nerves.

Ion	[Na$^+$]	[K$^+$]
Inside	low	high
Outside	high	low

Relationship between E°, n, ΔG° and K

The E° values for the cells can be converted to Gibbs Free Energy (ΔG°) values by means of the relationship; $\Delta G° = -nFE°$ where n is the number of electrons transferred in the balanced equation during the reaction, F is the Faraday constant $(96500 J \cdot V^{-1} \cdot mol\ e^{-1})$ and E° is the cell voltage. Because $\Delta G° = -RT \ln K$ (chapter 9), E° values can also be used to calculate equilibrium constants. By combining the two equations, $\ln K = (nF/RT) E°$ or $\ln K = nE°/0.0257$ at 25°C.

For the $Zn(s)$, $Zn^{2+}(aq)$, $Cu^{2+}(aq)$, $Cu(s)$ reaction,

$\Delta G° = -2(96500\ J \cdot V^{-1} \cdot mol^{-1})(1.10\ V)$ $\qquad \Delta G° = -212000\ J$

$\ln K = 2(1.10)/0.0257$ $\qquad \ln K = 85.60$ $\qquad K = 1.50 \times 10^{37}$

while for the $Cu(s)$, $Cu^{2+}(aq)$, $Ag^+(aq)$, $Ag(s)$,

$\Delta G° = -2(96500\ J \cdot V^{-1} \cdot mol^{-1}e^-)(0.46\ V)$ $\qquad \Delta G° = -88800\ J$

$\ln K = 2(0.46)/0.0257$ $\qquad \ln K = 35.80$ $\qquad K = 3.52 \times 10^{15}$

The negative ΔG° values indicate that these reactions are spontaneous, consistent with their positive E° values. The extremely large K values show that both of these reactions will go essentially to completion.

Electrolytic cells involve the conversion of electrical energy into chemical energy by providing a voltage that is high enough to cause a non-spontaneous process to occur. The identity of the product(s) formed depends on the reduction (or oxidation) potential of the substance to be produced while the quantity formed is a function of the amount of charge used as specified by Faraday's Laws (discussed below). Electrolysis is used to produce some substances in industry (such as Na or Cl_2 from molten salts or brine and Al from bauxite), to purify others (e.g. Cu and H_2), or to deposit a metallic layer on an appropriate surface.

The electrolysis process consists of sending a direct current (from a battery or a rectified alternating current source) between two electrodes. If the voltage between the electrodes is sufficient an oxidation product will be formed at the anode and a reduction product will be produced at the cathode. As an example, when molten sodium chloride is electrolyzed chlorine gas will be produced at the anode while sodium metal is formed at the cathode.

Predicting the products formed upon electrolysis of multiple species

When molten NaCl is electrolyzed the only products that could be formed are Na metal and Cl_2 gas. In contrast, if an aqueous KI solution is electrolyzed, two possible products could be formed at each electrode. The potential oxidation products are I_2 (from I^-) and O_2 (from H_2O) and the possible reduction products are K (from K^+) and H_2 (from H_2O). The first substance produced at each electrode can be predicted by considering the relevant oxidation and reduction potentials. From the Table of SRPs above, the pertinent equations and values are

$$O_2(g) + 4\,H_3O^+(aq) + 4\,e^- \rightarrow 6\,H_2O(l) \qquad E° = +1.229\ V$$
$$I_2(aq) + 2\,e^- \rightarrow 2I^-(aq) \qquad E° = +0.535\ V$$
$$2\,H_2O(l) + 2\,e^- \rightarrow H_2(g) + 2\,OH^-(aq) \qquad E° = -0.8277$$
$$K^+(aq) + e^- \rightarrow K(s) \qquad E° = -2.925$$

When the first two equations are reversed they give the possible oxidation reactions with the corresponding oxidation potentials while the second pair of equations represent the possible reduction processes with their SRPs.

possible oxidation reactions
$$6\,H_2O(l) \rightarrow O_2(g) + 4\,H_3O^+(aq) + 4\,e^- \qquad E° = -1.229\ V$$
$$2\,I^-(aq) \rightarrow I_2(aq) + 2\,e^- \qquad E° = -0.535\ V$$

possible reduction reactions
$$2\,H_2O(l) + 2\,e^- \rightarrow H_2(g) + 2\,OH^-(aq) \qquad E° = -0.8277$$
$$K^+(aq) + e^- \rightarrow K(s) \qquad E° = -2.925$$

All of these potentials are negative as expected for reactions that are not spontaneous and have to be forced electrically. The reaction that occurs at each electrode will be the one that requires the smaller expenditure of energy. Thus, the anode reaction will be the formation of $I_2(aq)$ with $E = -0.535\ V\,(\Delta G° = 103\ kJ/mol)$ rather than $O_2(g)$ with $E° = -1.229\ V\,(\Delta G° = 354\ kJ/mol)$ and the cathode reaction will be the production of H_2(g) and OH^-(aq) for which $E° = -0.8277\ V\,(\Delta G° = 160\ kJ/mol)$ rather than K with $E° = -2.925\ V$ and $\Delta G° = 282\ kJ/mol$.

These results can be demonstrated by electrolyzing an aqueous KI solution in a Petri dish using graphite (pencil lead) electrodes connected to a 9 volt battery. The I_2 can be detected near the anode with a drop of starch solution and the presence of OH^- ions can be shown near the cathode by adding a drop of phenolphthalein indicator.

Determining the quantity of product formed during electrolysis

Michael Faraday (1791–1867) was one of the most productive scientists of his day. He made several chemical discoveries and developed an understanding of electromagnetism but is perhaps best known for the rules of electrochemistry which bear his name. They are stated below in modern terms rather than those used by him.

1. The mass of a substance that is produced at an electrode is directly proportional to the quantity of electricity passed through the electrode.

2. For a given quantity of electricity or electric charge the mass of material altered at an electrode is directly proportional to the material's molar mass divided by the number of electrons required for the alteration of one mole.

Some terms relating to electrolysis are given in the following table.

Quantity	Unit	Defining Relation	Conversion Factors
Charge	coulomb (C)	$1\,C = 1\,A \cdot s = 1\,J/V$	$1\,mol\ e^- = 96500\,C$
Current	ampere (A)	$1\,A = 1\,C/s$	
Potential	volt (V)	$1\,V = 1\,J/C$	
Energy	joule (J)	$1\,J = 1\,V \cdot C$	

The use of these laws will be illustrated with two different examples.

1. Sodium metal, Na, is produced by the reduction of molten sodium chloride. What mass of Na is produced by the passage of a current of 5.0 amperes for 3.5 hours?
    $3.5\,hr \times 60\,min/hr \times 60\,s/min = 12600\,s$
    $12600\,s \times 5.0\,C/s = 63000\,C$
    $63000\,C \times 1\,mol\ e^-/96500\,C = 0.65\,mol\ e^-$
    $0.65\,mol\ e^- \times 23.0\,g\ Na/mol\ e^- = 15.0\,g\ Na$

2. Water can be electrolyzed to produce hydrogen, H_2, and oxygen, O_2. What volume of O_2 measured at STP can be produced by the passage of 5.0 amperes for 24 hours?
    $24\,hr \times 60\,min/hr \times 60\,s/min = 86400\,s$
    $86400\,s \times 5.0\,C/s = 432000\,C$
    $432000\,C \times 1\,mol\ e^-/96500\,C = 4.48\,mol\ e^-$
    $4.48\,mol\ e^- \times 1\,mol\ O_2/4\,mol\ e^- = 1.12\,mol\ O_2$
    $1.12\,mol\ O_2 \times 22.4\,L/mol = 25.1\,L$

Oxidation-Reduction Titrations

When an oxidation-reduction is carried out an unknown quantity of one reactant can be determined by measuring the quantity of the other by titration. In order to be useful in such titrations a reagent must:

a. undergo a known change in oxidation state
b. be easily measured
c. be stable in solution
d. exhibit a detectable end point.

Chemists have developed a variety of reagents which meet these criteria to use as oxidizing titrants and others that behave as reducing titrants. The principles of titration that were mentioned briefly in chapter 5 (Solutions) and covered more extensively in chapter 10 (Acids and Bases) apply to redox titrations and will not be discussed further here.

Oxidizing Titrants

Name	Formula	Conditions	Product	Oxid. Sts.	No. e^-	Red. Pot.
Permanganate	MnO_4^-	acid	Mn^{2+}	$+7 \rightarrow +2$	5	1.512
		neutral	MnO_2	$+7 \rightarrow +4$	3	0.588
Dichromate	$Cr_2O_7^{2-}$	acid	$2\ Cr^{3+}$	$+6 \rightarrow +3$	6	1.33
Triiodide	I_3^-	acid	$3\ I^-$	$0 \rightarrow -1$	2	0.534

Reducing Titrants

Name	Formula	Conditions	Product	Oxid. Sts.	No. e^-	Red. Pot.
Iron(II)	Fe^{2+}	acid	Fe^{3+}	$+2 \rightarrow +3$	1	-0.771
Tin(II)	Sn^{2+}	acid	Sn^{4+}	$+2 \rightarrow +4$	2	-0.15
Iodide	$2\ I^-$	acid	I_2	$-1 \rightarrow 0$	2	-0.621
Thiosulfate	$2\ S_2O_3^{2-}$	acid	$S_4O_6^{2-}$	$+2 \rightarrow +2.5$	2	-0.09

Many redox titrations require the addition of a special indicator that exhibits either change in color or voltage with an excess of one of the reactants. Permanganate ion in acid solution serves as its own indicator because the MnO_4^- ion is purple while the Mn^{2+} ion is colorless so the solution will appear colorless as long as the reducing species is present but will turn purple at the end point.

MULTIPLE-CHOICE QUESTIONS

Questions 1–2 should be answered referring to the structures of four ions shown below, which the dichromate $(Cr_2O_7^{2-})$, permanganate (MnO_4^-), thiosulfate $(S_2O_3^{2-})$ and triiodide (I_3^-) ions.

| A | B | C | D |

1. Which structure best represents the permanganate ion?

    (A) A
    (B) B
    (C) C
    (D) D

2. Which structure best represents the dichromate ion?

    (A) A
    (B) B
    (C) C
    (D) D

Questions 3–5 should be answered with reference to the unbalanced half-reaction:

$$Cr_2O_7^{2-} + H^+ \rightarrow Cr^{3+} + H_2O$$

3. What is the oxidation number of Cr in $Cr_2O_7^{2-}$?

    (A) −2
    (B) +3
    (C) +5
    (D) +6

4. How many H^+ ions are in the balanced half reaction?

(A) 5
(B) 8
(C) 12
(D) 14

5. How many electrons are needed (and on which side of the half-reaction) to balance the electron transfer?

(A) 4 on the right
(B) 8 on the right
(C) 3 on left
(D) 6 on left

6. Which equation represents an oxidation-reduction reaction?

(A) $2\,HCl(aq) + Na_2CO_3(s) \rightarrow 2\,NaCl(aq) + CO_2(g) + H_2O(l)$
(B) $2\,HCl(aq) + Zn \rightarrow H_2(g) + ZnCl_2(aq)$
(C) $HCl(aq) + AgNO_3(aq) \rightarrow AgCl(s) + HNO_3(aq)$
(D) $HCl(g) + NH_3(g) \rightarrow NH_4Cl(s)$

7. Which is the net ionic equation for the nitric acid oxidation of iron(II) chloride to form iron(III) chloride and nitrogen(II) oxide?

(A) $3\,FeCl_2 + 4\,HNO_3 \rightarrow 2\,FeCl_3 + Fe(NO_3)_3 + N + 2H_2O$
(B) $3\,Fe^{2+} + 6\,Cl + 4\,NO_3^- + 4\,H^+ \rightarrow 3\,Fe^{3+} + 6\,Cl + 3\,NO_3^- + NO + 2\,H_2O$
(C) $3\,Fe^{2+} + NO_3^- + 4\,H^+ \rightarrow 3\,Fe^{3+} + NO + 2\,H_2O$
(D) $3\,Fe^{2+} + NO_3^- + 6\,H^+ \rightarrow 3\,Fe^{3+} + N^{2+} + 3\,H_2O$

8. Of the substances listed, in which one can the nitrogen atom not be oxidized further?

(A) N_2
(B) NH_3
(C) N_2O_5
(D) $NaNO_2$

9.
$$2\,MnO_4^- + 5\,H_2O_2 + 6\,H^+ \rightarrow 2\,Mn^{2+} + 5\,O_2 + 8\,H_2O$$

What volume of 0.0100 M KMnO$_4$ solution is needed to react with 10.0 mL of 0.200 M H$_2$O$_2$?

(A) 20.0 mL
(B) 80.0 mL
(C) 200. mL
(D) 500. mL

10.
$$Sn^{2+} + MnO_4^- + H^+ \rightarrow Sn^{4+} + Mn^{2+} + H_2O$$

What is the Sn^{2+}/MnO_4^- ratio when the oxidation-reduction reaction above is correctly balanced?

(A) 1/2
(B) 2/3
(C) 5/2
(D) 7/2

11. Electrons are transferred through the external circuit from the

(A) anode to the cathode in both electrolytic and galvanic cells
(B) cathode to the anode in both electrolytic and galvanic cells
(C) anode to the cathode in electrolytic cells and from the cathode to the anode in galvanic cells
(D) cathode to the anode in electrolytic cells and from the anode to the cathode in galvanic cells

Questions 12–13 should be answered with reference to the following standard reduction potentials.

$$Cu^{2+}(aq) + 2\,e^- \rightarrow Cu(s) \qquad E^\circ = 0.337\ V$$
$$Fe^{3+}(aq) + e^- \rightarrow Fe^{2+}(aq) \qquad E^\circ = 0.769\ V$$

12. According to the standard reduction potentials above, which species will release electrons most readily?

(A) $Cu^{2+}(aq)$
(B) $Cu(s)$
(C) $Fe^{3+}(aq)$
(D) $Fe^{2+}(aq)$

13. What is the potential for the galvanic cell based on the above half-reactions and their standard reduction potentials?

(A) +0.432 V
(B) +1.106 V
(C) +1.201 V
(D) +1.875 V

Questions 14–16 should be answered with reference to the standard reduction potentials below.

$$Cd^{2+}(aq) + 2\,e^- \rightarrow Cd(s) \qquad E° = -0.402 \text{ V}$$
$$Tl^+(aq) + e^- \rightarrow Tl(s) \qquad E° = -0.336 \text{ V}$$
$$Co^{2+}(aq) + 2\,e^- \rightarrow Co(s) \qquad E° = -0.282 \text{ V}$$
$$Cu^{2+}(aq) + 2\,e^- \rightarrow Cu(s) \qquad E° = +0.337 \text{ V}$$

14. How many spontaneous reactions can be written from the half-reactions and SRPs above?

(A) 3 only
(B) 4 only
(C) 6 only
(D) 12

15. Which substance will reduce $Co^{2+}(aq)$ but not $Cd^{2+}(aq)$?

(A) $Cu^{2+}(aq)$
(B) $Cu(s)$
(C) $Tl^+(aq)$
(D) $Tl(s)$

16. Which reaction will give a galvanic cell with the highest E°?

(A) $2\,Tl(s) + Cu^{2+}(aq) \rightarrow 2\,Tl^+(aq) + Cu(s)$
(B) $2\,Tl(s) + Cd^{2+}(aq) \rightarrow 2\,Tl^+(aq) + Cd(s)$
(C) $Cu^{2+}(aq) + Cd(s) \rightarrow Cd^{2+}(aq) + Cu(s)$
(D) $Cd^{2+}(aq) + Cu(s) \rightarrow Cu^{2+}(aq) + Cd(s)$

17.
$$Pb^{2+}(aq) + 2 e^- \to Pb(s) \qquad E° = -0.127 \text{ V}$$

When $SO_4^{2-}(aq)$ is added to a solution of $Pb^{2+}(aq)$ to form slightly soluble $PbSO_4$, how will the potential be affected?

(A) It will become more negative.
(B) It will not change.
(C) It will change sign.
(D) It will become less negative.

18.
$$O_2(g) + 4 H_3O^+(aq) + 4 e^- \to 6 H_2O(l) \qquad E° = +1.229 \text{ V}$$
$$Br_2(l) + 2 e^- \to 2 Br^-(aq) \qquad E° = +1.08 \text{ V}$$
$$Ni^{2+}(aq) + 2 e^- \to Ni(s) \qquad E° = -0.25$$
$$2 H_2O(l) + 2 e^- \to H_2(g) + 2 OH^-(aq) \qquad E° = -0.8277$$

According to the standard reduction potentials above, what are the first products formed when a 1 M aqueous solution of nickel(II) bromide is electrolyzed?

(A) $O_2(g)$ at the anode and $H_2(g)$ at the cathode
(B) $O_2(g)$ at the anode and $Ni(s)$ at the cathode
(C) $Br_2(l)$ at the anode and $H_2(g)$ at the cathode
(D) $Br_2(l)$ at the anode and $Ni(s)$ at the cathode

Questions 19–21 should be answered with reference to the cell based on the reaction

$$Cu(s) + 2 Ag^+(aq) \to Cu^{2+}(aq) + 2 Ag(s) \qquad E° = +0.460 \text{ V}$$

19. The E° value of the cell based on the reaction above is +0.460 V under standard conditions. An increase in which of the following will produce a higher voltage?

(A) size of the copper electrode
(B) volume of the $Cu^{2+}(aq)$ solution
(C) concentration of the $Ag^+(aq)$ solution
(D) size of the silver electrode

20. Which process occurs in the cathode compartment of this cell?

(A) $Ag^+(aq)$ ions move toward the electrode.
(B) $Ag^+(aq)$ ions move away from the electrode.
(C) $Cu^{2+}(aq)$ move toward the electrode.
(D) $Cu^{2+}(aq)$ move toward the electrode.

21. The value of the free energy change ($\Delta G°$) for this reaction is given by

(A) $-(0.460)$ F
(B) (0.460) F
(C) $2(0.460)$ F
(D) $-2(0.460)$ F

_____

22. How many moles of aluminum metal can be deposited when 0.600 moles of electrons are passed through 4.00 moles of molten Al_2O_3?

(A) 0.100
(B) 0.200
(C) 1.33
(D) 1.80

23.
$$Cu^{2+}(aq) + 2\,e^- \rightarrow Cu(s)$$

A current of 2.50 amperes is used to electrolyze a solution of copper(II) sulfate for 2.00 hours. Which expression represents the number of moles of copper metal (M = 63.54 g/mol) deposited according to Faraday's Laws?

(A) $(2.00 \times 2.50/96500)$
(B) $(2.00 \times 60.0 \times 60.0 \times 2.50/96500)\,/2.00$
(C) $(2.00 \times 2.50 \times 60.0/96500)\,/2.00$
(D) $(2.00 \times 60.0 \times 60.0 \times 2.50 \times 63.54/96500)\,/2.00$

24. An electrolysis experiment results in the deposition of 1.27 g of copper metal (M = 63.54 g/mol). What is the minimum number of electrons transferred?

(A) 6.0×10^{21}
(B) 1.2×10^{22}
(C) 2.4×10^{22}
(D) 4.8×10^{22}

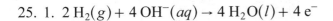

25. 1. $2\,H_2(g) + 4\,OH^-(aq) \rightarrow 4\,H_2O(l) + 4\,e^-$

2. $H_2(g) + 2\,H^+(aq) + 2\,e^- \rightarrow 2\,H_2O(l)$

3. $NO(g) + 2\,H_2O(l) \rightarrow NO_3^-(aq) + 4\,H^+(aq) + 3\,e^-$

Which of the half-reactions above will be shifted toward the products with an increase in pH?

(A) 1 only
(B) 2 only
(C) 1 and 3 only
(D) 1, 2, and 3

26. $$Au^{3+}(aq) + 3\,Ag(s) \rightarrow 3\,Ag^+(aq) + Au(s) \qquad E° = +0.70$$

According to the Nernst equation, which change will produce the greatest increase in the value of the cell potential, $E°$?

(A) doubling the $[Au^{3+}]$
(B) doubling the $[Ag^+]$
(C) cutting the $[Au^{3+}]$ in half
(D) cutting the $[Ag^+]$ in half

27. $$2\,H_3O^+(aq) + 2\,e^- \rightarrow H_2(g) + 2\,H_2O(l) \qquad E° = 0.00\ V$$

According to the Nernst equation, $E = 0.00 - (0.025/2)\ \ln[\text{prod}]/[\text{reac}]$, what is the potential for this reaction at pH = 7.00?

(A) -0.414
(B) -0.207
(C) $+0.207$
(D) $+0.414$

CHAPTER 11

CONSTRUCTED-RESPONSE QUESTIONS

1. For the Standard Reduction Potentials

$$Cr^{3+}(aq) + 3\,e^- \to Cr(s) \qquad\qquad E° = -0.744 \text{ V}$$
$$Ni^{2+}(aq) + 2\,e^- \to Ni(s) \qquad\qquad E° = -0.236 \text{ V}$$

   (a) Write a balanced equation for the reaction that could be used for a galvanic cell and calculate its E° value.
   (b) Sketch the cell shown below.

$$Cr/Cr^{3+}//Ni^{2+}/Ni$$

   i. Show clearly the location of the reaction components
   ii. Add and label any components required for the cell to produce electricity.
   iii. State the conditions for each reactant in the standard cell.

   (c) Calculate the value of $\Delta G°$ for this reaction.

2. Answer the following questions having to do with voltaic and electrolytic cells.

(a) Use the standard reduction potentials below to write the cell reaction that would produce the greatest potential in a voltaic cell.

(b) $Cd^{2+}(aq) + 2\,e^- \rightarrow Cd(s)$ $E° = -0.402$ V
$Tl^+(aq) + e^- \rightarrow Tl(s)$ $E° = -0.336$ V
$Cu^{2+}(aq) + e^- \rightarrow Cu^+(aq)$ $E° = +0.161$ V

     i. For the galvanic cell based on the reaction above, calculate the cell potential and list three different ways of changing the cell potential.

    ii. For each of the changes listed in (b) i., state whether it will cause the potential to increase or decrease relative to the value of E° and account for these effects.

(c) List three factors that influence the mass of metal that can be deposited from a 1 *M* aqueous solution of its ions. For each of these factors state how it will affect the mass of metal deposited. Justify your answer.

3. One means of producing a known quantity of iodine, I_2, is to react a measured amount of primary standard potassium iodate, KIO_3, with an excess of aqueous sodium iodide.

   (a) Write a balanced equation for the reaction of IO_3^- with I^-.
   (b) Based on the equation in 3(a) calculate the number of moles of I_2 formed from the reaction of 3.56 g of KIO_3 (M = 214 g/mol) with an excess of aqueous KI.
   (c) If the quantity of I_2 in 3(b) is reacted with aluminum metal to form aluminum triiodide, calculate the mass of AlI_3 formed.

WRITING NET IONIC EQUATIONS

Big Idea 3 states that "changes in matter involve the rearrangement and/or reorganization of atoms and/or the transfer of electrons." Learning Objective 3.2 goes on to require that "The student can translate an observed chemical change into a balanced chemical equation and justify the equation type (molecular, ionic, or net ionic) in terms of utility for the given circumstances."

In the past, one of the major sections of the free-response section of the Advanced Placement Chemistry examination was Question 4, wherein students were asked to demonstrate their accumulated skills in chemistry by writing net ionic equations. Given a verbal prompt for three different sets of reactions, a student was required to predict the reactants and a complete set of products and to balance all of the equations. This will no longer be the case with the new format of the examination. Question 4 is gone but the skills of writing net ionic equations will still be tested. The style of examining is apt to change and the equations may well appear in parts of other questions. Students will still need to practice writing net ionic equations (NIE)!

Historically, students have typically felt completely overwhelmed by the task of writing net ionic equations. How could they possibly memorize the thousands of different reactions that are possible in chemistry? The answer, of course, lies in recognizing that this sort of memorization is not necessary and indeed is counterproductive. Rather, students should endeavor to learn a discrete and finite set of facts and patterns, then apply these facts and patterns to the reactants that are offered. By careful review of the equations offered, a student should be able to successfully address these reactions. Some of the reactions may not appear on the exam in this form.

Knowing the Elements and the Ions

The elements

1. Most elements are in monatomic form. Hence gold is written as Au, iron as Fe, and so on.

2. Some elements occur in diatomic form. One easy way to remember these is to use the mnemonic device "Horses Need Oats For Clear Brown Eyes", since the initial letter of each word prompts one element (Hydrogen, Nitrogen, Oxygen, Fluorine, Chlorine, Bromine, Iodine appear as H_2, N_2, O_2, F_2, Cl_2, Br_2, I_2 respectively).

3. One element appears as a triatomic form. Ozone (O_3) is an allotrope of diatomic oxygen, the more stable form. An allotrope is a different form of an element in the same phase under the same conditions. O_3 and O_2 both exist under standard conditions as a gas. Ozone is unstable and spontaneously decomposes to form O_2.

4. Elemental phosphorus and arsenic appear in molecules of four atoms (P_4 and As_4).

5. Elemental sulfur's molecular form includes eight atoms (S_8) in a ring form. This form is frequently abbreviated as "S".

6. The most common elemental form of carbon is the buckminsterfullerene C_{60} but this is commonly abbreviated as "C".

Monatomic ions and binary compounds

The charge on monatomic ions can be determined by the position of the parent atom on the Periodic Table. Group I, the alkali metals, form 1+ cations. Group II, the alkaline earth metals, form 2+ cations. All other metals will include a Stock system Roman numeral to indicate the charge of the cation. This includes transition metals, inner transition metals, and metals beneath the "staircase" dividing metals from non-metals on the Periodic Table. Three metals form cations with the same charge so often that the Stock system is sometimes omitted: silver(I) or Ag^+; zinc(II) or Zn^{2+}; and aluminum(III) or Al^{3+}.

Binary ionic compounds are formed by adjusting the number of each cation and anion in the compound such that neutrality (an algebraic zero) is reached. Thus three chloride anions are required to match with an iron(III) cation: $FeCl_3$. Two fluoride anions link with a barium cation: BaF_2. One sodium cation and one iodide anion pair perfectly: NaI.

Polyatomic ions: the Big Five, the Little Five, and various others by extension, analogy, and prefix

Hundreds and hundreds of polyatomic ions exist. It would be a daunting task to try to memorize all of them. In fact, some textbooks simply present lists of fifty or more ions to learn. It is MUCH easier to learn a system that will permit you to learn just a little, yet be able to generate the name, formula, and charge for many common polyatomic ions.

THE BIG FIVE

Here is a very short list of ions to learn. The beginning of each name contains a stem representing the non-metal atom at the center of the ion. Notice that each name ends in –ATE, a suffix that indicates that the polyatomic ion contains oxygen. The suffix does not tell you how many oxygen atoms are included in the ion; nor does it indicate the charge. You must learn these!

Chlorate	ClO_3^-
Nitrate	NO_3^-
Carbonate	CO_3^{2-}
Sulfate	SO_4^{2-}
Phosphate	PO_4^{3-}

Once you have learned The Big Five, you may use this short list to expand your knowledge of ions.

IONS BY ANALOGY: PERIODICITY

As you read down the column on the Period Table known as the halogens (group VII), note that bromine (Br) and iodine (I) are found directly under chlorine (Cl). Since the elements in a family are known to have similar chemical characteristics, knowing the Big Five member chlorate (ClO_3^-) means that you automatically know bromate (BrO_3^-) and iodate (IO_3^-). You can use this comparison technique in many situations.

Example:

Give the formula and charge for the ions selenate and arsenate.

Solution: Consult your Periodic Table. Selenium is in the same column as sulfur. Since you have already learned that sulfate is SO_4^{2-}, then selenate must be SeO_4^{2-}. Arsenic is the same family as phosphorus. Since you already know that phosphate is PO_4^{3-}, then arsenate must be AsO_4^{3-}.

IONS BY EXTENTION

There are a number of oxyanions containing chlorine as the central atom. As long as you know the formula and charge of the ion chlorate (ClO_3^-), then you can predict the others. Note that although the central atom and overall charge do not change, the number of oxygen atoms does. The suffix–*ite* means one less oxygen than the –*ate* form. The prefix *hypo*– means one oxygen less than the –*ite* form, while the prefix *per*– (short for *hyper*–) means one more oxygen than the –*ate* form.

Hypochlorite	ClO^-
Chlorite	ClO_2^-
Chlorate	ClO_3^-
Perchlorate	ClO_4^-

> **Example**:
>
> Give the formula for each name: bromite; periodate; hypochlorite; peroxide.
>
> *Solution*: Follow the logic trail from chlorate (ClO_3^-) to bromate (BrO_3^-) to bromite (BrO_2^-). For periodate, follow from chlorate (ClO_3^-) to iodate (IO_3^-) to periodate (IO_4^-). For hypochlorite, step from chlorate (ClO_3^-) to chlorite (ClO_2^-) to hypochlorite (ClO^-). For peroxide, travel from oxide (O^{2-}) to peroxide (O_2^{2-}).

IONS BY HYDROGENATON

Any anion with a charge of 2- (or more negative) can be modified by adding a proton (H^+) to it, thus changing the charge by one. If more than one proton can be added to the parent anion to form new anions, then the anions are distinguished by adding the Greek counters mono-, di-, tri-, and so on.

SO_4^{2-}	sulfate	PO_4^{3-}	phosphate
HSO_4^-	hydrogen sulfate	HPO_4^{2-}	monohydrogen phosphate
		$H_2PO_4^-$	dihydrogen phosphate

In the past, the addition of a hydrogen ion was signified by adding the prefix "bi". This practice is outdated and no longer used, although "sodium bicarbonate" (baking soda) is occasionally seen.

> **Example**:
>
> Give the formula for each name: hydrogen selenate; dihydrogen stibnite (or antimonite); hydrogen tellurite; dihydrogen phosphite.
>
> *Solution*: Think sulfate to hydrogen sulfate to hydrogen sellenate, $HSeO_4^-$; phosphate to dihydrogen phosphate to dihydrogen stibnate, $H_2SbO_4^-$; sulfate to hydrogen sulfate to hydrogen sulfite to hydrogen tellurite, $HTeO_3^-$; phosphate to dihydrogen phosphate to dihydrogen phosphite, $H_2PO_3^-$

THE LITTLE FIVE

Here is a small group of additional anions that you will see frequently. Learn them now.

1. Polyatomic cations

NH_4^+	ammonium
Hg_2^{2+}	mercury(I)

2. Polyatomic anions named as if monatomic

OH^-	hydroxide
CN^-	cyanide

3. Polyatomic anions with characteristic colors
    MnO_4^- permanganate (purple)
    CrO_4^{2-} chromate (yellow)
    $Cr_2O_7^{2-}$ dichromate (orange)

4. Organic polyatomic anions
    $C_2H_3O_2^-$ acetate
    $C_2O_4^{2-}$ oxalate

5. Anions with the prefix *thio* (indicating that a sulfur atom has displaced an oxygen atom)
    $S_2O_3^{2-}$ thiosulfate
    CN^- cyanide to CNO^- cyanate to CNS^- thiocyanate

You are likely to learn other polyatomic ions in context as you explore other topics, especially laboratory work.

What is NIE?

Net ionic equations (NIE) are chemical shorthand. They eliminate spectator ions, ions which appear in identical form on both the reactant and product sides of a larger equation. Note well that the term means "net with respect to ions" only. All other elements and compounds in all physical states are expected to be included.

Precipitation reactions

In order to write a precipitation reaction, you must be able to predict potential insoluble products, those compounds that will fall from solutions as they form. You may be encouraged to memorize a long list of solubility rules. A different tactic would be to learn a set of simplified guidelines that allow you to make accurate predictions most of the time. Learning these condensed guidelines will allow you a wide variety of precipitation prognostications. While they may not be 100% accurate, they will be close enough to allow confident prediction of many situations without forcing you to memorize tens or dozens of solubility rules.

The simplified solubility guidelines:

CATIONS:

a. All salts containing the cation Na^+, K^+, or NH_4^+ are soluble.

ANIONS:

b. All salts containing the anion NO_3^-, $C_2H_3O_2^-$, ClO_3^-, or ClO_4^- are soluble.

c. The HALIDE guideline: All salts containing the halide anions Cl^-, Br^-, or I^- are soluble EXCEPT when paired with cations of the Silver Group: Ag^+, Hg_2^{2+}, or Pb^{2+}.

d. The SULFATE guideline: All salts containing the sulfate anion SO_4^{2-} are soluble EXCEPT when paired with the cations Ba^{2+}, Sr^{2+}, and those of the Silver Group.

e. ALL OTHER SALTS ARE INSOLUBLE! (at room temperature)

Test strategy: questions of this type are usually given in the form "solution of this soluble salt plus solution of that soluble salt are mixed." The trick is to pair the cation from one salt with the anion from the other salt. If this combination represents an insoluble salt according to the guidelines, then write the insoluble salt as a product. Immediately move back to the left side of the equation to write each ion of that insoluble salt separately. Be sure to check the other possible pairing since another insoluble salt may precipitate. Note well that in all cases a reaction occurs. According to Mr. Spock, to write "NR" for "no reaction" or "NAR" for "no apparent reaction" is not logical.

Remember to balance the equation. You must end up with conservation of mass (same number of atoms of each type on each side of the reaction) and conservation of charge (same total charge on each side).

You may recognize this pattern as a "double replacement reaction" from your Chemistry I days.

Example:

Solutions of silver nitrate and sodium chloride are mixed.

Solution: $Ag^+ + Cl^- \rightarrow AgCl$

Example:

A barium chloride solution is dripped into a potassium sulfate solution.

Solution: $Ba^{2+} + SO_4^{2-} \rightarrow BaSO_4$

Acid-base reactions

Acids have several unique characteristics. They taste sour, turn the indicator litmus red, react with carbonates to liberate carbon dioxide, react with active metals to produce hydrogen gas, and neutralize bases. On the other hand, bases taste bitter, turn litmus blue, precipitate with most cations, and neutralize acids. According to Arrhenius, an acid causes the concentration of protons in solution, H^+, to increase while a base causes an increase in hydroxide concentration, OH^-. A Danish chemist, Johannes Bronsted, and a British chemist, Thomas Lowry, altered this definition. They redefined an acid-base reaction in terms of the transfer of a proton, with the acid being the proton donor and the base being the proton acceptor. While this new definition had no effect on the population of acids, it did allow many more substances that lacked hydroxide ion to be considered bases.

Bronsted-Lowry proton transfer theory requires moving a proton from and acid to a base. Thus pairs of species can be identified: the acid which has the proton and the base which is to receive it. Such a pair is called a conjugate acid-base pair. The term conjugate comes from the Latin and it means that the acid and base are married together, with the exchanged proton as the shared essential in the marriage. Note that there are two conjugate acid-base pairs in an acid–base reaction. One acid is found in the reactants with its conjugate base partner on the product side. The other pair shows the acid on the product side and the base on the reactant side. Each acid-base pair differs only by a proton.

In order to use the Bronsted-Lowry theory of proton transfer to predict reactions, you must make some fundamental distinctions about the strength of acids. A strong acid is one that dissociates 100% in aqueous solution. These acids are

1. Binary acids of the halogens HCl, HBr, HI

2. Oxidizing acids HNO_3 and H_2SO_4

3. $HClO_4$

To help assemble these in your memory, note that there are three binary acids and three oxyacids.

A weak acid dissociates less than 100%, typically far less. Some weak acids that are "wannabe" strong acids are $HClO_3$, HSO_4^-, and $H_2C_2O_4$ since they dissociate well but in this scheme they are simply considered weak. Many students would like to transform hydrofluoric acid, HF, and phosphoric acid, H_3PO_4, into strong acids but they do not dissociate well enough to be considered as such.

Strong bases are considered to be hydroxides of metals that dissociate 100%. These include the hydroxides of Periodic Table Group I (LiOH, NaOH, KOH, RbOH, CsOH) and those of lower Periodic Table Group II ($Ba(OH)_2$ and $Sr(OH)_2$). "Wannabe" strong bases are $Ca(OH)_2$ and $Mg(OH)_2$ but these hydroxides do not dissociate 100%. In fact, each is assigned a K_{sp} value, characteristic of a sparingly soluble substance, so they do not dissociate the required 100%. Your instructor may prefer a different definition of strong base and therefore include calcium and magnesium hydroxides.

Bronsted-Lowry acid-base chemistry

Now armed with the distinction between strong acids (SA) and weak acids (WA) and that between strong bases (SB) and weak bases (WB), you can now perform some acid-base chemistry. If you consider the situation for just a moment, you will realize that there are only four possible combinations of acids and bases:

1. SA + SB

2. SA + WB

3. WA + SB

4. WA + WB

For predictive purposes, note these things:

1. Strong acids are always written as hydronium ion (H_3O^+, the combination of a proton and a water molecule) while strong bases are always hydroxide ion (OH^-).

2. Weak acids and weak bases are written in molecular form (HF(aq) or $Mg(OH)_2$(aq), for example).

3. The presence of a strong *anything*, either acid or base, as a reactant means that water must appear as a product.

4. The presence of a weak *anything*, either acid or base, means that its conjugate will appear on the other side of the reaction. Thus

    SA + SB → water

    SA + WB → water + the conjugate acid of the weak base

    WA + SB → water + the conjugate base of the weak acid

    WA + WB → conjugate base of weak acid + conjugate base of weak base

Example:

Solutions of ammonia and hydrofluoric acid are mixed.

Solution: this is a weak base and weak acid combination, so $NH_3 + HF \rightarrow NH_4^+ + F^-$

Example:

Solutions of sodium hydroxide and hydrochloric acid are mixed.

Solution: strong base and strong acid combination, $OH^- + H_3O^+ \rightarrow 2\,H_2O$

Example:

Solutions of ammonia and hydrochloric acid are mixed.

Solution: weak base and strong acid, $NH_3 + H_3O^+ \rightarrow H_2O + NH_4^+$

Example:

Solutions of sodium hydroxide and hydrofluoric acid are mixed.

Solution: strong base and weak acid, $OH^- + HF \rightarrow H_2O + F^-$

The Phantoms

There are acid-base reactions that can create one of the Phantoms, a small set of unstable products. These are certain weak acids and bases whose formulas can be written but they never persist as products. These unstable products spontaneously break down into a predictable set of products, always in the pattern of water and a gas:

$$H_2CO_3 \rightarrow H_2O + CO_2(g)$$
$$H_2SO_3 \rightarrow H_2O + SO_2(g)$$
$$NH_4OH \rightarrow H_2O + NH_3(g)$$

Example:

Nitric acid solution is poured into a solution of sodium sulfide.

Solution: $S^{2-} + 2H_3O^+ \rightarrow 2\,H_2O + H_2S(g)$

Example:

Hydrochloric acid is added to a solution of sodium hydrogen sulfide.

Solution: $H_3O^+ + HS^- \rightarrow H_2O + H_2S(g)$

The Anhydrides

The term anhydride means "without water". Thus an acid anhydride is a substance which, when added to water, yields an acidic solution. Oxides of non-metals are acid anhydrides. Since these acid-base reactions are not oxidation-reduction reactions, be sure to produce an acid form with the non-metal in the same oxidation state.

Example:

Sulfur dioxide gas is bubbled through water.

Solution: $SO_2 + H_2O \rightarrow H_3O^+ + HSO_3^-$

A basic anhydride is the oxide of a metal. When soluble, these metallic oxides will produce a basic solution. Again, there is no change in the oxidation number assigned to the metal in the compound.

Example:

Powdered calcium oxide is sprinkled over water.

Solution: $CaO + H_2O \rightarrow Ca(OH)_2$

In most general terms, an acid solution plus a basic solution yields water and a salt. Anhydrides do not have any water but they behave in a similar way. Thus an acid anhydride plus a basic anhydride yields a salt anhydride. You may not have thought of this category of reactions as acid-base reactions in the past!

Example:

Hot sulfur trioxide gas is passed over solid calcium oxide.

Solution: $SO_3 + CaO \rightarrow CaSO_4$

Many decomposition reactions are acid-base reactions in reverse. Decomposition reactions can frequently be considered the opposite of an acid anhydride-basic anhydride reaction. That is, a salt containing an oxyanion decomposes into a metallic oxide and a non-metal oxide.

Example:

Carbon dioxide gas is passed over a heated sample of magnesium oxide.

Solution: $CO_2 + MgO \rightarrow MgCO_3$

In reverse…

Example:

A sample of magnesium carbonate is strongly heated.

Solution: $MgCO_3 \rightarrow MgO + CO_2$

A notable exception to this pattern is the thermal decomposition of potassium chlorate or potassium perchlorate, which result in elemental oxygen gas. A catalyst (typically powdered manganese(IV) oxide) is needed for this.

Solution: $2\,KClO_3 \rightarrow 2\,KCl + 3\,O_2$

The Hydrolysis

Certain salts react with water to create acid or basic solutions by attracting part of the water molecule. Since the water molecule is taken apart, this process is called "hydrolysis", the breaking apart of water. If you remember that a salt is one product of an acid-base reaction, you can predict the relative pH of a salt solution just by remembering the characteristics of the parent acids and bases.

An anion can be either a neutral anion or a basic anion. Neutral anions are easily identified as the non-proton component of a strong acid. Thus chloride, bromide, and iodide ions (Cl^-, Br^-, and I^-) are neutral anions, as are nitrate and chlorate ions (NO_3^- and ClO_3^-). The anion of a weak acid is a basic anion because it extracts a proton from a water molecule, leaving a molecule of the weak acid and a hydroxide ion.

Example:

Sodium fluoride is added to water.

Solution: $F^- + H_2O \rightarrow HF + OH^-$

A cation can be either a neutral cation or an acidic cation. Neutral cations are the cations of the strong bases, the hydroxides of group I metals and the lower part of the Group II metals (LiOH, NaOH, KOH, RbOH, CsOH, $Ba(OH)_2$, $Sr(OH)_2$). Cations of weak bases will extract hydroxide from a water molecule to form the molecule of the weak base, thus freeing protons into solution.

Example:

Magnesium nitrate powder is added to water.

Solution: $Mg^{2+} + 4\,H_2O \rightarrow Mg(OH)_2 + 2\,H_3O^+$

Lewis acid-base reactions

The American physical chemist Gilbert Newton Lewis further developed the transfer idea of Bronsted-Lowry but changed the nature of the particle. He considered an acid-base reaction to be one where a new covalent bond was formed when a species with an orbital filled with two electrons, the Lewis base, inserted into a species with an empty orbital, the Lewis acid. In essence, the acid can be considered an electron pair acceptor and the base the electron pair donor where the end result is a covalent bond between the Lewis acid and the Lewis base. Lewis' work greatly expanded the number of substances that could be considered acids. While Lewis acid-base theory will not be tested on the new AP Chemistry exam, it does explain many reactions that seem like acid-base reactions but do not fit the Bronsted-Lowry definition.

Lewis acid-base reactions feature the creation of a new covalent bond, with the Lewis base inserting the pair of electrons from a filled orbital into an empty orbital in a Lewis acid. Note that this greatly expands the number of species that can be considered as acids, compared to a Bronsted-Lowry definition. These typically occur in two patterns:

1. The elements beryllium and boron are frequently electron deficient after they combine. They cannot make up a valence octet of electrons since they start with only two and three valence electrons respectively, thus typically forming two and three covalent bonds. Examples are BeH_2 and BF_3, the former having two empty orbitals and the latter three. They can then combine with a species with a lone pair of electrons that can be shared into an empty orbital in the Lewis acid.

Example:

Boron trifluoride and ammonia gases are mixed.

Solution: $BF_3 + NH_3 \rightarrow BF_3NH_3$ (or $F_3B–NH_3$, with a covalent bond between boron and nitrogen)

2. The formation of a complex ion can be considered a Lewis acid-base reaction since the central metal cation has empty orbitals and the ligands have at least one lone pair of electrons to share, forming a covalent bond.

Example:

Potassium thiocyanide solution is dropped into a solution of iron(III) nitrate.

Solution: $Fe^{3+} + SCN^- \rightarrow FeSCN^{2+}$ [thiocyanoiron(III) cation]

Example:

A solution of sodium hydroxide is added to a solution of aluminum(III) nitrate.

Solution: $Al^{3+} + 4\,OH^- \rightarrow Al(OH)_4^-$ [tetrahydroxoaluminate(III) anion]

Example:

Eexcess concentrated ammonia solution is added to a solution of silver(I) nitrate.

Solution: $Ag^+ + 2\,NH_3 \rightarrow Ag(NH_3)_2^+$

How can one tell how many ligands to park on the central metal cation? A convenient rule of thumb is to double the charge on the central metal cation. Thus iron(III) cation should carry $3 \times 2 = 6$ ligands. See the examples above.

A notable exception is aluminum(III) cation, which has a coordination number of 4. See the example above.

There are some situations that hint at a complexation reaction. The term "excess concentrated" may be an indication that a surplus of ligands is being supplied, thus adding the maximum possible number of ligands to the central metal cation.

Example:

Excess concentrated sodium hydroxide is dropped into a slurry of water and solid aluminum hydroxide.

Solution: $Al(OH)_3 + OH^- \rightarrow [Al(OH)_4]^-$

Another pattern to see is the addition of a species with a common anion. At first glance it might seem that no reaction could take place but the additional source of ligands means a push towards a complex ion.

Example:

Excess concentrated hydrochloric acid is added to a solution of manganese(II) chloride.

Solution: $Mn^{2+} + 6\,Cl^- \rightarrow [MnCl_6]^{4-}$

Oxidation-reduction reactions

Redox with elemental forms ANY reaction containing an elemental form as a reactant (or a product, for that matter) must be a redox reaction. Of course, this implies that you would recognize the elemental forms. You may review these forms at the beginning of the chapter.

Oxidation-reduction reactions with elements appear in several forms:

1.   Element + element to form a compound ("combination reaction" from your Chemistry I days)

2.   Element + compound solution form element + compound solution (a "single replacement" reaction from Chemistry I). You may recognize these reactions in the form of an "activity series".

The oxidation number on monatomic ions can be determined by the position of the parent atom on the Periodic Table. Group I, the alkali metals, form 1+ cations, so the oxidation number is +1. Group II, the alkaline earth metals, form 2+ cations, so the oxidation number is +2. All other metals will include a Stock system Roman numeral to indicate the charge of the cation and therefore the oxidation number. This includes transition metals, inner transition metals, and metals beneath the Zintl boundary, the "staircase" dividing metals from non-metals on the Periodic Table. Three metals form cations with the same charge so often that the Stock system is sometimes omitted: silver(I) or Ag^+; zinc(II) or Zn^{2+}; aluminum(III) Al^{3+}.

Example:

A piece of calcium metal is heated in a nitrogen atmosphere.

Solution: $3\,Ca + N_2 \rightarrow Ca_3N_2$

Example:

A piece of magnesium metal is dropped into a solution of silver nitrate.

Solution: $Mg + 2\,Ag^+ \rightarrow 2\,Ag + Mg^{2+}$

Example:

A piece of copper metal is dropped into a dilute solution of nitric acid.

Solution: $3\,Cu + 8\,H^+ + 2\,NO_3^- \rightarrow 3\,Cu^{2+} + 2\,NO + 4\,H_2O$

Redox of ions in solution

In the course of a redox reaction, one species must be oxidized (causing reduction of another species and thus called the reducing agent) while another is itself reduced (causing oxidation of another species and therefore the oxidizing agent).

To identify these agents, look for species at the end of their range. The chlorine atom can attract another electron to form chloride anion, thus completing a valance set of electrons. So chloride anion cannot be reduced any further. It can only lose electrons and be oxidized to chlorine atom or hypochlorite, chlorite, chlorate, or perchlorate anions. Note that the oxidation number on the chlorine each case has increased from the previous case. So chloride cannot be reduced. It can only be oxidized and therefore is itself only a reducing agent. Similarly, iron(III) cation has lost as many electrons as it possibly can. It can only be reduced to iron(II) cation or to iron metal. Since it must be reduced itself, it causes oxidation of another species and is therefore an oxidizing agent only.

Other common oxidizing agents include permanganate ion (reduced to Mn^{2+} in acidic solution) and the chromate/dichromate twins (reduced to Cr^{3+} in acidic solution).

One tip that the reaction might be a redox reaction is the term "acidified" or "alkaline" found in the prompt. Students frequently forget that there must be a proton/water pairing in acid solution and a hydroxide/water pairing in basic solution. Here is a case where it might be worth your time to learn a method to balance an oxidation-reduction equation. Following the "never-fail" method of balancing redox reactions will prevent you from forgetting to include one of the pairs. Here is a summary of a technique that always works:

Identify the elements oxidized and reduced. Separate them into half-reactions with those elements in the complete species on both reactant and product side (i.e., keep manganese as part of MnO_4^- rather than singling it out as Mn^{7+}).

Balance each half-reaction separately.

· First balance the element being oxidized or reduced.
· Balance the elements other than hydrogen or oxygen.
· Balance oxygen by adding water in the form of H_2O.
· Balance hydrogen by adding H^+ (if in acid solution). If in basic solution, balance hydrogen by adding water in H-OH form, then immediately add the same number of OH^- on the other side.
· Balance the total charge on each side by adding electrons to the more positive side.

Equalize the exchange of electrons so that the number lost equals the number gained. Each half-reaction must be multipled by a factor to get to the least common multiple of the loss and gain.

Add the balanced half-reactions to produce a net ion equation. Be sure to cancel species appearing on both sides of the equation, typically H_2O and H^+ or OH^-.

This type of redox balancing may no longer be expected to appear on the AP Chemistry examination.

Example:

A solution of sodium sulfite is mixed with an acidified solution of sodium dichromate.

Solution: $3\,SO_3^{2-} + 8\,H^+ + Cr_2O_7^{2-} \rightarrow 3\,SO_4^{2-} + 4\,H_2O + 2\,Cr^{3+}$

Combustion

A combustion reaction is just a specialized form of a redox reaction including an elemental form, oxygen gas. It can be presented as "heated in oxygen" or "burned in air".

Example:

Magnesium ribbon is ignited.

Solution: $2\,Mg + O_2 \rightarrow 2\,MgO$

Combustion of organic compounds

Organic compounds called hydrocarbons are frequent candidates for combustion reactions. Hydrocarbons are combusted in predictable ways. The oxidized form of hydrogen is water. Complete oxidation of carbon leads to carbon dioxide. Incomplete combustion of carbon will generate carbon monoxide. Severely limited oxygen might lead to elemental carbon in the form of soot.

Example:

Methane gas is burned in the atmosphere.

Solution: $CH_4 + 2 O_2 \rightarrow CO_2 + 2 H_2O$

Example:

Ethanol is burned in a limited quantity of oxygen gas.

Solution: $C_2H_5OH + 2 O_2 \rightarrow 2 CO + 3 H_2O$

You should know the basic formations of carbon and hydrogen atoms in simple organic compounds. Alkanes, alkenes, and alkynes are all hydrocarbons, named according to a simple formula by the number of carbon atoms present. Alkanes have all single bonds and the generic formula C_nH_{2n+2}. Alkenes have a double bond between two carbons and have the generic formula C_nH_{2n}. The alkyne series features a triple bond between two carbons; the generic formula C_nH_{2n-2}. Here is an easy way to keep them straight: the mnemonic device "Me eat peanut butter!" for the first four members of the alkane series methane, ethane, propane, and butane. After that, a Greek counting prefix is used to indicate the number of carbon atoms: pentane, hexane, heptane, octane, nonane, and decane complete the first ten in the series. Alkenes substitute "–ene" in place of "–ane" in the corresponding alkane while alkynes substitute "–yne" instead.

#carbons	Alkane	Formula	Alkene	Formula	Alkyne	Formula
1	methane	CH_4	———	———	———	———
2	Ethane	C_2H_6	Ethane	C_2H_4	Ethyne	C_2H_2
3	Propane	C_3H_8	Propene	C_3H_6	Propyne	C_3H_4
4	Butane	C_4H_{10}	Butane	C_4H_8	Butyne	C_4H_6
5	Pentane	C_5H_{12}	Pentene	C_5H_{10}	Pentyne	C_5H_8
6	Hexane	C_6H_{14}	Hexane	C_6H_{12}	Hexyne	C_6H_{10}
7	Heptane	C_7H_{16}	Heptane	C_7H_{14}	Heptyne	C_7H_{12}
8	Octane	C_8H_{18}	Octane	C_8H_{16}	Octyne	C_8H_{14}
9	Nonane	C_9H_{20}	Nonene	C_9H_{18}	Nonyne	C_9H_{16}

There are even reactions which resemble strongly combustion reactions.

> **Example**:
>
> Magnesium ribbon is heated strongly in nitrogen gas.
>
> *Solution*: $3\,Mg + N_2 \rightarrow Mg_3N_2$

Electrolysis

An electrolytic cell is the opposite of a galvanic cell. In it, electrical energy is converted to chemical energy by causing a chemical change, forcing a non-spontaneous reaction. There are two situations to consider: electrolysis of a fused (melted) salt and electrolysis of an aqueous solution of electrolytes.

Electrolysis of a fused salt: A metal is produced by reduction of the metal's cation at the cathode. A non-metal is formed by oxidation of the non-metal's anion at the anode.

> **Example**:
>
> An electric current is passed through a melted sample of potassium iodide.
>
> *Solution*: $2\,I^- + 2\,K^+ \rightarrow I_2 + 2\,K$

Electrolysis of an aqueous solution of a salt: Look for competition for electrons at each electrode; in other words, water must be considered as a possible participant at each electrode. It is easy to remember which process happens at which electrode if you remember the vowel-consonant link: oxidation (begins with a vowel) occurs at the anode (vowel), possibly producing acid (vowel) and oxygen (vowel) gas if water is involved. At the cathode (consonant), reduction (consonant) occurs and, if water is involved, a basic (consonant) solution and hydrogen (consonant) gas is evolved. Consult the Table of Standard Reduction Potentials to determine which process occurs at each electrode. At the cathode, a cation might be reduced or water instead. At the anode, the anion is oxidized (or the water). Whichever process requires less energy will be favored.

> **Example**:
>
> An electric current is passed through a solution of sodium iodide.
>
> *Solution*: $2\,I^- + 2\,H_2O \rightarrow I_2 + H_2 + 2\,OH^-$

Overall strategy

Consider each situation in this order:

- Precipitation reaction
- Acid-base reaction
- Redox reaction

It is likely that you will be able to identify a reaction as belonging to one of these categories and one of the subcategories.

CHAPTER EXERCISES

Write a balanced net ionic equation to describe each reaction.

1. Solutions of lead(II) nitrate and potassium carbonate are mixed.

$$Pb^{+2} + CO_3^{-2} \rightarrow PbCO_3$$

2. Solutions of strontium chloride and sodium sulfate are mixed.

$$SrCl_2 + Na_2SO_4 \rightarrow SrSO_4 + NaCl$$
$$Sr^{+2} + SO_4^{-2} \rightarrow SrSO_4$$

3. Solutions of silver(I) nitrate and ammonium fluoride are mixed.

$$AgNO_3 + NH_4F \rightarrow NH_4NO_3 + AgF$$
$$Ag^+ + F^- \rightarrow AgF$$

4. Solutions of barium hydroxide and sulfuric acid are mixed.

$$Ba(OH)_2 + H_2SO_4 \rightarrow BaSO_4 + H_2O$$

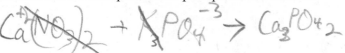

5. Solutions of calcium nitrate and potassium phosphate are mixed.

$$Ca(NO_3)_2 + K_3PO_4^{-3} \rightarrow Ca_3PO_4{}_2$$

6. Solutions of hydrochloric acid and potassium phosphate are mixed.

$$HCl + PO_4^- \rightarrow HPO_4^-$$

7. Equal volumes of identical concentrations of hydrochloric acid and potassium monohydrogen phosphate are mixed.

$$H^+Cl^- + HPO_4^- \rightarrow H_2PO_4$$

8. Solutions of nitric acid and potassium hydroxide are mixed.

$$HNO_3 + KOH \rightarrow KNO_3 + H_2O$$

9. Solid sodium hydride is sprinkled over water.

$$NaH + H_2O \rightarrow H_2 + OH^- + Na^+$$

Metallic hydrides yield metallic hydroxides

H_2

10. An electric current is passed through a melted sample of sodium chloride.

$$NaCl_2 \rightarrow Na^+_{(s)} + Cl_2$$

11. An electric current is passed through an aqueous solution of sodium chloride.

$$NaCl \rightarrow Cl_2 + H_2 + OH + Na^+$$

12. Sulfur dioxide gas is bubbled through an acidified solution of potassium permanganate.

$$2H_2O + 5SO_2 + 2MnO_4^- \rightarrow 2Mn^{+2} + 5SO_4 + 4H^+$$

13. Chlorine gas is bubbled into a solution of sodium hydroxide.

$$Cl_2 + OH^- \rightarrow ClO^- + Cl^- + H_2O$$

14. Powdered iron is sprinkled over a solution of iron(III) nitrate.

$$Fe + Fe^{+3}(NO_3)_3 \rightarrow Fe^{+2}(NO_3)_2 + Fe$$

15. Solutions of acetic acid and potassium hydrogen carbonate are mixed.

$$HC_2H_3O H^+ + K HCO_3^- \rightarrow H_2CO_3 +$$

16. Equal volumes of equimolar sodium hydroxide and sodium monohydrogen phosphate are mixed.

$$OH^- + HPO_4^{-2} \rightarrow H_2O + PO_4^{-3}$$

17. A stream of carbon dioxide gas is directed over a solid sample of potassium oxide.

$$CO_2 + K_2 O_2^{-2} \rightarrow CO_3^{-2}$$

18. Liquid ethanol combusts in the air.

$$C-C-OH$$

$$C_2H_6O + O_2 \rightarrow CO_2 + H_2O$$

19. A sample of solid ammonium carbonate is heated.

$$(NH_4)_2 CO_3 \rightarrow NH_3 + H_2CO_3$$

20. Solid potassium perchlorate is heated with a potassium permanganate catalyst.

$$KClO_4 \; + \; KMnO_4$$

$$HClO_4 \xrightarrow{KMnO_4} KCl + O_2$$

21. Solutions of strontium hydroxide and copper(II) sulfate are mixed.

$$2OH^- + Cu^{+2}\cancel{SO_4} \rightarrow Cu(OH)_2$$

22. Solutions of ammonium nitrate and sodium hydroxide are mixed.

$$NH_4^+ \cancel{NO_3} + OH^- \rightarrow NH_3 + H_2O$$

23. Solutions of nickel(II) nitrate and potassium sulfide are mixed.

$$Ni^{+2}\cancel{NO_3} + \cancel{K}S^{-2} \rightarrow \cancel{KNO_3} + NiS$$

24. Solutions of zinc(II) nitrate and sodium phosphate are mixed.

$$Zn^{+2}\cancel{NO_3} + \cancel{Na}PO_4^{-3} \rightarrow Zn_3(PO_4)_2$$

25. Propene gas is ignited in excess oxygen gas.

$$-\overset{|}{\underset{|}{C}}=\overset{|}{C}-\overset{|}{\underset{|}{C}}-$$

$$C_3H_8 + O_2 \rightarrow CO_2 + H_2O$$

SAMPLE EXAMINATION 1

Questions 1–4 refer to oxidation numbers of the non-oxygen element in each species.

(A) Carbonate
(B) Chlorate
(C) Nitrite
(D) Sulfate

1. Greatest oxidation number

2. Lowest oxidation number

3. Can be oxidized to a +7 oxidation number

4. Same oxidation number as nitrogen in nitrogen dioxide

Questions 5–7 should be answered using the following responses.

(A) Li
(B) B
(C) N
(D) F

223

5. Has the largest number of unpaired electrons of the elements listed.

6. Has the highest ionization energy of the elements listed.

7. Forms an ion with a +1 charge.

_____

Questions 8–11 refer to the following types of bonds.

(A) Ionic bond
(B) Metallic bond
(C) Non-polar covalent bond
(D) Polar covalent bond

8. Type of bond in PCl_5

9. Type of bond in the alloy brass

10. Type of bond between ammonium and chloride in NH_4Cl

11. Type of bond between nitrogen atoms in N_2

_____

Questions 12–14 should be answered with the following responses.

(A) Phosphoric acid
(B) Potassium permanganate
(C) Methylamine
(D) Zinc(II) hydroxide

12. Used frequently to oxidize other substances

13. Is amphoteric

14. Forms a colored solution

_____

Questions 15–16 refer to the Table below and the responses that follow.

Metal	Physical appearance	Reaction product with HCl(*dilute*)	Reaction product with HNO$_3$(*dilute*)
I	Reddish solid	No reaction	Reddish-brown bubbles
II	Lustrous light grey solid	No reaction	Reddish-brown bubbles
III	Yellowish solid	No reaction	No reaction

(A) Ag, silver
(B) Au, gold
(C) Cu, copper
(D) Zn, zinc

15. Identity of metal III

16. One of the components of both brass and bronze

Questions 17–19 should be answered with reference to the following reaction profiles

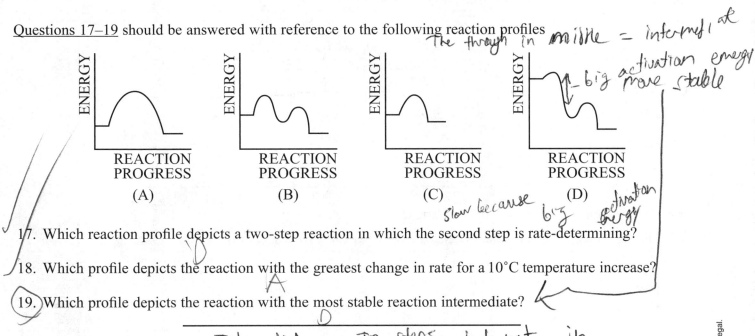

The through in middle = intermediate

big activation energy
more stable

ENERGY

REACTION PROGRESS
(A)

REACTION PROGRESS
(B)

REACTION PROGRESS
(C)

REACTION PROGRESS
(D)

slow because big activation energy

17. Which reaction profile depicts a two-step reaction in which the second step is rate-determining?

18. Which profile depicts the reaction with the greatest change in rate for a 10°C temperature increase?

19. Which profile depicts the reaction with the most stable reaction intermediate?

Intermediate — In steps but not in product.

$$O_3 \rightarrow O_2 + \boxed{O}$$
$$NO + \boxed{O} \rightarrow NO_2$$
$$NO + O_3 \rightarrow O_2 + NO_2$$

Questions 20–22 should be answered with reference to the reaction
$$CO(g) + NO_2(g) \rightarrow CO_2(g) + NO(g)$$
which is believed to occur by the mechanism below
$$NO_2(g) + NO_2(g) \rightarrow NO_3(g) + NO(g)$$
$$CO(g) + NO_3(g) \rightarrow CO_2(g) + NO_2(g)$$

(A) NO(g)
(B) NO₂(g)
(C) NO₃(g)
(D) CO(g)

20. Which substance is a reaction intermediate?

21. This substance appears in the rate equation only if the second step is rate-determining.

22. This substance appears in the rate equation regardless of which mechanism step is rate-determining.

Questions 23–25 refer to the heating curve for water.

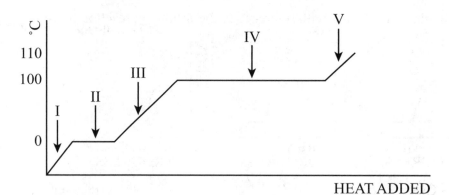

23. During which segment is the increase in potential energy the greatest?

(A) II
(B) III
(C) IV
(D) V

24. During which segment is the increase in kinetic energy the greatest?

(A) II
(B) III
(C) IV
(D) V

25. Which section represents the greatest increase in entropy (ΔS)?

(A) II
(B) III
(C) IV
(D) V

Questions 26–27 refer to the dissolving of potassium nitrate represented by the equation $KNO_3(s) \rightarrow K^+(aq) + NO_3^-(aq)$. This reaction was carried out in a Styrofoam insulated calorimeter and the following data were recorded:

$q = mc\Delta T$

$100\,(4.18)(8.4)$

Mass of solid KNO_3 dissolved	10.1 g
Mass of aqueous solution (sp. heat = 4.18 J/g°C)	100 g
T initial	30.0°C
T final	21.6°C
Molar Mass of KNO_3	101 g

$\dfrac{10.1\,g}{101\,amu} = .10n$

Therefore 3.51 KJ
for .10n but 35.1 KJ for

26. Which of the following equations correctly shows the heat of solution (kJ/mole) for the dissolving of KNO_3?

1 n

(A) $KNO_3(s) + 35.1\,kJ \rightarrow K^+(aq) + NO_3^-(aq)$
(B) $KNO_3(s) + 3.51\,kJ \rightarrow K^+(aq) + NO_3^-(aq)$
(C) $KNO_3(s) \rightarrow K^+(aq) + NO_3^-(aq) + 8.4\,kJ$
(D) $KNO_3(s) \rightarrow K^+(aq) + NO_3^-(aq) + 3510\,kJ$

27. If the mass of KNO_3 solid dissolved were doubled while all other experimental conditions were kept the same, what change would occur in ΔT, J per reaction, J/g of KNO_3 and kJ/mole KNO_3?

	ΔT of solution	J per reaction	J/gram KNO_3	kJ/mole KNO_3
			Constant	Constant
(A)	Larger	Larger	Larger	Larger
(B)	Larger	Larger	Larger	No change
(C)	Larger	Larger	No change	No change
(D)	Larger	No change	No change	No change

Weak acid

Questions 28–30 should be answered with reference to the curve below for the titration of the acid HA with NaOH

only NaOH + Salt

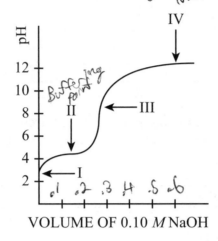

VOLUME OF 0.10 M NaOH

(A) I
(B) II
(C) III
(D) IV

28. At which point are the concentrations of HA and A^- equal to one another?

B

29. Which point has the highest electrical conductivity?

D

30. Which point is the equivalence point?

C

31. Consider two gases, O_2 and SO_2, in fixed containers pictured below:

d = 64 g/L   d = 32 g/L

64 g O_2	64 g SO_2
1.0 Liters 273 K	2.0 Liters 273 K

$\frac{g}{L}$

All of the following statements comparing the two gases are correct EXCEPT

(A) Their average kinetic energies are equal.
(B) The density of O_2 is twice the density of SO_2.
(C) The pressure of O_2 is twice the pressure of SO_2.
(D) The average molecular velocity of O_2 is greater than SO_2.

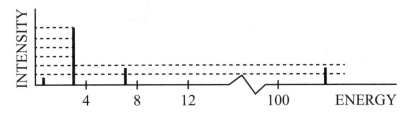

32. The complete PES diagram of a certain element is shown below.

[Graph: INTENSITY (y-axis) vs ENERGY (x-axis) with markings at 4, 8, 12, 100]

How many valence electrons does this element have?

(A) One
(B) Two
(C) Seven
(D) Nine

33. An aqueous solution of HCl is standardized by reacting it with a dried 0.212 g sample of Na_2CO_3 (M = 106 g/mol) according to the equation;

$$Na_2CO_3 + 2 HCl \rightarrow 2 NaCl + H_2O + CO_2$$

What is the molarity of the HCl solution if 25.0 mL is required for the reaction?

(A) 0.16 M
(B) 0.080 M
(C) 0.040 M
(D) 0.016 M

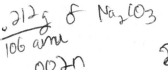

34. In the analysis of concentration vs time data, which linear graphs and reaction orders are correctly matched?

(A) [ ] vs time - first order; 1/[ ] vs time - zero order
(B) ln [ ] vs time - first order; 1/[ ] vs time - second order
(C) [ ] vs time - second order; ln [ ] vs time - first order
(D) [ ] vs time - zero order; 1/[ ] vs time - first order

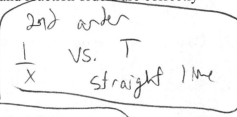

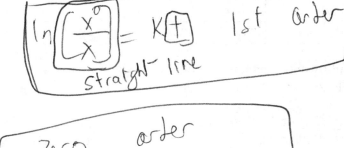

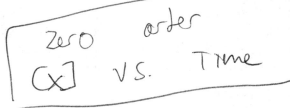

35. An ice cube readily melts at room temperature by the following equation:
$$6.0 \text{ kJ} + H_2O(s) \rightarrow H_2O(l)$$
Which set of thermodynamic properties best describes this process?

	$\Delta H°$	$\Delta S°$	$\Delta G°$
(A)	+	+	−
(B)	−	−	+
(C)	+	−	+
(D)	−	+	−

36. Which of the following best describe the particles present in a 2.0 M aqueous solution of $Al(NO_3)_3$? (All contain an abundance of water molecules.)

(A) 2 M $Al(NO_3)_3(aq)$
(B) 2 M $Al^{3+}(aq)$ and 3 M $(NO_3)^{3-}(aq)$
(C) 2 M $Al^{3+}(aq)$ and 6 M $NO_3^-(aq)$
(D) 2 M $Al^{3+}(aq)$ and 18 M $NO^-(aq)$

37. The formation of a measured quantity of zinc(II) sulfide from weighed quantities of zinc metal and sulfur can be used to illustrate all of the following Laws **EXCEPT**

(A) Law of Constant Composition
(B) Law of Conservation of Mass
(C) Law of Definite Proportions
(D) Law of Multiple Proportions — Many possibilities

38. Consider the reactions below along with their free energy values:

	Reaction	$\Delta G°$ (kJ/mole)
Reaction 1	$Cu_2S(s) \rightarrow 2\,Cu(s) + S(s)$	+ 86.2
Reaction 2	$SO_2(g) \rightarrow S(s) + O_2(g)$	+ 300.1
Reaction 3	$Cu_2S(s) + O_2(g) \rightarrow 2\,Cu(s) + SO_2(s)$	

Which of the following statements is correct for reaction 3 which shows the extraction of copper from copper(I) sulfide ore?

(A) $\Delta G° = -127.7$ kJ/mole, Keq $\ll$ 1, extraction of copper *cannot* occur
(B) $\Delta G° = +213.9$ kJ/mole, Keq $\ll$ 1, extraction of copper *cannot* occur
(C) $\Delta G° = -213.9$ kJ/mole, Keq $\gg$ 1, extraction of copper *can* occur
(D) $\Delta G° = -426$ kJ/mole and Keq $\gg$ 1, extraction of copper *can* occur

39. Separate 100.0 mL solutions of the acids HOCl, HOClO, HOClO$_2$, and HOClO$_3$ are prepared to each have pH = 6.0. Which solution requires the highest number of moles of acid to reach this pH?

(A) HOCl
(B) HOClO
(C) HOClO$_2$
(D) HOClO$_3$

40. Which gas is produced when nitric acid acts as an oxidizing agent in air?

(A) yellowish-green Cl$_2$
(B) colorless H$_2$
(C) colorless NO
(D) reddish-brown NO$_2$

H NO$_2$

41. Which of these transitions by an electron between energy levels in the Bohr model of the hydrogen atom emits visible light?

(A) n = 6 to n = 1
(B) n = 5 to n = 4
(C) n = 4 to n = 2
(D) n = 4 to n = 3

$E = 1375.4$
$E = 29.52$
$E = 246$
$E = 63.8$

$E = \dfrac{-1312}{n^2} = KJ/n$

$E = \dfrac{1.196 \times 10^5}{\lambda} = KJ/n \big/ nm$

visible light
Balmer series

42. Consider the boiling points of the halogen group as given below

Halogen	Boiling Point (K)
Fluorine	85.1
Chlorine	239.2
Bromine	331.9
Iodine	452.5

Which of the following statements best *explains* the trend in boiling points from fluorine to iodine?

(A) Covalent bonds within the molecules strengthen as the molecules become larger.
(B) London dispersion forces strengthen as the molecules become larger and more polarizable.
(C) London dispersion forces strengthen due to increasing molecular mass.
(D) London dispersion forces are enhanced by permanent dipole forces as the molecules become larger.

Ca_2O_3

43. Which is the same for samples of calcium carbonate in limestone deposits from different areas of the world?

(A) percentage of calcium carbonate in different deposits
(B) mass ratios of the constituent elements
(C) ratio of the isotopes C-12 and C-14
(D) crystalline form

44. Carbon monoxide, CO, and nitrogen dioxide, NO_2, react to form carbon dioxide, CO_2, and nitric oxide, NO. Which of the molecular orientations below is most likely to lead to a successful reaction?

(A) $O=N-O-C\equiv O$
(B) $C\equiv O-O=N-O$
(C) $O=N-C=O$
           $|$
           O
(D) $C\equiv O-N=O$
              $\backslash$
               O

45. A thermometer is lowered into a sample of water. The temperature displayed by the thermometer is $30°C$. Which of the following statements is correct?

(A) All water molecules in the sample have the same kinetic energy.
(B) Water molecules in the sample have a range of kinetic energies.
(C) If the temperature of the sample were doubled to $60°C$, the average kinetic energy of the water would double.
(D) If the temperature of the sample were lowered to $0°C$, the average kinetic energy of the water molecules would fall to zero.

46. Ascorbic acid, $H_2C_6H_6O_6$, ionizes as shown below
$$H_2C_6H_6O_6 + H_2O \rightleftharpoons HC_6H_6O_6^- + H_3O^+ \qquad K_{a1} = 8.0 \times 10^{-5}$$
$$HC_6H_6O_6^- + H_2O \rightleftharpoons C_6H_6O_6^{2-} + H_3O^+ \qquad K_{a2} = 1.60 \times 10^{-12}$$
Which substance has the highest concentration in a 0.20 M solution of ascorbic acid?

(A) $H_2C_6H_6O_6$
(B) $HC_6H_6O_6^-$
(C) H_3O^+
(D) $C_6H_6O_6^{2-}$

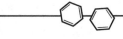

47. For which of the following compounds does hydrogen bonding affect its physical properties?

(A) Ethane, CH_3—CH_3
(B) Ethanol, CH_3—CH_3—OH
(C) Dimethyl ether, CH_3—O—CH_3
(D) Methyl fluoride, CH_3—F

48. According to the Standard Reduction Potentials in the Table below, which metal listed would be the most effective sacrificial anode in the presence of the other metals?

Selected Standard Reduction Potentials at 25°C	E°, volts
$Cl_2(aq) + 2\,e^- \rightarrow 2\,Cl^-(aq)$	$+1.36$
$I_2(s) + 2\,e^- \rightarrow 2I^-(aq)$	$+0.54$
$Ag^+(aq) + e^- \rightarrow Ag(s)$	$+0.80$
$Cu^{2+}(aq) + 2\,e^- \rightarrow Cu(s)$	$+0.34$
$Pb^{2+}(aq) + 2\,e^- \rightarrow Pb(s)$	-0.12
$Mg^{2+}(aq) + 2\,e^- \rightarrow Mg(s)$	-2.36

(A) Cu
(B) Ag
(C) Pb
(D) Mg

49. For the reaction, $2\,NO + O_2 \rightarrow N_2O_4$, what is its K value in terms of the K values for Reaction 1 and Reaction 2 below?

Reaction 1: $N_2 + 2\,O_2 \rightarrow N_2O_4$ K_1
Reaction 2: $N_2 + O_2 \rightarrow 2\,NO$ K_2

(A) $K = K_1 - K_2$
(B) $K = K_1 \times K_2$
(C) $K = K_1/K_2$
(D) $K = K_2/K_1$

50. Which of the following solids conducts electricity when melted?

(A) Sand, SiO_2
(B) Ice, H_2O
(C) Wax, $C_{25}H_{52}$
(D) Salt, $NaCl$

51. The conversion of $O_3(g)$ to $O_2(g)$ is thought to occur by the two step process
$$O_3(g) \rightleftharpoons O_2(g) + O(g)$$
$$O_3(g) + O(g) \rightarrow 2\,O_2(g)$$
In the energy diagram below which point represents the O(g)?

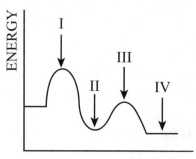

REACTION PROGRESS

(A) I
(B) II
(C) III
(D) IV

52. Chlorine consists of two isotopes with masses of 35 and 37. If the average atomic mass of a sample of chlorine atoms is 35.5, what is the $^{35}Cl/^{37}Cl$ ratio?

(A) 1/1
(B) 2/1
(C) 3/1
(D) 4/1

$35.5 = 35(x) + 37(1.0-x)$

$35.5 = 35x + 370 - 37x$

$.75 = x \qquad -2x + 37$

53. The decomposition of hydrogen peroxide, H_2O_2, into H_2O and O_2 is thermodynamically favorable at room temperature with a free energy change ($\Delta G°$) of -112 kJ/mol but the reaction is slow and very few bubbles of oxygen are observed. Which statement best accounts for this behavior?

(A) The system is at equilibrium.
(B) The K_{eq} value is much less than 1.
(C) LeChatelier's principle shifts the reaction toward the reactants upon the production of oxygen gas.
(D) The reaction lacks the necessary activation energy.

54. A buffer in our bloodstream involves the hydrogen carbonate ion, HCO_3^-, and carbonic acid, H_2CO_3, in this equilibrium system:

$$HCO_3^-(aq) + H^+(aq) \rightleftharpoons H_2CO_3(aq)$$

When an excess of OH^- enters the bloodstream, which reaction of the buffer system above stabilizes the pH of the blood?

(A) $OH^-(aq) + H^+(aq) \rightleftharpoons H_2O(aq)$
(B) $OH^-(aq) + HCO_3^-(aq) \rightleftharpoons CO_3^{2-}(aq) + H_2O(aq)$
(C) $OH^-(aq) + H_2CO_3(aq) \rightleftharpoons HCO_3^-(aq) + H_2O(aq)$
(D) $2OH^-(aq) + H_2CO_3(aq) \rightleftharpoons CO_2^{2-}(aq) + 2H_2O(aq)$

55. .....$Cr_2O_3(s)$ + ..3..$CO(g)$ → ......3..$CO_2(g)$ + ...2..$Cr(s)$

When the above equation is properly balanced and reduced to lowest whole numbers, the coefficient for CO is

(A) 1
(B) 2
(C) 3
(D) 4

56. The K_{sp} values for AgCl, AgSCN and Ag_2CrO_4 are given in the table below.

	AgCl	Ag_2CrO_4	AgSCN
K_{sp}	1.8×10^{-10}	1×10^{-12}	8×10^{-12}

When saturated solutions of these three salts are arranged in order of increasing $[Ag^+]$, which order is correct?

(A) $AgSCN < Ag_2CrO_4 < AgCl$
(B) $AgSCN < AgCl < Ag_2CrO_4$
(C) $Ag_2CrO_4 < AgSCN < AgCl$
(D) $Ag_2CrO_4 < AgSCN < AgCl$

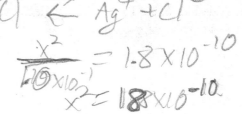

57. What is the effect of temperature on a reaction for which the signs of $\Delta H°$ and $\Delta S°$ are both negative?

(A) Always spontaneous
(B) Never spontaneous
(C) Non-spontaneous at low temperature but spontaneous at high temperatures
(D) Spontaneous at low temperature but non-spontaneous at high temperatures

58. Which of the following carbon-oxygen species has a lone pair of electrons on the carbon atom?

    (A) CO
    (B) CO_2
    (C) CO_3^{2-}
    (D) HCO_3^-

59. The reaction $4\,HCl(g) + O_2(g) \rightleftharpoons 2\,Cl_2(g) + 2\,H_2O(g)$ has a $K_c = 1.5$ at a certain temperature. If the initial concentration of each substance in the reaction system is $0.10\ M$, in which direction will the reaction shift to attain equilibrium and which substance(s) will remain in the highest concentration?

    (A) The reaction will shift toward the reactants and $HCl(g)$ will have the highest concentration at equilibrium.
    (B) The reaction will shift toward the reactants and $O_2(g)$ will have the highest concentration at equilibrium.
    (C) The reaction will shift toward the products and $Cl_2(g)$ will have the highest concentration at equilibrium.
    (D) The reaction will shift toward the products and $Cl_2(g)$ and $H_2O(g)$ will have the highest concentrations at equilibrium.

60. A student is doing a titration using potassium permanganate solution, $KMnO_4$, to determine the amount of H_2O_2 in a sample. The balanced equation for the reaction in the titration is given below.

$$2\,MnO_4^- + 6\,H^+ + 5\,H_2O_2 \rightarrow 2\,Mn^{2+} + 8\,H_2O + 5\,O_2$$

A student calculates an amount of moles of H_2O_2 that is larger than the actual value. Which of the following errors could correctly explain the larger value?

    (A) The student failed to rinse the buret with $KMnO_4$ solution after rinsing it with distilled water.
    (B) The student did not swirl the flask appropriately and therefore stopped short of the endpoint.
    (C) The student added an extra 15 mL of distilled water to the H_2O_2 solution.
    (D) The student failed to wear goggles.

CONSTRUCTED-RESPONSE QUESTIONS

$$v = f\lambda$$

$$3.00 \times 10^8 \frac{m}{s} = (f)(651)$$

Question 1

1. The visible portion of the electromagnetic spectrum has wavelengths measuring 400 to 750 nm.

   (a) What is the frequency of red light with wavelength 651 nm?

   $$f = 4.61 \times 10^{14}$$

   (b) What is the energy (J) for one photon of this red light?

   $$3.05 \times 10^{-19}$$

2. Data to establish an absorption spectrum for the permanganate anion were taken across the visible spectrum:

Absorbance	0	0.40	0.91	1.02	0.42	0.37	0
λ (nm)	400	450	500	550	600	650	700

   (a) On the axes below, sketch the absorbance curve for the permanganate anion. Label each axis.

   (b) Although maximum absorbance occurs in the yellow (550-580 nm) part of the spectrum, permanganate anion has a characteristic purple color. Explain.

   It has d electrons. when light hits it, it jumps to other d and subshells and will show other colors.

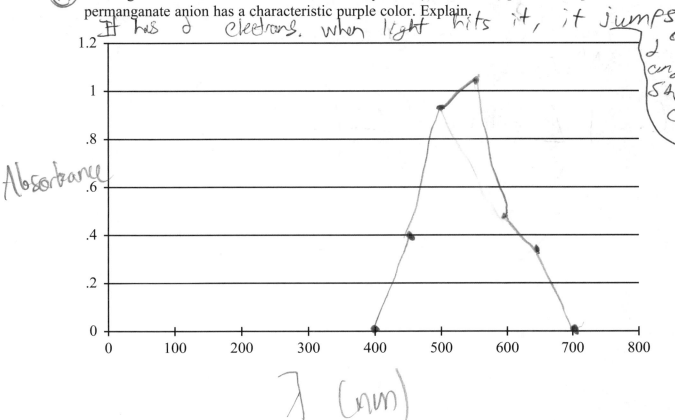

237

3. At 25°C, gaseous dinitrogen pentoxide decomposes into the gaseous products nitrogen dioxide and oxygen. The product nitrogen dioxide has a reddish-brown color while both dinitrogen pentoxide and oxygen gases are colorless. The progress of the reaction can be followed by measuring the absorbance as the reddish-brown product accumulates.

(a) Write a balanced net ionic equation with lowest whole number coefficients to describe the decomposition.

(b) The reaction is found to be first-order. Which function of $[N_2O_5]$ would give a straight line if plotted against time t? What is the significance of the slope of that line?

(c) At 25°C, the rate constant k for the reaction is 4.12×10^{-3} min^{-1} but at 67°C, its value is 0.35 min^{-1}. Describe how you could use these values to determine the activation energy E_a for the reaction.

a. $2N_2O_5 \rightarrow 4NO_2 + O_2$

b. In a first order reaction the $\ln[C_{an}]$ vs. Time gives a straight line.
K is the slope of the line. that is the rate constant.

c. $\ln\left(\dfrac{4.12 \times 10^{-3}}{.35}\right) = \dfrac{E_{ACT}}{8.314}\left(\dfrac{1}{340} - \dfrac{1}{298}\right)$

$\ln K$ vs T

Question 2

1. Using concepts of interparticulate Coulombic forces, explain the trend in boiling point temperatures among noble gases. *As the atomic weight increases, the more electrons which increases the inter-particulate Coulombic forces which makes the electrons more polarizable, the higher the charge of e and the higher the London dispersion forces*

Noble gas	He	Ne	Ar	Kr
Molar mass	4.00	20.18	39.95	83.80
Boiling point (°C)	−269	−246	−186	−152

2. Using concepts of interparticulate Coulombic forces, explain the trend in boiling point temperatures among the halogens.

Halogen	F_2	Cl_2	Br_2	I_2
Molar mass	38.0	70.9	159.8	253.8
Boiling point (°C)	−188	−34	59	184

3. Using concepts of interparticulate Coulombic forces, explain the trend in boiling point temperatures among straight-line (normal) hydrocarbons.

Hydrocarbon	CH_4	C_2H_6	C_3H_8	C_4H_{10}
Molar mass	16.05	30.08	44.11	58.14
Boiling point (°C)	−161	−88	−42	0

4. Among diatomic molecules with similar molar masses, boiling points vary widely.

Molecule	N_2	O_2	CO	NO
Molar mass	28.02	32.00	28.01	30.01
Boiling point (°C)	−196	−183	−192	−151

Using concepts of interparticulate Coulombic forces, explain why

(a) The boiling point of oxygen is greater than that of nitrogen. — *More electrons stronger London dispersion forces*
(b) The boiling point of nitrogen monoxide is greater than either nitrogen or oxygen. *Polar vs. Non polar*
(c) The boiling point of nitrogen monoxide is greater than the boiling point of carbon monoxide.

NO is more polar because of its paramagnetic nature.

CO is diamagnetic

5. Among molecules with similar shapes, boiling points can vary widely.

Molecule	H$_2$O	H$_2$S	H$_2$Se	H$_2$Te
Molar mass	18.02	34.03	80.98	129.62
Boiling point (°C)	100	−60	−42	−2

One molecule does not fit the established trend. On the table of data above, circle the column of data which does not fit. Explain your choice. Be sure to evaluate each member of the series in your comparisons. Hydrogen bonding

0.385g Pill

0.0112 M MnO$_4^-$

20.8×10^{-3} L

$\left(\dfrac{55.85g}{n}\right)$ 1.6 5 ×10^{-4} n = 5 × 2.3246×10^{-4} n MnO$_4^-$
Fe^{+2}

$\dfrac{.06505g \; Fe}{0.385 g}$ × 100 = 16.9%

Question 3

Answer the following questions concerning an oxidation-reduction titration experiment.

1. Experiments frequently require a "primary standard". What is a primary standard?

2. In preparation for a redox titration, a student dissolved 0.919 g "FAS" ("ferrous ammonium sulfate" or iron(II) ammonium sulfate, $Fe(NH_4)_2(SO_4)_2 \cdot 16H_2O$, *MM* 392.13) in more than 30 mL distilled water. The student then added a small amount of 6 *M* H_2SO_4 to acidify the solution, then filled a buret with a solution of ~0.02 *M* $KMnO_4$.

   (a) Why is it unnecessary for the student to know the exact volume of distilled water used to dissolve the solid FAS? *It is purely a solution. Not needed.*

   (b) The half-reactions for the redox reaction are $Fe^{2+} \rightarrow Fe^{3+}$ and $MnO_4^- \rightarrow Mn^{2+}$. What is the ratio of $Fe^{2+}: MnO_4^-$ in a balanced equation? *$\frac{5}{1}$*

   (c) If the student used 21.07 mL MnO_4^- solution to titrate 0.919 g FAS solution to a persistent pale pink, what is the apparent concentration of the solution? *.02234 M*

3. In an experiment to determine the % mass of Fe in an iron-containing vitamin tablet, the student takes a tablet weighing 0.385 g, grinds it with a pestle in a mortar, and dissolves it in sufficient distilled water. The solution is then acidified and titrated with a potassium permanganate solution previously standardized as 0.0112 *M* MnO_4^-. The titration requires 20.8 mL to reach a persistent pale pink color.

   (a) What is the mass of Fe in the vitamin tablet? *= .06505 g*

   (b) What is the mass percent of iron in the vitamin tablet? *= 16.9%*

HCl

MnO_4 (1 MnO_4

1. A primary standard.
a solid that must be titrated to find out the Molarity of the strong Acid/Base.
Double titration. Much more accurate titration.

NaOH

tartaric acid

2. FAS = 392.13 AMU

oxid: $(Fe^{+2} \rightarrow Fe^{+3} + 1e) 5$

$(5e + 8H^+ + MnO_4^- \rightarrow Mn^{+2} + 4H_2O)$

$\frac{0.919}{392.13} = .00234 n$ of Fe^{+2}

$21.07 \times 10^{-3} \ell$

$.00234 / 1 mol =$

$\frac{.00646 n \ MnO_4}{21.07 \times 10^{-3}} = .02234 M$

Question 4

Indicator	Color change	pH at change
Methyl red	Red to yellow	5-7
Bromthymol blue	Yellow to blue	6-8
Phenolphthalein	Colorless to pink	8-10

A student performing acid-base titrations is given a choice of three indicators to signify the equivalence point.

(a) In the first titration, the student adds a solution of sodium hydroxide from a buret to a solution of hydrochloric acid in an Erlenmeyer flask. NaOH is added until color change, the endpoint of the indicator.

$$H^+ + OH^- \rightarrow H_2O$$

i. Write a balanced net ionic equation to describe the reaction.

$pH = 7$

ii. Select an indicator for this titration and explain your choice.

~~Phenolphthalein NaOH strong base~~ Bromthymol blue

It would have changed from yellow to green to blue, giving a end point and an equivalence point

(b) The second titration adds the sodium hydroxide solution to a solution of ethanoic acid (acetic acid).

$$HC_2H_3O_2 + OH^- \rightarrow H_2O + C_2H_3O_2^-$$

i. Write a balanced net ionic equation to describe the reaction.

ii. Select an indicator for this titration and explain your choice.

phenolphthalein. — Looking for pink at equivalence point.

pH = 9 - 9.5

Question 5

(a) For most reactions, the reaction rate increases as the temperature increases. Explain this observation on a particulate basis.

(b) The decomposition of dinitrogen pentoxide gas into nitrogen dioxide and oxygen gases is a first-order reaction.

   i. Write a balanced net ionic equation for this reaction using smallest whole number coefficients.

   ii. Suppose that an evacuated rigid container is charged with 1.0 atm dinitrogen pentoxide and the gas is allowed to react. After the partial pressure of dinitrogen pentoxide becomes 0.80 atm, what is the total pressure in the container? Explain.

a. As the temperature ↑ the molecules move faster, creating more collisions. and increasing the rate of the reaction

bi. loses -2 (2 N₂O₅ → (4 NO₂ + O₂)
1.0 $.80$ $.4$ $.1$

$P_A = P_T$

$1.3 = .8 + .4 + .1$
atm

Stoichiometry — mole ratio

Question 6

(a) Why is a burn caused by steam so much worse than one caused by the same amount of boiling water?

(b) Burning 1.00 g methane (CH_4) in a Bunsen burner can cause 250. g water (H_2O) in a beaker to change temperature from 25 to 78°C.

$$CH_4 + 2O_2 \rightarrow CO_2 + 2H_2O$$

   i. Write a balanced net ionic equation to describe the reaction. Use smallest whole number coefficients.

   ii. Calculate ΔH_{rxn} (kJ/mol) for the combustion of one mole of methane.

$$\boxed{-886 \text{ KJ}}$$
$$\boxed{-840 \text{ KJ}}$$
exothermic

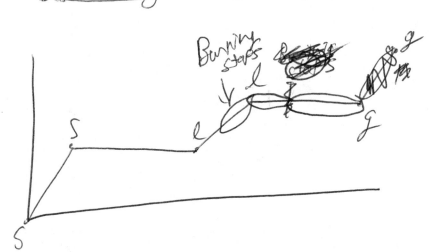

a. A gas has a much higher Average

a. The steam has more energy. The boiling water has maximum at 100 °C. The steam can be hotter than the water. In addition as the steam burns you and water cools, it will become boiling and burn you longer.

b. $q = mC\Delta T$

$q = 250 (4.18)(53) = 55385 J (16g) = 886 KJ$

Question 7

Answer the following questions concerning gaseous equilibria containing dinitrogen tetraoxide.

Consider this equilibrium: $2 NO_2(g) \longleftrightarrow N_2O_4(g)$

Will the change favor formation of more products, more reactants, or neither? Explain.

(a) Adding N_2O_4
(b) Removing NO_2
(c) Increase volume
(d) Use the following data to calculate K for the reaction between one mole of dinitrogen monoxide and sufficient oxygen gas to form one mole of dinitrogen tetraoxide.

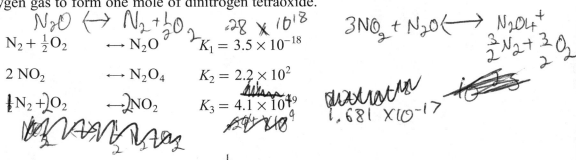

$$N_2 + \tfrac{1}{2}O_2 \longleftrightarrow N_2O \qquad K_1 = 3.5 \times 10^{-18}$$

$$2 NO_2 \longleftrightarrow N_2O_4 \qquad K_2 = 2.2 \times 10^2$$

$$\tfrac{1}{2}N_2 + O_2 \longleftrightarrow NO_2 \qquad K_3 = 4.1 \times 10^{9}$$

$$H_2S \rightleftarrows HS^- + H^+ \qquad K_1 = 1 \times 10^{-7}$$

$$HS^- \rightleftarrows S^{-2} + H^+ \qquad K_2 = 1 \times 10^{-13}$$

$$H_2S \rightleftarrows S^{-2} + 2H^+ \qquad K_7 = (K_1)(K_2) =$$

$$N_2O + \tfrac{3}{2}O_2 \longrightarrow N_2O_4$$

$$N_2O + \tfrac{3}{2}O_2 \longleftrightarrow N_2O_4$$

SAMPLE EXAMINATION 2

Questions 1–4 refer to the following sublevels when n = 3.

    (A) 3*s*
    (B) 3*p*
    (C) 3*d*
    (D) 3*f*

1. Ends in the transition metal block

2. Ends with a noble gas

3. Unpaired electrons in this block lead to colored solutions

4. Non-existent orbital

_____

Questions 5–6 refer to the mass spectrum below for element X that consists of three isotopes with the masses and % abundances shown below.

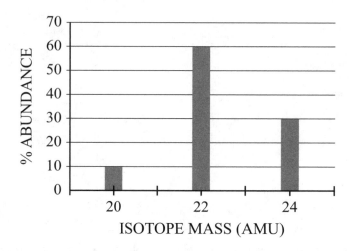

5. Which isotope of element X is the LEAST abundant?

   (A) They are equally abundant
   (B) X-20
   (C) X-22
   (D) X-24

6. What is the average atomic mass of element X?

   (A) 21.5 amu
   (B) 22.0 amu
   (C) 22.4 amu
   (D) 23.0 amu

$$20\,(.10) + (.60)(22) + (.30)(24)$$
$$2 + 13.2 + 7.2$$

Questions 7–9: Hydrated calcium sulfate is heated producing water vapor and the anhydrous salt, $CaSO_4$, by the following reaction: $CaSO_4 \cdot xH_2O \rightarrow CaSO_4 + xH_2O$

Mass of $CaSO_4 \cdot xH_2O$ before heating	17.21 g
Mass of solid residue after first heating	13.68 g
Mass of solid residue after second heating	13.61 g
Mass of solid residue after third heating	13.60 g

7. Which expression correctly identifies the moles of water found in the hydrate and released during the reaction?

(A) $(17.21 \text{ g} - 13.60 \text{ g}) \div 18.0 \text{ g}$
(B) $(17.21 \text{ g} - 13.68 \text{ g}) \times 18.0 \text{ g}$
(C) $(13.68 \text{ g} - 13.60 \text{ g}) \times 18.0 \text{ g}$
(D) $(13.68 \text{ g} - 13.60 \text{ g}) \div 18.0 \text{ g}$

8. After recording the mass of hydrate, $CaSO_4 \cdot xH_2O$, a small amount was unknowingly lost prior to heating. Which of the following statements is true with respect to the calculated % (by mass) of the water in the hydrate?

(A) The mass of the hydrate heated is less than recorded but the calculated % by mass of water is not affected.
(B) The mass of the hydrate heated is less than recorded and the calculated % by mass of water is less than it should be.
(C) The mass of the hydrate heated and the mass of water calculated decrease in proportion and the % by mass of water calculated is not affected.
(D) The mass of the hydrate heated is less than recorded causing the calculated % by mass of water to be more than it should be.

9. Which of the following most accurately describes the composition of the solid residue after the first heating?

(A) mostly hydrate; a small amount of anhydrous salt
(B) equal amounts of hydrate and anhydrous salt
(C) a small amount of hydrate; mostly anhydrous salt
(D) no hydrate; all anhydrous salt

Questions 10–13 should be answered with reference to the following substances.

(A) HNO_3

(B) N_2

(C) NH_2OH

(D) NO *—paramagnetic*

NO_2

Sigma bond - in same plane of atoms

Pi bond - In Plane above and below Sigma bond

10. Which substance would exhibit the highest electrical conductivity when dissolved in water at room temperature? *A*

11. Which substance contains only sigma bonds? *C*

12. Which substance contains the bond with highest energy? *B*

13. Which substance contains an unpaired electron? *D*

Questions 14–16 refer to the following acid-base forms.

(A) Strong acid

(B) Acid anhydride

(C) Basic anhydride

(D) Weak base

14. Soluble oxide that forms an alkaline solution when added to water *C*

15. A soluble oxide of a non-metal *B*

16. 100% dissociation *A*

Questions 17–18 should be answered from the following responses

(A) Fe^{2+}

(B) MnO_4^-

(C) Cl^-

(D) Al

17. Can only be reduced *B*

18. Can be either oxidized or reduced *A*

Questions 19–21 refer to the following choices

    (A) zero-order
    (B) first-order
    (C) second-order
    (D) third-order

$HL = \dfrac{.693}{K}$

19. The half-life of a reaction with this order does not depend on reactant concentration.

B

20. A graph of concentration vs time is linear for a reaction with this order.

A

21. What is the overall order of the reaction with the rate equation; Rate $= k[A][B]$?

C

Questions 22–24 should be answered with reference to the diagram below and the responses below it.

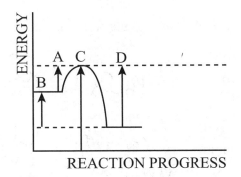

    (A) A — Activation E
    (B) B — ΔH
    (C) C — Activated complex
    (D) D

22. This interval represents the activation energy for the forward reaction.

A

23. This interval remains unchanged upon the introduction of a catalyst.

B

24. This interval represents the potential energy stored in the activated complex.

C

Questions 25–27 refer to the reversible reaction below in a flexible container at 25 °C

$$2\,C(s) + O_2(g) \rightleftharpoons 2\,CO(g) \qquad\qquad \Delta H° = -221\,\text{kJ/mol}$$

(A) Increasing the temperature
(B) Decreasing the pressure
(C) Adding a small amount of C(s)
(D) Removing CO(g)

25. Which change will not affect the position of the equilibrium?

    C

26. Which change will shift the equilibrium toward the reactants?

    A

27. Which change will produce the greatest range of molecular kinetic energies?

    A

Questions 28–30 should be answered on the basis of the following Ksp values.

(A) $BaCO_3$ $K_{sp} = 8.1 \times 10^{-9}$
(B) $CaSO_4$ $K_{sp} = 2.4 \times 10^{-5}$
(C) $PbCrO_4$ $K_{sp} = 1.8 \times 10^{-14}$
(D) ZnC_2O_4 $K_{sp} = 1.4 \times 10^{-9}$

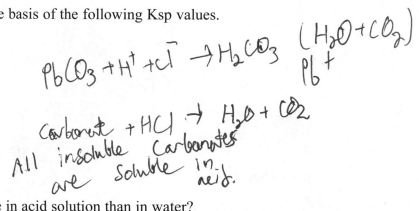

28. Which substance is the most soluble?

    B

29. Which substance is the least soluble?

    C

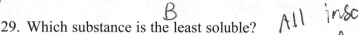

30. Which substance is much more soluble in acid solution than in water?

    A

31. An ideal gas occupies 2.5 L, exerts a pressure of 750 mm Hg, and has a temperature of 30°C. The gas is compressed to 1.5 L and cooled to 15°C. Which expression gives the pressure of the gas as a result of these changes?

(A) $750 \times (15/30) \times (2.5/1.5)$
(B) $750 \times (30/15) \times (1.5/2.5)$
(C) $750 \times (288/303) \times (2.5/1.5)$
(D) $750/760 \times (288/303) \times (1.5/2.5)$

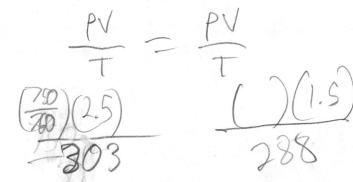

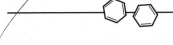

32. A weighed piece of magnesium ribbon is added to a dried crucible, which is reweighed and heated in air to form the compound MgO. The crucible is cooled and reweighed to find the mass of MgO. Which error could lead to a mass percentage of magnesium that is too low?

   (A) The crucible contains a small amount of H_2O when it is reweighed with the Mg.
   (B) The crucible is sill warm when it is weighed with the product.
   (C) The magnesium ribbon has an oxide coating.
   (D) The MgO formed absorbs moisture before it is weighed.

33. The half-life for a particular first order reaction is 10.0 seconds. What is the value of k, the first order rate constant?

   (A) 0. 0693 s^{-1}
   (B) 0. 100 s^{-1}
   (C) 0. 693 s^{-1}
   (D) 6.93 s^{-1}

34. A can of compressed gas is at room temperature at normal atmospheric pressure. When the gas is released from the can as a spray, the nozzle of the can becomes cold. Which statement below best *explains* this event?

   (A) An endothermic chemical reaction occurred between the air and the gas molecules.
   (B) As the gas expanded coming out of the can, it did work on the opposing air pressure and lost kinetic energy.
   (C) As the gas sprayed out, a vacuum was created inside the can.
   (D) Pressure and temperature of a gas are directly related.

35. The pH of an aqueous solution that is 0.100 M in acetic acid, $HC_2H_3O_2$, $(K_a = 1.8 \times 10^{-5})$ and 0.100 M in sodium acetate, $C_2H_3O_2^-Na^+$ $(NaC_2H_3O_2)$, is closest to

   (A) 1.00
   (B) 3.00
   (C) 5.00
   (D) 7.00

36. Consider the boiling points of alcohols as given below

Alcohol	Boiling Point (°C)
CH_3OH (methanol)	65.0
CH_3CH_2OH (ethanol)	78.5
$CH_3CH_2CH_2OH$ (1-propanol)	97.4
$CH_3CH_2CH_2CH_2OH$ (1-butanol)	117.3

Which statement best *explains* the trend in boiling points from methanol to 1- butanol?

(A) Increasing surface area of the longer carbon chain promotes stronger dispersion forces between molecules.
(B) Increasing mass promotes stronger dispersion bonds between molecules.
(C) Increasing the number of carbons in the chain creates a more polarized H and strengthens the hydrogen bonds between molecules.
(D) Increasing the number of carbons in the chain increases the covalent bonding of the carbons within the molecule.

37. A strip of copper metal is placed in an aqueous sodium chloride solution. According to the standard reduction potentials below, which of the following would be observed?

Selected Standard Reduction Potentials at 25°C	E°(volts)
$Cl_2(aq) + 2e^- \rightarrow 2Cl^-(aq)$	+1.36
$I_2(s) + 2e^- \rightarrow 2I^-(aq)$	+0.54
$Ag^+(aq) + e^- \rightarrow Ag(s)$	+0.80
$Cu^{2+}(aq) + 2e^- \rightarrow Cu(s)$	+0.34
$Pb^{2+}(aq) + 2e^- \rightarrow Pb(s)$	−0.12
$Mg^{2+}(aq) + 2e^- \rightarrow Mg(s)$	−2.36
$Na^+(aq) + e^- \rightarrow Na(s)$	−2.71

(A) No reaction occurs.
(B) Bubbles of gas would be observed.
(C) A blue color would form in the solution.
(D) Crystals of copper (II) chloride would form on the strip of copper.

38. The purpose of adding a catalyst to a chemical reaction is to increase the

    (A) concentration of reactants at equilibrium
    (B) fraction of reactant molecules with sufficient kinetic energy to undergo reaction
    (C) activation energy for the reverse reaction
    (D) enthalpy change for the reaction

39. All of the following reactions show an increase in entropy EXCEPT

    (A) $C_2H_5OH(l) \rightarrow C_2H_5OH(aq)$
    (B) $CO_2(g) \rightarrow CO_2(aq)$
    (C) $C_2H_5OH(l) + 3\,O_2(g) \rightarrow 2\,CO_2(g) + 3\,H_2O(g)$
    (D) $2\,NH_3(g) \rightarrow N_2(g) + 3\,H_2(g)$

40. The value of K_w (1.0×10^{-14} at $25\,^\circ C$) increases as the temperature is raised. Which of the following statements about the behavior of water at $50\,^\circ C$ is true?

    (A) The pH is below 7.00 and H_2O is more acidic.
    (B) The pH is below 7.00 and H_2O is neutral.
    (C) The pH is above 7.00 and H_2O is less acidic.
    (D) The pH is above 7.00 and H_2O is neutral.

41. The following diagrams represent the particle composition of HX, an aqueous acid. (Water molecules are present but not shown.)

If HX is a weak acid, which diagram best represents its particle composition?

PARTICLE KEY

HX ○

H_3O^+ ◔

X^- ●

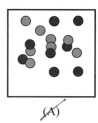

(A)

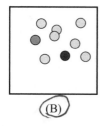

(B)

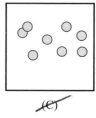

(C)

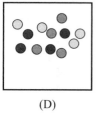

(D)

42. A student is doing a titration using potassium permanganate solution, $KMnO_4$, to determine the amount of H_2O_2 in a sample. The balanced equation for the reaction in the titration is given below.

$$2\,MnO_4^-(aq) + 6\,H^+(aq) + 5\,H_2O_2(aq) \rightarrow 2\,Mn^{2+}(aq) + 8\,H_2O(e) + 5\,O_2(g)$$

What species undergoes oxidation in the reaction?

(A) MnO_4^-
(B) H_2O_2
(C) H^+
(D) O_2

43. The reaction $2\,ClO_2(aq) + 2\,OH^-(aq) \rightarrow ClO_3^-(aq) + ClO_2^-(aq) + H_2O$ was studied with the results given below

$[ClO_2]$, M	$[OH^-]$, M	Rate, mol/L·s
0.020	0.030	0.0036
0.040	0.030	0.0144
0.040	0.060	0.0288

What is the rate equation for this reaction?

(A) Rate $= k[ClO_2][OH^-]$
(B) Rate $= k[ClO_2]^2[OH^-]^2$
(C) Rate $= k[ClO_2]^2[OH^-]$
(D) Rate $= k[ClO_2][OH^-]^2$

44. The combustion of 1 mole of methanol is described by this equation:
$$CH_3OH(g) + 3/2\,O_2(g) \rightarrow CO_2(g) + 2\,H_2O(g)$$

Substance	ΔH_f (kJ/mole)
$CH_3OH(g)$	−210
$O_2(g)$	0
$CO_2(g)$	−394
$H_2O(g)$	−241

$\mathcal{E}\,H_P - \mathcal{E}\,H_R$

From the heats of formation $(\Delta H_f°)$ above, which calculation would give the Heat of Combustion for 1 mole of methanol?

(A) $\Delta H_{combustion} = (-241) + (-394) - (-210)$
(B) $\Delta H_{combustion} = 2(-241) + (-394) - (-210)$
(C) $\Delta H_{combustion} = 2(+241) + (+394) - (+210)$
(D) $\Delta H_{combustion} = (-210) - 2(-241) + (-394)$

45. The reaction $2\,SO_2(g) + O_2(g) \rightleftharpoons 2\,SO_3(g)$ has an equilibrium constant of K_1. What is the value of K for the reaction $SO_3(g) \rightleftharpoons SO_2(g) + 1/2\,O_2(g)$ in terms of K_1?

(A) $1/2\,K_1$
(B) $1/K_1$
(C) $(1/K_1)^{1/2}$
(D) $K_1^{1/2}$

46. Which of the following contains the greatest number of phosphorus atoms?
(A) 11.2 L of gaseous P_2O_5 at STP conditions
(B) 500 mL of aqueous 6 M H_3PO_4
(C) 124 g of red phosphorus, P_4
(D) 2.5 moles of the ionic compound calcium phosphate

47. Melting of this solid requires the breaking of covalent bonds.

(A) Sand, SiO_2
(B) Ice, H_2O
(C) Wax, $C_{25}H_{52}$
(D) Salt, NaCl

48. Which chemical species can function *both* as a Bronsted-Lowry acid and as a Bronsted-Lowry base?

(A) F^-
(B) HSO_4^-
(C) H_3O^+
(D) CO_3^{2-}

49. At low temperatures the reaction of $CO(g)$ and $NO_2(g)$ is proposed to follow the two step mechanism;

$$NO_2(g) + NO_2(g) \rightarrow NO(g) + NO_3(g)$$
$$NO_3(g) + CO(g) \rightarrow CO_2(g) + NO_2(g)$$

$NO_2 + CO \rightarrow NO + CO_2$

What is the equation for the overall reaction?

(A) $2\,NO_2(g) + CO(g) + NO_3(g) \rightarrow CO_2(g) + NO(g) + NO_2(g) + NO_3(g)$
(B) $2\,NO_2(g) + CO(g) \rightarrow CO_2(g) + NO(g) + NO_2(g)$
(C) $NO_2(g) + CO(g) \rightarrow CO_2(g) + NO(g)$
(D) $NO_3(g) + CO(g) \rightarrow CO_2(g) + NO_2(g)$

50. Cylinders of Cu, Fe and Al with the same mass and temperature were heated on a hot plate as shown below: [Specific heats(J/g·°C): Al 0.90, Cu 0.39, Fe 0.45]

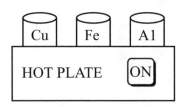

What is the result after heating for two minutes?

(A) The three cylinders would have the same temperature.
(B) The Cu cylinder would have the highest temperature.
(C) The Fe cylinder would have the highest temperature.
(D) The Al cylinder would have the highest temperature.

51. The emission of a positron (a positively-charged electron) tends to increase the stability of a nucleus by

(A) increasing the neutron:proton ratio
(B) decreasing the mass number
(C) increasing the atomic number
(D) decreasing the number of electrons

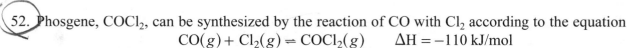

52. Phosgene, $COCl_2$, can be synthesized by the reaction of CO with Cl_2 according to the equation

$$CO(g) + Cl_2(g) \rightleftharpoons COCl_2(g) \qquad \Delta H = -110 \text{ kJ/mol}$$

Which reaction conditions will optimize the yield of $COCl_2(g)$?

(A) high temperature, high pressure
(B) high temperature, low pressure
(C) low temperature, low pressure
(D) low temperature, high pressure

53. Which of the following systems would show the *lowest* vapor pressure?

(A) 25 mL of diethyl ether, $(CH_3CH_2—O—CH_2CH_3)$, at 15°C, in beaker
(B) 25 mL of ethyl alcohol $(CH_3—CH_2—OH)$, at 25°C, in a graduated cylinder
(C) 50 mL of diethyl ether, $(CH_3CH_2—O—CH_2CH_3)$, at 25°C, in a graduated cylinder
(D) 50 mL of ethyl alcohol $(CH_3—CH_2—OH)$, at 15°C, in a beaker

54. When the equation for the following reaction is balanced using lowest whole number coefficients, the number of moles of electrons transferred in the oxidation is

$$\underline{} C + \underline{} HNO_3 \rightarrow \underline{} CO_2 + \underline{} NO_2 + \underline{} H_2O$$

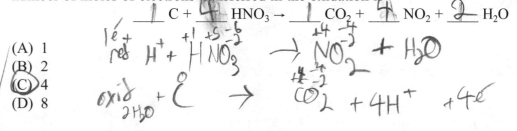

(A) 1
(B) 2
(C) 4
(D) 8

55. The rate-determining step in a reaction mechanism is always the

(A) first step
(B) slowest step
(C) step with the fewest collisions
(D) step with the lowest activation energy

56. The distribution of gaseous N_2 molecules at a certain temperature is depicted below.

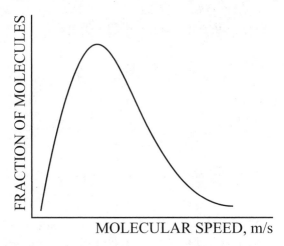

If the Kelvin temperature is doubled what change will occur in this distribution?

(A) The area under the curve will double.
(B) The curve will shift toward higher molecular speeds.
(C) The maximum of the curve will become higher.
(D) The maximum molecular speed will double.

57. Which solution has the largest buffer capacity and a pH near 4?

(A) 1.0 M HOCl $(K_a = 2.9 \times 10^{-8})$ and 1.0 M NaOCl
(B) 0.50 M $HC_3H_5O_3$ $(K_a = 1.4 \times 10^{-4})$ and 0.50 M $NaC_3H_5O_3$
(C) 1.0 M $HC_3H_5O_3$ $(K_a = 1.4 \times 10^{-4})$ and 0.20 M $NaC_3H_5O_3$
(D) 1.0 M NH_3 $(K_b = 1.8 \times 10^{-5})$ and 1.0 M NH_4Cl

58. Which of the following carbon-oxygen species has the longest average C—O bond length?

(A) CO
(B) CO_2
(C) $CH_3CO_2^-$
(D) CO_3^{2-}

59. Calcium carbonate solid, $CaCO_3$, is only slightly soluble in water. Which of the following would increase the solubility of this solid in a saturated solution?

(A) Add more water.
(B) Add a solution containing calcium ions, $Ca^{2+}(aq)$, and carbonate ions, $CO_3^{2-}(aq)$.
(C) Add a solution containing hydronium ions, $H_3O^+(aq)$.
(D) Add a solution containing hydroxide ions, $OH^-(aq)$.

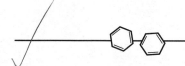

60. A reaction will always be spontaneous if

(A) ΔH° is negative
(B) ΔG° is positive
(C) ΔS° is negative
(D) E° is positive

CONSTRUCTED-RESPONSE QUESTIONS

Question 1: Part I

A solution of $KMnO_4$ of unknown concentration is poured into a buret and standardized with solid, oven-dried potassium oxalate (molar mass 166.0) according to the following equation:

$$16 H^+(aq) + 2 MnO_4^-(aq) + 5 K_2C_2O_4(s) \rightarrow 2 Mn^{2+}(aq) + 10 CO_2(g) + 8 H_2O + 10K^+(aq)$$

The solid $K_2C_2O_4$ is weighed, dissolved in 25 mL of water, and 5 mL of H_2SO_4 is added to acidify the solution in the flask. The solution is then titrated in 3 trials with the $KMnO_4$ from the buret until a persistent pale color remains. The data table for the 3 different trials is below.

166

Trial	Mass of solid $K_2C_2O_4$	Volume of $KMnO_4$ solution
1	0.250 g	31.15 mL
2	0.250 g	31.05 mL
3	0.250 g	31.05 mL

(a) Is the $C_2O_4^{2-}$ ion undergoing oxidation or reduction? Explain.

Oxidation (charge ↑)

(b) Calculate the moles of $K_2C_2O_4$ reacted in Trial 2.

(0.00156n)5 = .00753n

(c) Calculate the molar concentration (M) of the $KMnO_4$ solution. Please show your work.

.047006 M

(d) Which experimental error below could account for the different volume of $KMnO_4$ solution in Trial 1? Explain.

i. The buret is rinsed with distilled H_2O but not with the $KMnO_4$ solution.

ii. Some solid $K_2C_2O_4$ remains in the "weighing boat."

PART II

A second standardized solution of 0.0214 M KMnO$_4$ is used to analyze an opened bottle of drugstore H$_2$O$_2$ solution to determine the % by mass of H$_2$O$_2$. The net ionic equation for this reaction is

$$6\,H^+(aq) + 2\,MnO_4^-(aq) + 5\,H_2O_2(aq) \rightarrow 2\,Mn^{2+}(aq) + 5\,O_2(g) + 8\,H_2O(aq)$$

A 3.00 mL sample of the H$_2$O$_2$ solution is placed in a flask, acidifed with 2 mL of 6M H$_2$SO$_4$, and titrated to the endpoint with the KMnO$_4$ delivered from the buret. The volume of 0.0214 M KMnO$_4$ required to reach the endpoint is 34.70 mL. Assume the density of the H$_2$O$_2$ solution is 1.00g/ mL.

Volume of ? % H$_2$O$_2$	3.00 mL
Volume of 0.0214 M KMnO$_4$	34·70 mL

(e) Calculate the % by mass of the H$_2$O$_2$ solution. Assume the density of the H$_2$O$_2$ solution is 1.00g/ mL.

(f) If the endpoint of the titration reaction is overshot, will the student's calculated value for the % H$_2$O$_2$ increase, decrease, or remain the same? Explain.

(g) i. Define the following terms
   Analyte:
   Titrant:

   ii. In this lab, there was a substance that served as both a titrant and an analyte. Identify the substance and explain how it acted as both.

Question 2

Given the following data: M → L + N

Potential energy of the reactants	50 kJ/mol
Activation energy (E_a) for the forward reaction	90 kJ/mol
ΔH for the reaction	30 kJ/mol

(a) Draw a potential energy diagram for the reaction above. Include *numerical values* on the vertical axis.

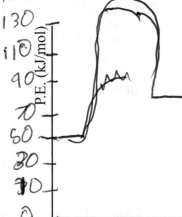

(b) On the graph, identify the region that shows the ΔH of the reverse reaction. Determine ΔH of the reverse reaction.

+30 KJ/mol

(c) What is the potential energy stored in the activated complex?

140 KJ

(d) What is the activation energy of the reverse reaction?

– 90 KJ

Refer to the diagram below for questions E and F

Flow Rates	System I	System II

A = 2 mL/s

A = 4 mL/s

A = 6 mL/s

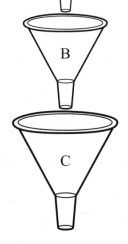

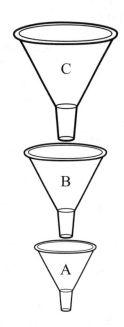

(e) What will be the overall output (flow rate) in rate mL/second in set-up I?

(f) What will be the overall output (flow rate) in rate mL/second in set-up II?

Questions 3

3. A student has numerous plastic sealable bags and four substances: two different white solid powders (substance A & substance B), one red solution (substance C), and distilled water. 5 mL of distilled water is poured into each plastic bag, and the data is summarized in the data table below. "Yes" means the substance is present; "no" means the substance is absent in the trial.

B+ water — endo

Trial #	Substance A	Substance B	Substance C	Outcome(s)
Trial 1	yes	yes	yes	Solution turns yellow, becomes hot, white precipitate forms, numerous bubbles appear
Trial 2	no	yes	yes	Solution becomes colder, magenta color, a few bubbles appear
Trial 3	yes	no	yes	Solution becomes hot, no bubbles, remains red
Trial 4	yes	yes	no	Solution becomes warm, colorless, a few bubbles form

(a) Which substance is responsible for the color changes in the reactions? Explain.

C - indicator

(b) The student hypothesizes that substance A is responsible for the production of heat in this reaction. Which trial provides the strongest evidence for her hypothesis? Explain.

Trial 2 — because it becomes colder without heat

(c) The student hypothesizes that the solution is colored because substance C is red food coloring, rather than an acid-base indicator. Is her hypothesis true or false? Explain.

False — because of constant color change

(d) Based on the data above, which two substances in Trial #1 are responsible for the production of a gas? Explain how you reached your selection.

A+B → gas. Gas is driven out because of heat C is indicator.

(e) It is learned that Substance B is an ionic compound with a general formula of XY. Write the thermal equation for the dissolving of XY in water.

$XY + H_2O + Heat → X^+_{(aq)} + Y^-_{(aq)}$

(f) Circle the correct potential energy diagram below for the dissolving of Substance B.

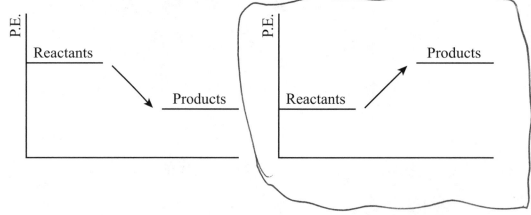

Question 4

Gaseous Element X is heated in a rigid cylinder in a mass spectrometer and released through a narrow nozzle.

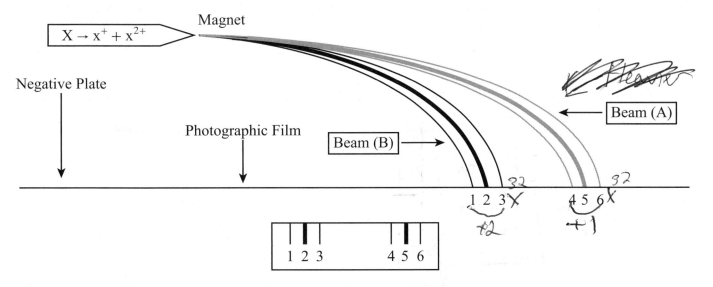

When gas X is released from a mass spectrometer , two different ions are formed (+1 and +2) and pass through a magnetic field. Three isotopes are detected, ^{30}X, ^{31}X and ^{32}X. When the photographic film is displayed, the results for the beams (1-6) are displayed in the rectangular box.

(a) Which beam of ions (A or B) represents the X^{+2} ion? Explain.

Beam B

(b) Which beams (1-6) represent the X-32 isotope? Explain.

3, 6

Question 5

Consider the equilibrium reaction
$$CH_4(g) + 2 H_2O(g) \longleftrightarrow CO_2(g) + 4 H_2(g)$$
A mixture containing 1.00 mole each of methane and water vapor is brought to equilibrium in a rigid 1.00 L flask at 600 K. The equilibrium mixture is found to contain 0.800 moles of H_2.

(a) What is the value of K_C for this reaction at 800 K?

(b) If a 2.00 L flask is substituted for the original flask, what is the value of K_C when equilibrium is re-established at 800K?

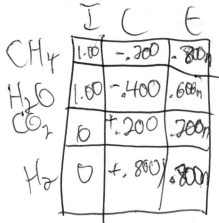

$$1.00 \quad 1.00$$
$$1 \times +2 \rightleftarrows 1 \quad C +0$$
$$-200 \quad -800$$

$$K_c = \frac{[CO_2][H_2]^4}{[CH_4][CH_2O]^2} \qquad \frac{(.200)(.4096M)}{[.8M][.36M]}$$

$$\frac{P_1 \not V_1}{T_1} = \frac{P_2 \not V_2}{T_2} \qquad K_c = .284 = \frac{.08192}{.288} \quad \text{at} \quad 600K$$

$$P = \frac{nRT}{V} \qquad P = \frac{(.800)(.0821)(600)}{1} \quad \text{at} \quad 600K$$

$$P = 39.408$$

Question 6

Substance	Molecular formula	Boiling point	Molar Mass (g/mole)
carbon tetrachloride	CCl_4	349 K	154
chloroform	$CHCl_3$	334 K	119.5
sulfur tetrafluoride	SF_4	236 K	107

Consider the liquids in the above chart.

(a) Draw a Lewis dot structure for SF_4.

(b) Which, if any, of the above molecules is/are polar?

(c) Account for the fact that the boiling point of carbon tetrachloride is higher than the boiling point of chloroform.

Question 7

$$Cu^{2+} + Zn \rightarrow Zn^{2+} + Cu$$

Use the reaction above to answer the questions (a)–(c) below.

A student adds some zinc dust to an aqueous solution of $CuSO_4$ in an insulated calorimeter, swirls the solution vigorously and observes that the temperature of the solution rises.

The student then places a clean metallic Cu strip in a beaker containing 0.1 M $CuSO_4$ solution and a cleaned Zn strip in a beaker, of 0.1 M $Zn(NO_3)_2$ solution. A wet piece of twine soaked in KNO_3 is draped between the beakers so that the two ends of the twine are submerged, one in the $CuSO_4$ solution and one in the $Zn(NO_3)_2$ solution. The metal strips are joined with wires leading to a voltmeter. The student observes the voltage reading to be a positive value.

(a) The student wishes to calculate ΔH for the first reaction. What data are needed here to make the ΔH calculation?

(b) Is the sign of ΔG for the second experiment positive or negative? Explain.

SAMPLE EXAMINATION 3

Questions 1–3 refer to the following terms.

    (A) Ionization Energy
    (B) Electron affinity
    (C) Electronegativity
    (D) Electropositivity

1. Energy change occurring when an atom gains an electron to form an ion.

2. Energy required to remove an electron from an atom to an infinite distance.

3. Provides a measure of the relative attraction for electrons in a chemical bond.

———————————————————————

Questions 4–7 pertain to the following gases.

(A) Chlorine
(B) Helium
(C) Nitrogen
(D) Oxygen

4. Monatomic

5. Paramagnetic

6. One sigma and two pi bonds

7. Colored

Questions 8–11 refer to the following substances.

(A) Sodium carbonate and ammonium nitrate
(B) Carbon-12 and Carbon-14
(C) Diethyl ether, $C_2H_5OC_2H_5$, and 2-hydroxybutane, $CH_3CH_2CHOHCH_3$
(D) Diamond and graphite

8. A pair of isotopes

9. A pair where each contains both covalent and ionic bonds

10. A pair of allotropes

11. A pair of isomers

Questions 12–15 refer to the following laboratory devices.

(A) Barometer
(B) pH meter and probe
(C) Separatory funnel
(D) Spectrophotometer

12. Used to create a titration curve

13. Used to make measurements to verify Beer's Law

14. Used to form layers of liquids of different densities

15. Used to find the molar mass of a volatile liquid

Questions 16–17 refer to the Table below and the responses that follow.

Metal	Physical appearance	Reaction product with dilute HCl	Reaction product with dilute HNO_3
I	Reddish solid	No reaction	Reddish-brown bubbles
II	Lustrous light grey solid	No reaction	Reddish-brown bubbles
III	Yellowish solid	No reaction	No reaction

    (A) Ag, silver
    (B) Au, gold
    (C) Cu, copper
    (D) Zn, zinc

16. Identity of metal I

17. Exists as two stable isotopes with atomic masses 107 and 109.

Questions 18–20 refer to the diagram below and the responses that follow.

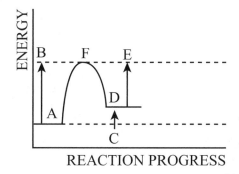

    (A) AB
    (B) CD
    (C) DE
    (D) F

18. Represents the ΔH of the forward reaction

19. Represents the activation energy for the reverse reaction

20. Represents the potential energy stored in the activated complex

Questions 21–23 refer to the reaction below for a specific mass of Zn(s) and volume of 1 M HCl(aq) with questions answered by the responses (A)-(D).

$$Zn(s) + 2\,H^+(aq) + 2\,Cl^-(aq) \rightarrow Zn^{2+}(aq) + 2\,Cl^-(aq) + H_2(g)$$

(A) temperature
(B) pressure of $H_2(g)$
(C) size of Zn(s) particles
(D) concentration of $H^+(aq)$ at a constant number of moles of $H^+(aq)$

21. A decrease in this factor will increase the reaction rate

22. An increase in this factor will increase the rate of the reaction and the volume of $H_2(g)$ formed when the reaction is complete.

23. A change in this factor will have no effect on the reaction rate.

Questions 24–26 should be answered with reference to the equations below.

(A) $S(s) + O_2(g) \rightleftharpoons SO_2(g)$ $\Delta H° = -296.8 \text{ kJ/mol}$
(B) $H_2(g) + I_2(g) \rightleftharpoons 2\,HI(g)$ $\Delta H° = +25.9 \text{ kJ/mol}$
(C) $PCl_5(g) \rightleftharpoons PCl_3(g) + Cl_2(g)$ $\Delta H° = +115 \text{ kJ/mol}$
(D) $2\,NO(g) + O_2(g) \rightleftharpoons 2\,NO_2(g)$ $\Delta H° = -57 \text{ kJ/mol}$

24. Which equilibrium will be shifted toward the products by an increase in pressure at constant temperature?

25. Which reaction occurs with the greatest increase in entropy, $\Delta S°$?

26. Which reaction will have the most negative $\Delta G°$ at 25°C?

Questions 27–29 refer to a saturated aqueous solution of MgF_2(s) at 25°C

$$MgF_2(s) \rightleftharpoons Mg^{2+}(aq) + 2\,F^-(aq) \qquad K_{sp} = 7 \times 10^{-11}$$

(A) Adding NaF(aq)
(B) Adding HCl(aq)
(C) Evaporating the solution to one- half its original volume.
(D) Increasing the temperature to 30°C

27. Which change will increase the $[Mg^{2+}]$ by the greatest amount?

28. Which change will not affect the $[Mg^{2+}]$ or the $[F^-]$?

29. Which change will change the value of K_{sp}?

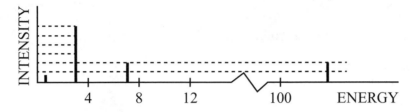

30. The complete PES diagram for a gaseous element is given below.

What is the identity of this element?

(A) Al
(B) F
(C) Na
(D) K

31. Which of the following gas samples will exhibit behavior that is *closest* to "ideal"?

(A) He(g) at 0.5 atm and 100 K
(B) He(g) at 0.5 atm and 400 K
(C) NH_3(g) at 0.5 atm and 100 K
(D) NH_3(g) at 2 atm and 100 K

32. The following diagrams represent the particle composition of HX, an aqueous acid. (Water molecules are present but not shown.)

Which diagram best represents the particle composition of a strong acid?

PARTICLE KEY

HX $\circ$

H_3O^+ ◓

$X-$ ●

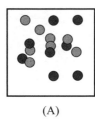
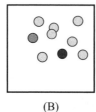
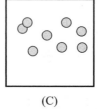
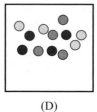

(A)   (B)   (C)   (D)

33. The melting of which solid requires the breaking of dispersion forces only?

(A) Sand, SiO_2
(B) Ice, H_2O
(C) Wax, $C_{25}H_{52}$
(D) Salt, NaCl

34. Which of the following ionic compounds would exhibit the highest melting point?

(A) NaF
(B) NaBr
(C) $MgCl_2$
(D) MgO

35. Which of the following carbon-oxygen species has the shortest C–O bond length?

(A) CO
(B) CO_2
(C) $CH_3CO_2^-$
(D) CO_3^{2-}

36. A weighed piece of magnesium ribbon is added to a dried crucible, which is reweighed and heated in air to form magnesium oxide. The crucible is cooled and reweighed to find its mass. What is the expected magnesium oxide/magnesium mass ratio?

(A) 0.67/1
(B) 1.67/1
(C) 2.33/1
(D) 2.5/1

37. When solid NH_4Cl is added to room temperature H_2O in a test tube the tube becomes cold to the touch. How should this process be described?

(A) endothermic with $\Delta H < 0$
(B) endothermic with $\Delta H > 0$
(C) exothermic with $\Delta H > 0$
(D) exothermic with $\Delta H < 0$

38. A student is doing a titration using potassium permanganate solution, $KMnO_4$, to determine the amount of H_2O_2 in a sample. The balanced equation for the reaction in the titration is given below.
$$2\, MnO_4^- + 6\, H^+ + 5\, H_2O_2 \rightarrow 2\, Mn^{2+} + 8\, H_2O + 5\, O_2$$
If 40 mL of 0.01 M $KMnO_4$ was required to reach the endpoint, how many moles of H_2O_2 are present in the sample?

(A) 0.0002 mol
(B) 0.0004 mol
(C) 0.001 mol
(D) 1 mol

39. According to the Standard Reduction Potentials in the table below, which of the following reactions will produce the greatest voltage?

Selected Standard Reduction Potentials at 25°C	$E°$, volts
$Cl_2(aq) + 2e^- \rightarrow 2Cl^-(aq)$	+1.36
$I_2(s) + 2e^- \rightarrow 2I^-(aq)$	+0.54
$Ag^+(aq) + e^- \rightarrow Ag(s)$	+0.80
$Cu^{2+}(aq) + 2e^- \rightarrow Cu(s)$	+0.34
$Pb^{2+}(aq) + 2e^- \rightarrow Pb(s)$	-0.12
$Mg^{2+}(aq) + 2e^- \rightarrow Mg(s)$	-2.36

(A) $Mg(s) + Pb^{2+}(aq) \rightarrow Mg^{2+}(aq) + Pb(s)$
(B) $Cl_2(aq) + 2 I^-(aq) \rightarrow 2 Cl^-(aq) + I_2(s)$
(C) $Mg(s) + 2 Ag^+(aq) \rightarrow Mg^{2+}(aq) + 2 Ag(s)$
(D) $Mg^{2+}(aq) + 2 Cl^-(aq) \rightarrow Mg(s) + Cl_2(aq)$

40. Which is correct as this voltaic cell operates?
$$Zn(s)|Zn^{2+} (1.0 \; M)||Cu^{2+} (1.0 \; M)| Cu(s)$$

(A) Oxidation happens at the copper electrode.
(B) Electrons move from the copper electrode to the zinc electrode.
(C) The concentration of Zn^{2+} will decrease.
(D) The mass of the zinc electrode will decrease.

41. .....$Cr_2O_3(s) +$ .....$CO(g) \rightarrow$ ....$CO_2(g) +$ ....$Cr(s)$

Which substance in the above reaction undergoes oxidation?

(A) Cr_2O_3
(B) CO
(C) CO_2
(D) Cr

42. Consider the following atoms and ions:
$$Cl^- \quad K° \quad K^+ \quad Ca^{2+}$$
Which of the following lists correctly shows the particles in order from smallest to largest?

(A) $Ca^{2+} < K^+ < Cl^- < K°$
(B) $Cl^- < K^+ < K° < Ca^{2+}$
(C) $Cl^- < Ca^{2+} < K^+ < K°$
(D) $Ca^{2+} < K^+ < K° < Cl^-$

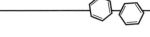

43. The formula for aluminum bromide is $AlBr_3$. What is the expected formula for aluminum selenide?

(A) $AlSe$
(B) $AlSe_2$
(C) $AlSe_3$
(D) Al_2Se_3

44. According to the spectral regions in which they are found, how do the energies required for the transitions compare?

      I. Promotion of a "d" electron (visible)
      II. Stretching of a C–H bond (infrared)
      III. Excitation of an electron in benzene (UV)

(A) $I < II < III$
(B) $II < I < III$
(C) $III < I < II$
(D) $I < III < II$

45. At low temperatures the reaction of $CO(g)$ and $NO_2(g)$ is proposed to follow the two step mechanism;
$$NO_2(g) + NO_2(g) \rightarrow NO(g) + NO_3(g)$$
$$NO_3(g) + CO(g) \rightarrow CO_2(g) + NO_2(g)$$
Which substance is an intermediate in this reaction?

(A) $NO(g)$
(B) $NO_2(g)$
(C) $NO_3(g)$
(D) $CO(g)$

46. Which reaction below does not involve a homogeneous catalyst?

(A) $2\,CO(g) + O_2(g) + Pt(s) \rightarrow 2\,CO_2(g) + Pt(s)$
(B) $2\,SO_2(g) + O_2(g) + 2\,NO_2(g) \rightarrow 2\,SO_3(g) + 2\,NO_2(g)$
(C) $RCOOR'(aq) + H_2O + H^+(aq) + Cl^-(aq) \rightarrow RCOOH(aq) + ROH\ (aq) + H^+(aq) + Cl^-(aq)$
(D) $2\,H_2O_2(aq) + 2\,Br^-(aq) + 2\,H^+(aq) \rightarrow 2\,H_2O + O_2(g) + 2\,Br^-(aq) + 2\,H^+(aq)$

47. Hydrogen peroxide, H_2O_2, reacts with iodide ions in the presence of H^+ ions to form I_2 according to the equation below.

$$2 H^+(aq) + 2I^-(aq) + H_2O_2(aq) \rightarrow I_2(aq) + 2 H_2O(l)$$

What is the rate equation for this reaction according to the following data?

[I⁻]	[H₂O₂]	Initial Rate, mol/L·min
0.020	0.030	0.0030
0.030	0.030	0.0045
0.020	0.040	0.0040

(A) Rate $= k[I^-][H_2O_2]$

(B) Rate $= k[I^-]^{3/2}[H_2O_2]^{4/3}$

(C) Rate $= k[I^-]^2[H_2O_2]$

(D) Rate $= k[I^-]^2[H_2O_2]^2$

48. Heat is released when solid carbon reacts with $O_2(g)$ according to the equation

$$2 C(s) + O_2(g) \rightarrow 2 CO(g)?$$

What are the signs for $\Delta H°$, $\Delta S°$ and $\Delta G°$ at $25°C$?

	$\Delta H°$	$\Delta S°$	$\Delta G°$ at $25°C$
(A)	+	+	+
(B)	+	−	−
(C)	−	+	−
(D)	−	−	+

49. The graph below is the result of measuring the volume of $H_2(g)$ produced by reacting an excess of Mg(s) with 50 mL of 2.0 M HCl. Which change will increase the rate of formation of $H_2(g)$ but not its volume?

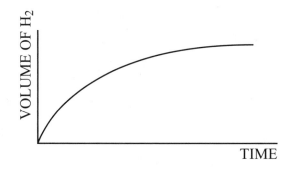

(A) Adding the same mass of Mg(s) to 50 mL of 3.0 M HCl

(B) Adding the same mass of Mg(s) in smaller pieces to 50 mL of 2.0 M HCl.

(C) Doubling the volume of 2.0 M HCl

(D) Increasing the temperature from $25°C$ to $35°C$

50. For the reaction: $H_2(g) + Cl_2(g) \rightarrow 2\,HCl(g)$ $\Delta H° = -184.6\,kJ$

Bond	Bond Energy (kJ/mole)
H–H bond	436
Cl–Cl bond	243
H–Cl bond	?

Which expression gives the bond energy (BE) for the H-Cl bond?

(A) $BE_{H-Cl} = -184.6 - (436 + 243)$

(B) $BE_{H-Cl} = \dfrac{-184.6 + 436 + 243}{2}$

(C) $BE_{H-Cl} = 184.6 + 436 + 243$

(D) $BE_{H-Cl} = \dfrac{184.6 + 436 + 243}{2}$

51. The heat of fusion and specific heat of water are:

Heat of Fusion	6.02 kJ/mole
Specific Heat	4.18 J/g°C

Which of the following expressions correctly shows the energy change when 2.0 moles of water at 25°C are converted to ice at 0°C?

(A) $(36)(4.18)(25) =$ kJ of energy released

(B) $\dfrac{(36)(4.18)(25)}{1000} - (2 \times 6.02) =$ kJ of energy released

(C) $\dfrac{(36)(4.18)(25)}{1000} + (2 \times 6.02) =$ kJ of energy released

(D) $(2 \times 6.02) =$ kJ of energy released

52. While using a calorimeter, a student demonstrates the use of the

(A) Law of Conservation of Mass
(B) First Law of Thermodynamics
(C) Hess' Law
(D) Law of Multiple Proportions

53. Consider the following kinetic energy distribution curve at 400 K. The activation energy, E_a, for a reaction is marked on the horizontal axis.

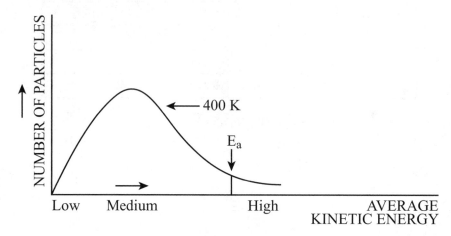

If the temperature of the system were decreased to 200 K, which statement is true?

(A) The reaction would slow down because the E_a would move to a higher average K.E. value causing fewer particles beyond the E_a.
(B) The reaction would slow down because the distribution curve would flatten out and fewer particles would exceed the E_a.
(C) The reaction would slow down because the peak of the curve would move to a lower average KE value, leaving fewer particles beyond the E_a.
(D) The reaction would slow down because both the peak of the curve and the E_a would move to a lower K.E. value, leaving fewer particles beyond the E_a value.

54. How does a change in temperature affect the spontaneity of a process with $\Delta H° > 0$ and $\Delta S° > 0$?

(A) Always spontaneous
(B) Never spontaneous
(C) Non-spontaneous at low temperature but spontaneous at high temperature
(D) Spontaneous at low temperature but non-spontaneous at high temperature

55. When detergents such as $H_3C(CH_2)_3C_6H_4CO_2^- \, Na^+$ dissolve in H_2O, they often clump together. The best explanation for this behavior is that

(A) $H_3C(CH_2)_3C_6H_4$ groups interact with one another.
(B) CO_2^- groups interact with one another.
(C) $H_3C(CH_2)_3C_6H_4$ groups interact with H_2O molecules.
(D) CO_2^- in $H_3C(CH_2)_3C_6H_4CO_2^-$ interact with Na^+ ions.

56. The pH of a 0.100 M solution of acetic acid, $HC_2H_3O_2$, ($K_a = 1.8 \times 10^{-5}$) in H_2O is closest to

(A) 1.00
(B) 3.00
(C) 5.00
(D) 7.00

57. Which is the same for separate 50.0 mL portions of 0.100 M solutions of HCl and lactic acid, $HC_3H_5O_3$, ($K_a = 1.4 \times 10^{-4}$)?

(A) pH
(B) percent ionization
(C) rate of reactivity with Mg metal
(D) volume of 0.050 M NaOH needed for neutralization

58. Which of the following would result in a buffer solution?

(A) 100 mL 0.5 M $HC_2H_3O_2$(aq) + 100 mL 0.5 M HCl(aq)
(B) 50 mL 0.5 M $HC_2H_3O_2$(aq) + 50 mL 0.5 M NH_3(aq)
(C) 100 mL 0.5 M $HC_2H_3O_2$(aq) + 50 mL 0.5 M NaOH(aq)
(D) 100 mL 0.5 M HCl (aq) + 50 mL 0.5 M NH_3(aq)

59. Dinitrogen tetroxide, N_2O_4, is in equilibrium with nitrogen dioxide, NO_2 according to the equation N_2O_4 (g) $\rightleftharpoons$ 2 NO_2 (g). Based on the following data for this system at a certain temperature, what is the value of K_p.

	Initial pressure, atm	Equilibrium pressure, atm
N_2O_4(g)	1.00	0.25
NO_2(g)	0.00	

(A) 2.3
(B) 3.0
(C) 6.0
(D) 9.0

60. According to VSEPR theory the geometry of the atoms in PH_3 is best described as

(A) square
(B) triangular planar
(C) triangular pyramidal
(D) tetrahedral

CONSTRUCTED-RESPONSE QUESTIONS

Question 1

Reduction Potentials	
$Cu^{2+} + 2e^- \rightarrow Cu$	0.34 volts
$Zn^{2+} + 2e^- \rightarrow Zn$	-0.76 volts

A student pours 125 ml of 0.152 M $CuSO_4$ solution into an insulated coffee cup calorimeter and measures the temperature of the solution. (Assume the density of the solution is the same as that of water.) 2.00 g of Zn metal dust is added to the $CuSO_4$ solution and the temperature rises 7.5°C.

(a) If the specific heat of the resulting solution is 4.31 $Jg^{-1}°C^{-1}$, determine the heat released in the reaction involving the Zn and $CuSO_4$ solution.
(b) Assuming the Zn to be in excess, how many moles of Cu^{2+} ion reacted?
(c) What is the heat of reaction, $\Delta H°$, in kJ per mole Cu^{2+} ion for the reaction?
(d) The student is given a box containing beakers, a voltmeter, a funnel, wires with alligator clips , filter paper and 1M $CuSO_4$ and 1M $ZnSO_4$ solutions along with polished Cu and Zn metal strips and asked to construct a galvanic cell. The student does so and obtains a voltage reading of 1.03 volts.
   i. Diagram the galvanic cell and, using an arrow, indicate the direction of electron flow through the wires.
   ii. What is the % error in the experimental voltage reading?

(e) Determine the value for $\Delta G°$ (in kJ/mol) for the cell reaction in D.
(f) Using your values from the above two experiments, determine the value of $\Delta S°$ for this reaction?

Question 2

Acid	Ionization constant K_a
Hydrofluoric acid, HF	7.2×10^{-4}
Nitrous acid, HNO_2	4.5×10^{-4}
Acetic acid, $HC_2H_3O_2$	1.8×10^{-5}
Hypochlorous acid, HClO	3.5×10^{-8}
Hypobromous acid, HBrO	2.0×10^{-9}
Hydrocyanic acid, HCN	6.2×10^{-10}

(a) Calculate the pH of 1 L of a 0.10 M solution of acetic acid.
(b) Calculate the pH of 1 L of a 0.10 M solution of potassium acetate.
(c) Calculate the pH of 1 L of a solution that is 0.10 M in both acetic acid and potassium acetate.
(d) What would be the effect on the pH of the solution described in (C) with the addition of a small amount of strong acid? Explain.
(e) What would be the effect on the pH of the solution described in (C) if 500 mL of distilled water were to be added to the flask?
(f) Which of the above acids would be the best choice to form a buffer of pH 8.00? What would be the base component of the buffer system?

Question 3

A solution of $KMnO_4$ of unknown concentration is poured into a buret and standardized with solid ferrous ammonium sulfate (FAS), $Fe(NH_4)_2(SO_4)_2$ with a molar mass of 284.05 g according to the equation:

$$8\,H^+(aq) + MnO_4^-(aq) + 5Fe^{2+}(aq) \rightarrow Mn^{2+}(aq) + 5Fe^{3+}(aq) + 4\,H_2O$$

The solid FAS is weighed, dissolved in 25 mL of water, and 5 mL of H_2SO_4 is added to acidify the solution in the flask. The FAS solution is then titrated in 3 trials with the $KMnO_4$ from the buret until a persistent pale color remains. The data table for the 3 different trials is below.

Trial	Mass of solid FAS	Volume of $KMnO_4$ solution
1	0.550 g	22.30 mL
2	0.550 g	22.40 mL
3	0.550 g	22.40 mL

(a) Is the MnO_4^- ion undergoing oxidation or reduction? Explain.
(b) Calculate the moles of (FAS), $Fe(NH_4)_2(SO_4)_2$, reacted in Trial 2 .
(c) Calculate the molar concentration (M) of the $KMnO_4$ solution.
(d) Which experimental error below could account for the different volume of $KMnO_4$ solution in Trial 1? Explain.
   i. Rinsing the buret with H_2O but not with the $KMnO_4$ solution.
   ii. Overshooting the endpoint of the reaction.
   iii. Some solid FAS remaining in the "weighing boat."

(e) A second standardized 0.0185 M $KMnO_4$ solution is used to analyze an oven-dried solid labeled "anhydrous $X_2C_2O_4$." The solid $X_2C_2O_4$ is believed to be one of 3 solids:

	Formula	Molar Mass (g/mol)
(1)	$H_2C_2O_4$	90
(2)	$Na_2C_2O_4$	134
(3)	$K_2C_2O_4$	166

The oxalate ion reacts with the $KMnO_4$ solution according to the reaction:

$$16\,H^+(aq) + 2\,MnO_4^-(aq) + 5\,C_2O_4^{2-}(aq) \rightarrow 2Mn^{2+}(aq) + 10\,CO_2(g) + 8\,H_2O(l).$$

When 0.2084 g of $X_2C_2O_4$ of the solid is dissolved in water, acidified and titrated, 33.62 mL of the $KMnO_4$ solution is required to reach the endpoint. Based on these data, what is the identity of the solid $X_2C_2O_4$?

Question 4

Photoelectron spectroscopy, using either ultraviolet or x-ray sources, can determine the energies of either valence electrons or inner electrons in atoms, molecules or solids. The PES spectrum of gaseous magnesium atoms consists of four peaks

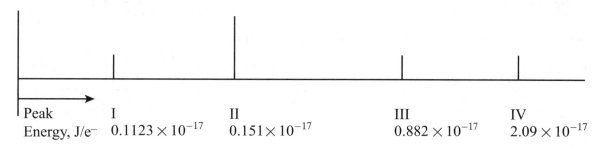

Peak	I	II	III	IV
Energy, J/e⁻	0.1123×10^{-17}	0.151×10^{-17}	0.882×10^{-17}	2.09×10^{-17}

(a) Calculate the energy of peak I in kJ/mol e⁻.

(b) Account for the appearance of four peaks in the magnesium spectrum and state how they relate to the electron structure of the magnesium atom.

Question 5

Substance	1-chloropropane, $CH_3CH_2CH_2Cl$	2-chloropropane, $CH_3CHClCH_3$
Molar mass	78.55 g mol^{-1}	78.55 g mol^{-1}
Boiling point at 1 atm	46.60°C	35.74°C

(a) In the boxes below, draw a structural formula for each molecule.

1-chloropropane, $CH_3CH_2CH_2Cl$	2-chloropropane, $CH_3CHClCH_3$

(b) Compare the normal boiling point of the two compounds and explain why they are different.

(c) Could mass spectroscopy be used to distinguish between the two molecules? Explain.

Question 6

Use the information in the following table to write chemical equations describing the following situations.

Substance	Equilibrium constant
$SrSO_4$	$K_{sp} = 3.2 \times 10^{-7}$
H_2SO_4	$K_{a1} = $ large; $K_{a2} = 1.2 \times 10^{-2}$
$Sr(OH)_2$	$K_{sp} = 3.2 \times 10^{-4}$

(a) Strontium sulfate is only slightly soluble in water. Write the equation for the dissociation of strontium sulfate in water.
(b) Write the solubility product constant expression for strontium sulfate.
(c) Write the balanced net ionic equation for the acid-base reaction which occurs when solutions of sulfuric acid and strontium hydroxide are mixed.
(d) How would the solubility of strontium sulfate vary (more soluble, less soluble, or the same) if the salt were to be dissolved in a solution of sulfuric acid rather than pure water?

Question 7

A student filled a 50 mL buret to the top with distilled water and timed the number of seconds it took for the water to pass from the zero mark to the 5 mL mark, the 10 mL line, the 15 mL and the 20 mL lines. The student was told the rate law $= k[H_2O]^m$, where m was the reactant order of the water flow through the buret. The student then graphed the water flow times and the remaining volumes as shown below.

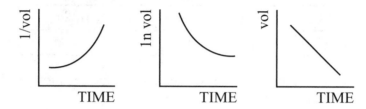

(a) Based upon the graphs above, what is the reactant order for water flowing through a buret? Explain.

(b) How is the rate constant determined from the graph you have selected?

(c) Would the rate data differ if the water were replaced with syrup or molasses at the same temperature? Explain.

SEMESTER 1 EXAMINATION

<u>Questions 1–3</u> should be answered with reference to the following equation for the combustion of ammonia

$$4\,NH_3(g) + 5\,O_2(g) \rightarrow 4\,NO(g) + 6\,H_2O(g)$$

1. If 10 moles of each reactant are available, what is the maximum number of moles of NO that can be formed?

   (A) 4 moles
   (B) 8 moles
   (C) 10 moles
   (D) 12 moles

2. When 3.4 g of NH_3 is mixed with 1.6 g of O_2, which of the following expressions shows the maximum mass of water that could be produced when the reaction occurs?

   (A) $3.4 \times 6/4 \times 18$
   (B) $3.4 \times 1/17 \times 6/4 \times 18$
   (C) $1.6 \times 1/32 \times 6/5 \times 18$
   (D) $(3.4 - 1.6) \times 1/32 \times 4/5 \times 1/18$

3. Which statement is true concerning the above reaction?

(A) The number of moles and atoms are conserved in this reaction.
(B) The number of atoms and molecules are conserved in this reaction.
(C) The total number of moles and the mass are conserved in this reaction.
(D) The number of atoms and mass are conserved in this reaction.

Questions 4–6 Consider the following table of first four ionization energies (IE) for elements I-IV:

	Element I	Element II	Element III	Element IV
First IE	2080	496	738	578
Second IE	3952	4562	1451	1817
Third IE	6122	6910	7733	2745
Fourth IE	9371	9543	10543	11577
Fifth IE	12177	13354	13630	14842

4. Which element shows the weakest attraction for the electron that is removed by the first ionization energy?

(A) I
(B) II
(C) III
(D) IV

5. Which element will most likely form a 3+ ion?

(A) I
(B) II
(C) III
(D) IV

6. Which one of the following outer subshell configurations most likely corresponds with element IV?

(A) ns^2
(B) $ns^2\, np^1$
(C) $ns^2\, np^3$
(D) $ns^2\, np^6$

Questions 7–9 should be answered with reference to the following elements and their positions in the Periodic Table.

(A) Mg
(B) Al
(C) P
(D) Cl

7. Which atom contains the largest number of unpaired electrons?

8. Which atom has its valence electrons in a single sublevel?

9. Which element forms a stable diatomic molecule?

_____

Questions 10–13 refer to the following types of solids.

(A) A molecular solid held together by London forces
(B) A covalent network solid
(C) An ionic solid
(D) A metallic solid

10. Diamond

11. Magnesium oxide

12. Graphene

13. Carbon dioxide

_____

Questions 14–15 should be answered with reference to the following cooling curve for the pure substance X$_2$.

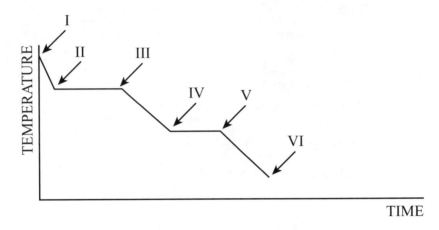

14. What change is occurring in X$_2$ molecules between II and III?

(A) X$_2$ molecules are slowing down.
(B) X$_2$ molecules are forming intermolecular attractions with one another.
(C) X$_2$ molecules are gaining potential energy.
(D) X$_2$ molecules are dissociating into X atoms.

15. What is the composition and molecular action of this X$_2$ sample between points III and IV?

(A) The sample is all liquid, molecules are slowing down, and bonds are unchanged.
(B) The sample is all liquid, molecules are slowing, and more bonds are forming.
(C) The sample is a 50-50 mixture of liquid and solid, molecules are slowing down, and more bonds are forming.
(D) The sample is a 50-50 mixture of liquid and gas, molecules are unchanged in their motion but bonds are breaking.

16. A 10.0 g sample of which of the following substances will contain the greatest number of particles?

(A) F$_2$
(B) Ne
(C) Na
(D) Ar

17. A student is asked to determine how many different dyes a water-soluble food coloring contains. Which technique is best suited to this task?

(A) column chromatography
(B) distillation
(C) filtration
(D) paper chromatography

18. Based on Coulomb's Law which acid is most likely to be a weak acid in aqueous solution?

(A) HF
(B) HCl
(C) HBr
(D) HI

19. Which solution requires the largest volume of 0.030 M NaOH for neutralization?

(A) 20.0 mL of 0.050 M HCl
(B) 40.0 mL of 0.020 M H$_2$SO$_4$
(C) 50.0 mL of 0.010 M HNO$_3$
(D) 10.0 mL of 0.050 M H$_2$SO$_4$

20. When a metallic oxide compound dissolves in water to form a solution,

(A) Oxygen gas is released
(B) The solution becomes acidic
(C) Metal precipitates
(D) The solution becomes alkaline

21. The NH$_3$ molecule can act as a(n)

(A) Bronsted-Lowry acid
(B) Bronsted-Lowry base
(C) Arrhenius acid
(D) Arrhenius base

22. When 0.65 g of zinc ($M = 65$ g/mol) is heated with 0.32 g of sulfur ($M = 32$ g/mol), 0.97 g of ZnS is formed. What will result if 1.30 g of zinc is heated with 0.32 g of sulfur?

    (A) 1.62 g of ZnS will be formed.
    (B) 1.62 g of Zn_2S will be formed.
    (C) 0.97 g of ZnS will be formed and 0.65 g of zinc will remain unreacted.
    (D) 0.97 g of ZnS will be formed and the extra zinc will sublime.

23. When solid $CaCl_2$ is added to room temperature H_2O in a test tube, the tube becomes warm to the touch. How should this process be described?

    (A) endothermic with $\Delta H < 0$
    (B) endothermic with $\Delta H > 0$
    (C) exothermic with $\Delta H > 0$
    (D) exothermic with $\Delta H < 0$

24. All of the following properties are characteristic of ionic compounds such as NaCl EXCEPT

    (A) brittleness
    (B) electrical conductivity as solid
    (C) high melting point
    (D) low volatility

25. All of the following are statements of the kinetic molecular theory of gases are true EXCEPT

    (A) Gases are mostly empty space.
    (B) Collisions between gas molecules are elastic.
    (C) Gas molecules are in constant chaotic motion.
    (D) Gas volumes equal zero at absolute zero.

26. What type of bonding is expected between nitrogen and fluorine atoms?

    (A) ionic
    (B) metallic
    (C) nonpolar covalent
    (D) polar covalent

27. When the following equation is balanced with lowest whole number coefficients, the sum of those coefficients is

$$\_\_\_P_2O_5 + \_\_\_Ba(OH)_2 \rightarrow \_\_\_Ba_3(PO_4)_2 + \_\_\_H_2O$$

(A) 4
(B) 8
(C) 12
(D) 16

28. As an open beaker of freshly distilled water sits out in the laboratory, its pH drops slowly from pH 7.0 to pH 5.7. This change occurs because

(A) Carbon dioxide from the atmosphere saturates the water.
(B) Nitrogen monoxide from the atmosphere saturates the water.
(C) Distillation removes basic impurities from water.
(D) The water undergoes auto-ionization.

29. Which of the following compounds shows the greatest % by weight for sodium?

(A) NaF
(B) NaCl
(C) Na_2O
(D) Na_2S

30. Which equation represents an oxidation-reduction reaction?

(A) $H_2O_2(l) \rightarrow H_2O(l) + O_2(g)$
(B) $NH_3(g) + HCl(g) \rightarrow NH_4Cl(s)$
(C) $SO_3(g) + H_2O(l) \rightarrow H^+(aq) + HSO_4^-(aq)$
(D) $I_2(s) \rightarrow I_2(g)$

CONSTRUCTED-RESPONSE QUESTIONS

Question 1

Answer the following questions pertaining to the composition of a brass alloy.

Brass is an alloy of the elements copper and zinc. While copper is unaffected by hydrochloric acid, zinc reacts to give hydrogen gas and an aqueous solution of zinc(II) chloride.

(a) Write a balanced net ionic equation to describe the reaction.
(b) A 1.00 g sample of brass was placed into a beaker and covered with excess concentrated hydrochloric acid. After the reaction stopped bubbling, the solution was poured through a funnel containing a piece of filter paper into a clean, dry 50 mL beaker. Unreacted copper remained in the filter paper while the aqueous solution of zinc(II) chloride moved into the beaker.

    i. The beaker was moved to a drying oven and baked until only a dry residue of zinc(II) chloride remained. The mass of the beaker increased by 0.195 g. What mass of zinc metal must have been in the original sample of brass?

    ii. What mass of copper metal remained in the filter paper?

    iii. What volume (in mL) of dry hydrogen gas, measured at 22.8°C and 751 torr, must have escaped during the reaction?

    iv. Assuming that there were only two elements in the alloy, calculate the percent by mass of zinc and copper in the alloy.

    v. Suggest an alternative method to analyze the amount of copper metal in the alloy.

Question 2

(a) Propanoic acid, CH_3CH_2COOH, is a monoprotic organic acid .

   i. Draw a Lewis dot structure for the molecule and circle the "acid hydrogen."

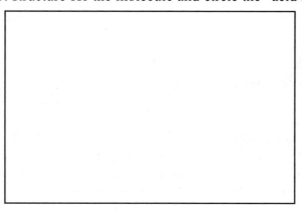

   ii. 1. Determine the number of sigma bonds and the number of pi bonds in the molecule above.

           sigma_____   pi_____

      2. Are the two C–O bond energies equivalent? Explain.

(b) Consider two chemical species: the CO_2 molecule and the CO_3^{2-} ion.

   i. Identify the shapes of these two chemical species.

        CO_2 _____ CO_3^{2-} _____

   ii. Determine the carbon-oxygen bond orders in each species and justify your choice in each case.

        CO_2 _____ CO_3^{2-} _____

Question 3

(a) Consider the 3 skeletal partial reactions below. Identify each process as an example of <u>oxidation</u>, <u>reduction</u> or <u>neither</u>. Justify your answer.

  i. $N_2 \rightarrow H_3N$
  ii. $H^+(aq) \rightarrow H_2O(l)$
  iii. $Al^{3+} \rightarrow Al$

(b) Consider the reaction between H_2 and N_2 to form gaseous NH_3.

$$\underline{\quad} H_2(g) + \underline{\quad} N_2(g) \rightarrow NH_3(g)$$

  i. Balance the equation above.
  ii. A student carries out the above reaction with 44.0 g of each reactant placed in the reaction vessel. What is the maximum mass of NH_3 which can form?
  iii. If the student obtains a value of 48.72 g for the mass of NH_3 formed, what is the percent error in this process?
  iv. A different student carries out the same reaction starting with 0.60 L of each reactant placed in a flexible reaction vessel at $0.0°C$. The reaction is heated and proceeds until all of the limiting reactant reacts, and then the reaction vessel is allowed to return to $0.0°C$.
   1. Identify the limiting reactant. Justify your choice.
   2. Will the final volume of the container be larger or smaller than the initial volume? Explain.

Question 4

	$Na_2SO_4(aq)$	$KOH(aq)$
$AlCl_3(aq)$	n.r.	ppt. (2)
$SrCl_2(aq)$	ppt. (1)	n.r.
$KCl(aq)$	n.r.	n.r.

Please refer to the chart above. All of the original solutions are 0.1 M and are clear solutions. The abbreviation n.r. = no reaction; the abbreviation for precipitate is "ppt."

(a) Write the complete balanced molecular equation for the reaction that forms precipitate (1). Underline the formula for the precipitate.

(b) Write the net ionic equation for the reaction that forms precipitate (2).

Question 5

Photoelectron spectroscopy, using either ultraviolet or x-ray sources, can determine the energies of either valence electrons or inner electrons in atoms, molecules, or solids. The PES spectrum of gaseous magnesium atoms consists of four peaks

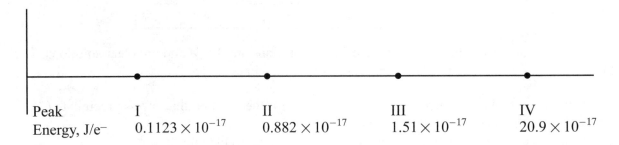

Peak	I	II	III	IV
Energy, J/e⁻	0.1123×10^{-17}	0.882×10^{-17}	1.51×10^{-17}	20.9×10^{-17}

(a) Light with a wavelength of 58.4 nm is used to eject the electron responsible for Peak I. Calculate the frequency of this light.

(b) Draw in Peak I and Peak II, with heights relative to one another, and identify which electrons they represent in the magnesium atom.